GENERAL AND APPLIED ENTOMOLOGY

GENERAL
AND APPLIED
ENTOMOLOGY

SECOND EDITION

BY

V. A. LITTLE

Professor of Entomology,
The Agricultural and Mechanical College of Texas

HARPER & ROW, PUBLISHERS
NEW YORK AND EVANSTON

CONTENTS

PREFACE

This textbook was written for students beginning a study of entomology. The student, his interest in and approach to the subject, and the type of information most worth while to him have been kept constantly in mind in the preparation of the text. Most students taking the subject may never have more than this one course. The most important question is "What subject matter should be given and how should it be presented?" This text is the result of more than 30 years of teaching a course in general and applied entomology and represents the author's thoughts and views on the subject.

The author has striven to write simply and clearly, and has attempted to present the subject as logically as possible. The more approved phylogenetic arrangement of natural groups has not always been followed, but they have frequently been arranged for study on the more sensible basis of habitat and metamorphosis.

One must always keep in mind that entomology is the study of insects—their recognition, biology, and control. Certainly, the study of taxonomy and biology of insects is most important for the beginner. Next in importance are the applied phases of the science. It is our thought that morphology and physiology should be limited to only a working knowledge in an elementary text.

The most effective teaching of economic entomology can be done along with taxonomic and biological studies, since, at this time, it is possible to tie control to the biology and the taxonomic group of the insect more satisfactorily. Most details of insect control are omitted because control measures vary so much in different parts of the country that one must depend largely on local recommendations. Also, much detailed information pertaining to dosages and applications of insecticides may be found on the manufacturer's label. Naturally, no textbook will fit the needs of every instructor. Adequate material has been included to allow considerable latitude in the choice of subject matter.

The study of insects is a most fascinating science, and this book attempts at every opportunity to arouse interest among the students. Although many injurious insects have been discussed, it is certainly not the desire to create the impression that all are harmful. The more important beneficial insects are stressed in their proper places. Rather simple and incomplete keys are given to the more important groups, chiefly for the purpose of acquainting the students with their use. Certainly, the student in his first course in entomology will not progress far in insect taxonomy. A chapter is included on making insect collections to encourage students to make collections and continue their studies. A glossary is included to aid with technical terms.

A textbook in entomology of a general nature only dips lightly into the vast amount of the accumulated knowledge of the science. A selected bibliography is included as an aid to both teacher and student. A number of the references contain excellent bibliographies which will be of further aid.

The subject material in this textbook has been taken from many sources. We are grateful to all authors and research workers from whose works this material has been drawn. The author is indebted to many people for helpful criticisms and suggestions, and for reading the manuscript. I especially wish to thank H. J. Reinhard, N. M. Randolph, J. C. Gaines, R. J. Dicke, D. R. King, M. A. Price, D. F. Martin, Ada Duncan, and Jo Ann Moss. The writer is grateful to Don Collins, C. O. Mohr, and Mrs. W. J. Dobson for help and suggestions with illustrations. Illustrations were loaned or permission was given for use of figures in the literature by a number of individuals and companies. Special thanks are due E. F. Knipling, L. S. Dillon, William W. Paul, Bruce B. Miner, G. H. Cale, G. F. Ferris, J. F. Cooper, P. J. Reno, H. B. Mills, E. O. Essig, Marjorie Mitchell, S. J. Carpenter, P. W. Oman, Mina Maxwell, W. W. Konkle, G. A. Bieberdorf, Marie Lonning, Gerald B. Spawn, Hans Nussbaum, G. F. Knowlton, W. P. Bradley, C. F. Garner, F. M. Fuller, John E. Simmons, Florence L. Batson, T. H. Mackintosh, and Blair Coursen.

V. A. LITTLE

College Station, Texas
February, 1957

PREFACE TO
THE SECOND EDITION

Many important developments in the science of entomology have taken place since the manuscript of the first edition of this textbook was prepared. Most changes have occurred in the field of insect control. One cannot appreciate the enormous amount of research being done and the continuous changes which are occurring until he attempts to review the published literature of the past several years.

Developments in the field of insecticides and the problems involved in their use have necessitated the rewriting of the chapter on the subject. The most logical manner of presentation of the subject matter is problematical. The general outline followed here is that which the writer has found to be reasonably satisfactory. The list of insecticides is quite incomplete, and detailed information on each is necessarily limited; but the attempt was made to include sufficient subject matter for most needs. Insect control is often quite involved, and, too, it is not possible to list all control methods with details. Local agricultural authorities are most helpful in supplying control programs and detailed information. Precautions given throughout the text concerning the safe use of insecticides are considered to be adequate.

Significant progress has been made in the fields of taxonomy and biology as well as in insect control. Correct identification of an insect and a knowledge of its relationships with other species is of paramount importance in insect control. Research taxonomists are constantly improving and increasing the knowledge of the natural relationships of insects, and in their classification are producing a more accurate interpretation of insect life. This research frequently necessitates the changing of scientific names. An attempt has been made to bring up to date the scientific names. A number of minor changes have been made throughout the text, and mistakes corrected. Regardless of how careful the worker may be, there will always be errors.

The author is indebted to a number of colleagues in preparation of this revision. Special thanks are due to the following persons: J. R. Brazzel, H. R. Burke, J. C. Gaines, C. F. Garner, O. H. Graham, R. L. Hanna, E. F. Knipling, M. A. Price, N. M. Randolph, and H. J. Reinhard.

College Station, Texas
August, 1962

GENERAL AND APPLIED ENTOMOLOGY

CHAPTER

I

INTRODUCTION

The place that insects occupy in the world of living things is important, as most all plants and animals are affected in some way by their presence. No other class of animals is so intimately involved in the intricacies and complexities of the biological world as are insects. They are essentially terrestrial in habitat; and are distributed from the permafrost line of the Arctic to the ice cap of the Antarctic, and from the mountain tops to the depths of caverns. Two-thirds or more of all species of animals are insects, and they are probably exceeded in number of individuals only by microscopic forms of life.

Insects are an ancient race of animals which has persisted for millions of years. Through the processes of evolution nature has superbly perfected them that they may survive under the most adverse conditions and in a diversity of environments. Nature has succeeded in combining in them certain advantageous characteristics, the combination of which is found in no other group of animals. An insect is protected by a suit of armor (exoskeleton) like knights of old. Associated with the exoskeleton is remarkable mobility and smallness of size. In addition to these characteristics, insects possess a unique and very efficient respiratory system, a varied and involved biology, and the ability to partake of food in a diversity of ways. Thus, in the insect world is found material worthy of man's best efforts in study, and problems which challenge him on every side.

Man's welfare is materially affected in a multiplicity of ways by insects. His body may be attacked, his food despoiled, and his diseases contracted in their feeding. Most of his stored possessions and the house in which he lives are subject to insect damage. Field crops, livestock, fruits, timber, and other agricultural products suffer great losses from the depredations of insects. Yet, man is also benefited

1

in a number of ways by their presence. Many are parasites or predators of other insects that are pests. They are useful in the pollination of many plants. Insects are nature's scavengers and reduce plant and animal matter to earth mold; they are a source of food for fishes and wildlife, and the products of some are of value in industry. On the basis of their relation to man, insects may be classed as either harmful or beneficial; however, the status of many is uncertain because their biologies are not adequately understood.

HARMFUL INSECTS

Insects and Public Health

When insects are considered on a world-wide basis perhaps they are most injurious to man as vectors of human diseases. Through the ages millions of people have died of diseases transmitted by insects. There are a number of insect-borne diseases, and these may be transmitted in different ways. A few of the more important may be mentioned.

Malaria is one of the important diseases of mankind. The disease is most prevalent in tropical regions where it exacts its greatest toll in human suffering and deaths. The disease is transmitted solely by certain species of *Anopheles* mosquitoes. Owing to improvement of health standards and mosquito control measures the disease is rarely found in the United States today.

Yellow fever is another dreaded disease of tropical and subtropical regions which is mosquito-borne. By means of mosquito control measures and the use of a protective vaccine the disease is kept in check. Filariasis, dengue, and encephalitis are other diseases transmitted by mosquitoes.

The pestiferous house fly has developed in the wastes of man and his animals and then persistently insisted upon sharing his food since the human race was young. Because of its filthy feeding and breeding habits it may transmit by mechanical means such diseases as typhoid, dysentery, and diarrhea.

Fleas are transmitters of bubonic plague and murine typhus of man. Bubonic plague is the Black Death of the Middle Ages that swept away millions of lives in Europe and Asia. Because of the knowledge of the disease, its transmitters and hosts, it should never again reach the proportions of a plague in civilized countries.

Louse-borne typhus is another scourge of the human race. The statement has been made that more people have died of this disease than have been killed in all wars. Typhus epidemics have always followed in the wake of wars due to lowered standards of sanitation and the crowding together of many people. This disease may now be controlled. Other diseases transmitted by insects are mentioned in the text with the discussion of their vectors.

Even though certain insects may not transmit pathogenic organisms, they may be pests through their stings, bites, and obnoxious presence. Every one is acquainted with the sting of wasps, bees, and ants. Some caterpillars bear nettling hairs or spines on their bodies which produce dermatitis and other symptoms when pressed against the skin. Body fluids of meloid beetles contain a poisonous compound, cantharidin, which produces blisters. Assassin bugs and others can inflict painful bites. Cockroaches with their nauseating odor and loathsome presence, pestiferous gnats, ants, and many other insects are nuisances of no mean importance.

Insects and Agriculture

Plants and animals are attacked and injured by insects in a number of ways. In addition to their feeding, diseases may be transmitted by them. The total loss produced by insects to agricultural products is extremely difficult to estimate due to the many variable and complicated factors involved. Perhaps the total figure would reach the stupendous sum of several billions of dollars annually.

A few outstanding insect pests to crops are mentioned. The boll weevil produced such serious economic repercussions in the South that a revolution in the methods of production of cotton was brought about. The European corn borer costs the farmers millions of dollars annually. Grasshoppers have plagued farmers in this country since pioneer days. Plant lice, the chinch bug, the codling moth, and others too numerous to mention have exacted a huge toll of crops.

Insects are important vectors of plant diseases. Plant lice, or aphids, and leafhoppers in particular are involved in the transmission of a large number of important virus diseases, some of which are transmitted only by insects. Cucumber beetles are the only known vectors of bacterial wilt of cucurbits. The Dutch elm disease is spread by bark beetles.

Injury to livestock by arthropods is caused by their sucking blood, feeding on the body tissues, transmitting diseases and parasitic worms, and annoyance. Horse flies, horn flies, stable flies, sucking lice, and ticks cause great losses to the livestock men by feeding on the blood of their animals. Heel flies annoy animals, and their larvae (cattle grubs) cause considerable loss by their feeding and damage to hides. The screw-worm is a most worrisome pest of the stockmen during warm weather, particularly in the Southwest. Its larva infests wounds and attacks live tissues. Lice are pestiferous in the cool seasons.

The blood-sucking arthropods in particular are important vectors of livestock diseases. Diseases may be transmitted by both mechanical and biological means. The disease-producing organisms are of two distinct types, animal microörganisms and plant microörganisms. Cattle fever is the best known of the protozoan diseases of livestock that is arthropod-transmitted. This disease exacted a toll of untold millions of dollars and the livestock industry could not fully develop in the South until its vector, the cattle tick, was eliminated. A related disease, anaplasmosis, is also tick-borne. Some of the most serious diseases of animals and man, such as nagana of animals and sleeping sickness of man, are caused by trypanosomes which are transmitted chiefly by tsetse flies. A number of virus diseases are transmitted wholly or in part by arthropods. Such bacterial diseases as anthrax and tularemia, although transmitted in other ways, may be spread by arthropods. Many species of parasitic worms are transmitted by insects.

Household and Stored-Products Pests

As insects are found in almost every conceivable environment in nature, the habitations of man would hardly be expected to be excepted. Man is plagued with a number of insects within the home. House flies and ants of several species are continual nuisances. Clothes moths feed on his clothing and other fabrics, and termites attempt to destroy the house in which he lives. The pantry may become infested with weevils, flour beetles, flour moths, and cockroaches. The food stores of man have always been raided by insects. Huge losses of food products in the aggregate occur annually in bins, grain elevators, warehouses, and on shelves of grocery stores. Rice and granary weevils, Angoumois grain moths, and flour moths are the more important pests.

BENEFICIAL INSECTS

The assumption that all insects are injurious would be wholly incorrect, inasmuch as only a small percentage of all the species are distinctly harmful, even though their number may appear large. Insects are so involved in the biological complex that they may be useful in a number of ways.

Insect Predators and Parasites

Perhaps insects are most beneficial in feeding upon each other. In their search for food many have become adapted to live upon others of their class, and so today every insect will be found to have other species feeding upon it. They are most important as they aid in maintaining a balance in insect populations, and without their services man would be unable to cope with his insect problems. These insects are classed as predators and parasites. Predators are generally larger than their prey, which they pounce upon and may devour in one meal. Parasites are smaller than their hosts, upon or within which they live continuously for at least a part of their life cycle. They feed successively upon the host, which is not immediately killed.

Among the insect predators none are more beneficial to the farmer and gardener than the familiar lady beetles. These small semihemispherical beetles not only have voracious appetites but they are prolific and long-lived. Both larvae and adults feed on a wide range of insects. Ground beetles are other common and well known predators. Aphis lions (larvae of lacewing flies) are beneficial as predators, as are dragonflies, ants, wasps, and many others.

Insect parasites are more numerous than the predators and are equally important. They are mostly quite small and usually escape notice. The tachinid flies are highly beneficial as they comprise a large family and all are parasitic. They parasitize caterpillars, beetles, and other groups of insects. The braconids are a large group of small wasp-like insects that parasitize a wide range of insects including plant lice and caterpillars. The chalcid flies are numerous and most species are parasites. There are thousands of species of ichneumon flies, all of which are parasites. Most groups of insects are plagued by ichneumon parasites.

Insects as Pollinators

Insects are invaluable in the pollination of plants. Some of the higher plants are self-pollinated, but most are cross-pollinated. Wind and insects are the chief factors in cross-pollination. Bees, wasps, ants, butterflies, beetles, flies, and thrips all render valuable service in the pollination of plants. Wild bees and honey bees are the most valuable pollinators. Honey bees are depended upon mostly when the services of insect pollinators are needed in the production of cultivated crops such as clovers, alfalfa, apples, pears, plums, and certain vegetables. Some plants, e.g., the yucca and the Smyrna fig, are completely dependent upon certain species of insects for pollination.

Other Ways in Which Insects Are Beneficial

Insects are an important source of food for many animals. The more common birds depend largely upon insects as a source of food and they consume huge quantities of them, especially during the nesting season. Insects such as bloodworms and the nymphs of mayflies are important as food for fresh-water fishes. Toads, frogs, lizards, skunks, armadillos, bats, and other animals also depend heavily upon insects as a source of food.

Insects are sometimes referred to as nature's scavengers. They are of much aid in reducing both plant and animal material to earth mold. Wood-boring beetles, carpenter ants, termites, and other insects help reduce logs, limbs, leaves, and related materials to humus. Mayfly nymphs and other aquatic insects feed on organic matter in ponds and streams, and thus help prevent pollution of these waters. Many insects aid in the elimination of animal wastes; however, flies which develop in such material may do much greater harm than good as disseminators of diseases.

Certain insect products have considerable commercial value. Honey has been a prized article of food since ancient days. There is always a demand in industry for beeswax for making such products as candles, polishes, and waxes. Silk is the product of the larva of an insect, the silkworm. Although silk is replaced largely by synthetic fibers, its production is still an important industry in some parts of the world. The production of shellac is a means of livelihood for a number of people, chiefly in Burma and India. Shellac is obtained from the lac scale insect.

A number of insects inhabit the soil and in so doing they have served to improve its texture somewhat, and also in some instances add some humus. The more important soil-inhabiting forms are ants and termites. Others are solitary bees and wasps which construct their nests in the soil, grubs of beetles, nymphs of some species, and larvae of certain flies.

Insects feed on weeds as well as other plants and they may aid materially in keeping them in check. The most successful use of an insect in the control of a plant was the introduction of the caterpillar of a moth (*Cactoblastis cactorum*) to control the prickly pear (*Opuntia* spp.) in Australia.

Another successful example was the importation of two species of leaf beetles, *Chrysolina quadrigemina* and *C. hyperici* into the United States to control the Klamath weed in the West.

2

INSECTS AND RELATED ANIMALS

In beginning the study of entomology, it is desirable to know the position of insects in the animal kingdom with special reference to related forms. The animal kingdom is divided into a number of groups known as *phyla* (singular *phylum*). The number of phyla studied by the student depends upon the authority followed; some combine certain related groups while others treat them separately. Eleven or twelve phyla are commonly studied.

The most familiar of all the phyla of animals are the *Chordata*

FIG. 1. A crayfish (Crustacea). (Courtesy of Carolina Biological Supply Co.)

which consist of mammals, birds, reptiles, amphibians, and other less well-known forms. However, it contains only a small percentage of the total number of species. At the other extreme of the animal kingdom are found the *Protozoa,* composed of such unicellular animals as the *Amoeba, Paramecium,* the malaria parasite, and the organism producing Texas fever of cattle.

Between these two widely separated phyla is a vast assemblage of diverse animal life. The phylum *Echinodermata* is represented by the common starfish. The earthworm is an example of the *Annelida.* The *Platyhelminthes* are commonly referred to as the flatworms, and the roundworms comprise the phylum known as the *Nemathelminthes.* The phylum *Mollusca* is a large group consisting of such common forms as oysters, mussels, and snails. In addition to the *Arthropoda,* there are several other less well known phyla.

Ranking high in the scale of animal life are the largest of all phyla, the *Arthropoda.* Probably three-fourths of all species of animals belong in this group. Here are found crayfish, spiders, ticks, mites, millipedes, centipedes, and insects. We will be concerned with this phylum in this study.

The word *Arthropoda* is derived from *arthron* (jointed) and *pous* (foot). The possession of jointed appendages is one of the chief characteristics of the *Arthropoda.* The bodies of these animals in the perfect state are composed of ring-like segments. In some groups, however, the segments have so completely grown together as to be indistinguishable. These animals have an exoskeleton composed in part of a chemical substance known as *chitin.* They are further characterized by being bilaterally symmetrical. No one characteristic is sufficient but all taken collectively will separate members of this group from those of other phyla.

A phylum is subdivided into classes. Thirteen classes of *Arthropoda* are recognized. For the purposes of this text, only the five most common classes will be considered. These classes are *Crustacea* (crayfish, sowbugs, and shrimps), *Arachnida* (spiders, ticks, and scorpions), *Diplopoda* (millipedes), *Chilopoda* (centipedes), and *Hexapoda* (insects).

KEY TO COMMON CLASSES OF ARTHROPODA

1. With two pairs of antennae and five or more pairs of legs;
   aquatic or semiaquatic in habitat; breathe by means of
   gills or body wall (Crayfish, Shrimps, and others)   **Crustacea,** p. 10

With one pair or no antennae; primarily terrestrial in habitat; breathe by means of air tubes, book lungs, or body wall   2
2. With no antennae and four pairs of legs (Spiders, Scorpions,
   and Ticks)   **Arachnida,** p. 11
   With one pair of antennae and three or more pairs of legs   3
3. With three pairs of legs and usually two pairs of wings
   (Insects)   **Hexapoda,** p. 35
   With more than three pairs of legs and no wings   4
4. With one pair of legs on each body segment (Centi-
   pedes)   **Chilopoda,** p. 34
   With two pairs of legs on each body segment (Milli-
   pedes)   **Diplopoda,** p. 33

CLASS CRUSTACEA (CRAYFISH, SHRIMPS, AND OTHERS)

The members of this class breathe by means of gills with the exception of small forms that respire through the body wall. They are
aquatic, or at least live in a moist environment. Two pairs of antennae are generally present on the head, and a number of pairs of
legs, often modified for swimming, are attached to the body. In a
number of cases, some of the body segments are fused with the head
to form a *cephalothorax* (head-thorax).

Crustacea (Fig. 1) are represented by such common forms as
crayfish, lobsters, pill bugs, sow bugs, crabs, and shrimps. They live
mostly in seas and fresh waters where they feed chiefly as scavengers on decaying vegetable and animal matter. The bulk of the zo-
oplankton material in water consists of small crustacean life.
Crustaceans supply much of the fish food; and they are also a source
of food for man (e.g., lobsters, shrimps, and crabs).

On the whole, Crustacea are considered beneficial but there are
some harmful species. Barnacles, sessile marine forms, do much
damage to shore installations and impede the speed of ships by at-
taching themselves to the bottom of the vessels. On rare occasions
crayfish have been known to damage lawns and destroy field crops
in humid regions where the soils have exceptionally high water lev-
els. Sow bugs and pill bugs are pests in greenhouses, flower beds,
and gardens. Sow bugs and pill bugs may be controlled with DDT
dusts and poison baits. Certain species of *Cyclops* serve as hosts of
the broad tapeworm (*Diphyllobothrium latum*) and the guinea
worm (*Dracunculus medinensis*).

CLASS ARACHNIDA (SPIDERS, SCORPIONS, AND TICKS)

This class includes such common forms as spiders, scorpions, ticks, and mites. The bodies of members of this group are usually composed of two divisions, the cephalothorax and abdomen. Antennae are absent and eyes are simple. Four pairs of legs are attached to the cephalothorax in the adult stage. The class is terrestrial, breathing by air tubes and book lungs.

Arachnida are divided into a number of orders. The following key will aid the student in recognizing members of the more common orders.

KEY TO COMMON ORDERS OF ARACHNIDA

1. Abdomen with distinct segments   2
   Abdomen not distinctly segmented   6
2. Abdomen with tail-like prolongation   3
   Abdomen with no tail-like prolongation   4
3. Tail stout and terminating in a sting (Scorpions)   **Scorpionida,** p. 14
   Tail long and slender without sting (Whip Scorpions)
                                                    Pedipalpida, p. 16
4. Palpi armed with pincer-like claws (Pseudoscorpions)
                              Chelonethida (Pseudoscorpionida), p. 17
   Palpi without pincer-like claws   5
5. Abdomen attached to cephalothorax by a slender stalk
      (Whip Scorpions)   **Pedipalpida,** p. 16
   Body oval and compact; legs usually quite long (Harvestmen
      or Daddy-long-legs)   **Phalangida,** p. 18
6. Cephalothorax and abdomen joined by short stalk (Spiders)
                                                      Araneida, p. 11
   Cephalothorax and abdomen broadly joined (Mites and
      Ticks)   **Acarina,** p. 18

Order ARANEIDA (Spiders)

This is the largest order of Arachnida and several thousand species are represented in North America fauna. Although a few species are poisonous to man, the group as a whole must be considered beneficial as its members prey chiefly upon insects.

Spiders (Fig. 2) may be readily separated from other Arachnida in having an unsegmented abdomen attached to the cephalothorax by means of a slender stalk or pedicel. There are usually two to eight simple eyes, but in some cave-inhabiting forms eyes may be absent. Mouthparts consist of paired *chelicerae* and a pair of *palpi* (pedipalpi). The chelicerae represent the modified second antennae of the Crustacea. Spiders do not devour their prey but crush it and suck the body fluids by means of a so-called sucking stomach. The palpi of the female are leg-like structures, but they are enlarged and modified in the male for use in transferring sperm to the female in mating. On the ventral surface of the abdomen are located the spinnerets (silk-spinning organs). Opening on the spinnerets are four types of tubes through which is spun four kinds of silk, each of which is utilized for a different purpose. Anterior to the spinnerets is a single spiracle. Book lungs are accessory respira-

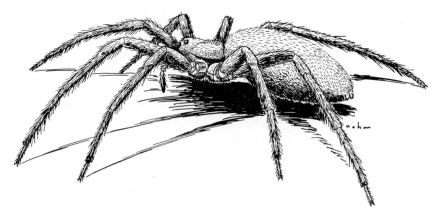

FIG. 2. A wolf spider. (From Illinois Natural History Survey. Drawn by C. O. Mohr.)

tory organs. They are sacs containing plates arranged as the leaves of a book. One or two pairs of book lungs are found in spiders and their openings are usually located on each side of the genital opening.

Spiders capture their prey by different means. Some species, such as jumping spiders and wolf spiders, stalk their victims. Crab spiders hide in flowers and pounce upon the insect visitors. Most spiders spin silken webs of some type in which their insect prey is snared. The webs are of various types, characteristic of the spider group. The orb-weavers spin the well-known orb webs. House spiders construct irregular webs. Others make funnel or triangular webs. When the prey is captured it is usually killed by the poison of the bite.

The mating habits of spiders are of interest to biologists. The males are generally smaller than the females and can be recognized by the enlarged and modified palpi. In some species mating is preceded by a courtship performance by the males which attempt to impress the females by dancing, circling, and showing off in other ways. Sometimes the females join in the performance. In many species the females may kill and eat the males following mating. This is why the black widow spider is so named.

The female spider lays her eggs in a silken sac. Great care is taken of the eggs and young spiders. The sac containing the eggs may be carried by the female or attached to some object. Some young spiders are cannibalistic and devour the weaker individuals.

As spiders are wingless they must depend upon means other than flight for dispersion. They may crawl or be transported by other animals or by air currents. Young spiders frequently make use of air currents for dispersion, especially in the autumn. They crawl to a high point, elevate the abdomen and spin out silken strands. When the silken threads create sufficient buoyancy in the breeze the spider is carried away, frequently to considerable distances. Strands of silk floating through the air on clear autumn days are as much a part of the season as flocks of wild geese on their southward journey.

Spiders are feared because of their bites. It is difficult to induce most of them to bite, and only a few of the North American species are poisonous to man. Only the bite of the black widow spider (*Latrodectus mactans*) is dangerously poisonous. Spiders bite with the chelicerae (fangs), which are normally provided with poison glands.

The Black Widow Spider (*Latrodectus mactans*). The mature female black widow spider (Fig. 3) is deep black with red markings in the form of an hourglass on the underside of the abdomen. It measures about 1/2 inch in length. The male is much smaller than the female. The abdomen of the male is marked dorsally with three transverse white bands and a median red stripe. It has enlarged and modified palpi. The males are relatively short-lived.

The black widow spider is most frequently found where insects are abundant. During the summer it is quite commonly found underneath bee hives. Occasionally it becomes relatively numerous where flies frequent.

The poison of the black widow spider is reported to be a neurotoxin. Man, however, is seldom bitten by this spider. When bitten, excruciating pain is experienced and severe symptoms may persist for several days. A physician should be consulted as soon as possible. In some cases fatalities have resulted.

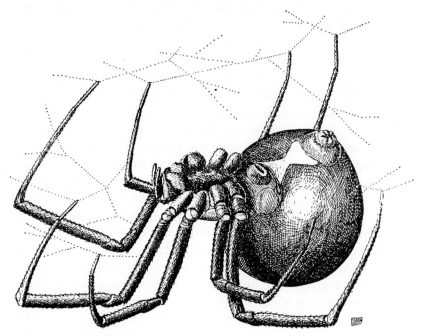

FIG. 3. The black widow spider (*Latrodectus mactans*) hanging on web. (From Utah Agricultural Experiment Station.)

Tarantulas (*Dugesiella* spp. and others).   Tarantulas (Fig. 4) are large hairy spiders which are much feared by some people. They occur in the southwestern states, Mexico, Central America, and South America. The size of tarantulas varies from one to three inches in length. The native forms live in holes in the ground or under logs and stones.

The time required for the development of tarantulas is believed to be about twelve years. The adult females may live for another twelve years or longer. Despite popular opinion to the contrary, the bite of the species of tarantulas found in the United States is not poisonous to man. However, the bite of certain tropical species is toxic and produces local reactions.

Order SCORPIONIDA (Scorpions)

Scorpions are widely distributed in tropical and temperate climates and within the United States they occur in the largest numbers

FIG. 4. A tarantula from southern Mexico. (Courtesy of the General Biological Supply House.)

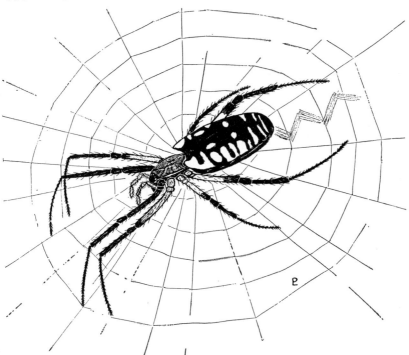

FIG. 5. A garden spider (*Argiope aurantia*). (From Borror and DeLong, *An Introduction to the Study of Insects,* Rinehart & Company, 1954. By permission of the publisher.)

in the Southwest. Probably more than 30 species occur in the United States. Members of this order are recognized by the jointed abdomen broadly joined to the cephalothorax and terminating in a sting, and by the long palpi with the terminal segments forming strong pincers. (See Fig. 6.)

The sting of the common species of scorpions is painful but the effects are not dangerous. The poison is a neurotoxin. In Mexico, however, five species are known whose sting may be fatal to small children. The poison injected by the sting of *Centruroides noxius* may be fatal to adults also. *Centruroides suffusus* is the commonly known Durango scorpion.

FIG. 6.   A common scorpion.

The biology of scorpions is not very well known. Scorpions are found in rotten logs; and under stones, bark, boards, and other similar places. Food consists of insects, spiders, and other small animals which are usually stung before being devoured. The female of the common striped scorpion produces about 30 to 40 young, which live, in their early stages of development, upon the back of the mother. However, they soon leave the female and fend for themselves, for the maternal instinct disappears rather early and they may be devoured by their own mother.

Should scorpions be commonly found around homes, garages, and other buildings, thorough spraying with a DDT solution in a light oil is recommended. The spray is quite effective although the DDT acts slowly and some time may elapse before the scorpions are eliminated.

Order PEDIPALPIDA (Whip Scorpions)

Whip scorpions are tropical in habitat and are found only in the southern part of this country. In body build they have the general form of scorpions. They differ from the latter in the form of the front legs. They are elongated, with the tarsi divided into a number of small segments which produce a whip-like appearance. Also, members in one family bear a long whip-like appendage on the end of the abdomen and are commonly known as vinegarroons, because,

when disturbed, they emit a fluid with a vinegar-like odor. They are thought by many to be poisonous, although no stinging organ is present. The fluid emitted could possibly cause some irritation on tender skin. Vinegarroons are also known as giant whip scorpions. The best known species is *Mastigoproctus giganteus* (Fig. 7). Whip scorpions are predaceous and secrete themselves under logs, boards, and other objects.

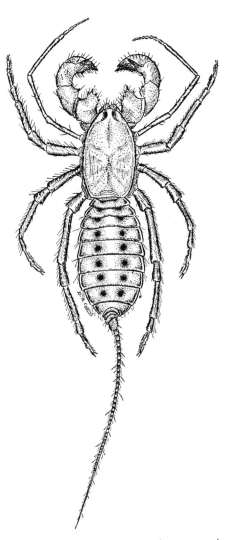

Order CHELONETHIDA (PSEUDOSCORPIONIDA) (Pseudoscorpions)

Members of the order are small, rarely more than 1/5 inch in length, and they have the general appearance of scorpions but the abdomen is broad and flat, and they have no sting (Fig. 8). Pseudoscorpions live under stones and bark of trees, in homes between pages of books, and in similar places. They have the peculiar habit of running sidewise and backwards. Food con-

FIG. 7. A vinegarroon (*Mastigoproctus giganteus*).

sists of small insects and mites. They may make use of large insects for transportation by clinging to their bodies. These animals have silk glands, the ducts of which are found on the chelicerae. The silk **is** used in the construction of hibernation cocoons.

Order PHALANGIDA (Harvestmen or Daddy-long-legs)

These common and widely distributed animals are readily recognized by the compact oval body and the long ungainly legs. Daddy-long-legs, as they are most commonly called, feed on juices of plants, dead insects, and possibly on some living insects also. Eggs may be laid in the soil, under stones, in cracks, and similar situations. Adults may hibernate in the South, but most species spend the winter in the egg stage in colder climates.

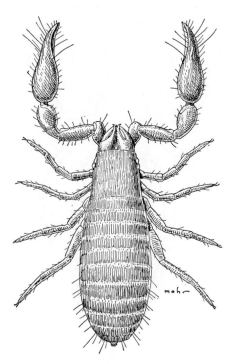

FIG. 8. A pseudoscorpion (*Microbisium confusum*) enlarged. (From Illinois Natural History Survey. Drawn by C. O. Mohr.)

Order ACARINA (Mites and Ticks)

The Acarina is the most important order of the Arachnida, for in this group is found a number of pests of both plants and animals. The Acarina may be separated from other Arachnida by the sac-like body with the abdomen not distinctly segmented and broadly joined to the cephalothorax. Mouthparts are for piercing and sucking.

Mites

Mites are generally quite small; many of them being microscopic in size. Taxonomy of the group is imperfectly known, but the number of species is indicated to be quite large. They are very abundant. Both plants and animals are attacked. Some are predators or parasites and others are scavengers. They may be found in the soil, rubbish, plant galls, under stones and bark, and in both fresh and salt water. Most species deposit eggs; however, a few are ovoviviparous, such as the straw itch mite (*Pyemotes ventricosus*). From the egg is hatched a six-legged larva. Following a period of feeding, the larva molts into a nymph with eight legs. The nymph feeds and molts one or more times before the adult stage is reached. The adult may be differentiated from the nymph by the presence of a genital pore. Only a few of the more important species can be mentioned here.

The Two-spotted Spider Mite (*Tetranychus telarius*).   The two-spotted spider mite (Fig. 9) is an important pest of many plants. Among the more common hosts of this species are cotton, beans, peas, cucumbers, cantaloupes, arbor vitae, and most flowers and greenhouse plants. The spider mite punctures the epidermis of the leaves with its mouthparts and sucks the plant juices. Leaves of lightly infested plants assume an ashy-gray stippled appearance, while those of heavily infested plants may turn reddish-brown and later drop. The two-spotted spider mite is oval in outline and the female is about $\frac{1}{50}$ inch in length; the male is smaller. The color may be red, reddish-yellow, yellow, greenish, or blackish. Normally a slight web to which the eggs are attached is spun on the under side of the leaf. In heavy infestations the entire plant may be enveloped by the web. (See Fig. 10.)

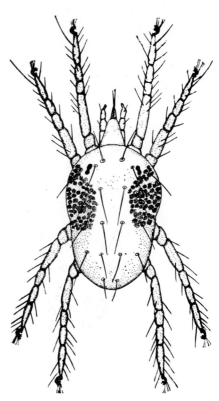

FIG. 9.   The two-spotted spider mite (*Tetranychus telarius*), highly magnified. (From Virginia Agricultural Experiment Station.)

The life history of the spider mite is dependent upon climatic conditions. A generation may be completed in slightly more than a week under optimum conditions, while more than a month may elapse before the completion of a life cycle when conditions are not favorable. An average of about 50 eggs are laid by each female. A

FIG. 10. Vetch plants heavily infested with spider mites. (From Texas Agricultural Experiment Station.)

FIG. 11. Ash flower gall produced by a gall mite (*Eriophyes fraxiniflora*). From Texas Agricultural Experiment Station.)

number of overlapping generations may occur in one season. Winter is spent on vetch, violets, geraniums, and other plants in the South. In the North it is reported that the mite overwinters in the soil.

Associated with the two-spotted spider mite are other closely related species which are extremely difficult to separate taxonomically. One of these is the desert spider mite (*Tetranychus desertorum*), which is the most important cotton mite in Texas. Morphologically the two species are most difficult to separate; however, *T. desertorum* is more uniformly red in color.

Several insecticides will control spider mites. Sulphur readily controls the desert spider mite, but it is not effective in the control of the two-spotted mite. Demeton, parathion, and malathion will control all species on field crops. Parathion aerosols are effective in greenhouses and malathion is recommended for use on a number of plants.

Other common mites attacking culti-vated plants (Fig. 11) are the citrus rust mite (*Phyllocoptruta oleivora*), citrus red mite (*Metatetranychus citri*), the pear leaf blister mite (*Eriophyes pyri,* Fig. 12), and the European red mite (*Metatetrany-chus ulmi,* Fig. 13).

A number of species of mites attack man and domestic animals. The more common species are chiggers, mange mites, scab mites, and the chicken mite.

Chiggers or Red Bugs (*Eutrombicula alfreddugesi*) and others. Humans be-come infested with chiggers (Fig. 14) in walking through grass, weeds, and other vegetation. Intense itching and red spots result from the feeding of these tiny red mites which are about $\frac{1}{150}$ inch in diam-eter and barely visible to the naked eye. Only the larval or six-legged stage attacks animals. The mouthparts are inserted into the skin and a fluid is injected which dissolves the tissues upon which the chig-ger feeds. Following feeding, the larval chigger drops to the ground and later molts into the nymphal stage. In addition to man, chiggers attack snakes, turtles, rab-bits, chickens, and other animals. Nymphs

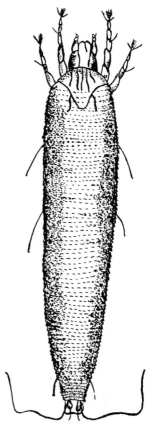

FIG. 12. The pear leaf blis-ter mite (*Eriophyes pyri*), greatly enlarged. (From Utah Agricultural Experiment Sta-tion.)

and adults are associated with the soil, feeding upon insect eggs, small insects and related organisms.

Chiggers may be controlled by spraying infested areas with chlordane, lindane, or toxaphene. Emulsion sprays provide more satisfactory control than those containing wettable powders. Dust-ing with sulphur is also recommended.

Chigger attacks on man may be prevented by treating the cloth-ing with sulphur, diethyl-meta-toluamide, 622 mixture or with inda-lone before going into infested areas. Swabbing chigger bites with a

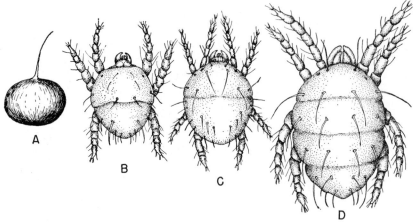

FIG. 13. The European red mite (*Metatetranychus ulmi*). **A,** Egg. **B,** Larva or 6-legged stage. **C,** Nymph. **D,** Adult. (Modified from Agricultural Research Service, U.S.D.A.)

50–50 mixture of chloroform and rubbing alcohol will kill the chiggers and relieve the severe itching; however the chloroform will burn for a short while.

Mange Mites. Mange or sarcoptic mites (Fig. 15) attacking man, hogs, horses, dogs, and other animals are varieties of the same species, *Sarcoptes scabiei*. They feed in the skin and produce definite burrows in which the eggs are laid. The female human itch mite is about $\frac{1}{60}$ inch in diameter, and the male is only one-half as large. The young female deposits ten to 25 eggs in the burrow of the skin and the eggs hatch in three to four days. Following three molts the adult stage is reached in ten to 12 days. The length of life of mites is a month or more.

Human itch is an old malady of man. In centuries past it was thought to be caused by bad blood or improper living. Benzyl benzoate formulations readily eliminate the itch

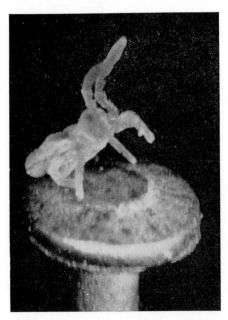

FIG. 14. Adult of a chigger (*Trombicula splendens*) on the head of a pin. (From *Scientific Monthly*.)

when the remedy is properly used. Following treatment, clothing, towels, and bed clothing should be sent to the dry cleaners or laundered to eliminate the mites which may be infesting them.

Hog mange is quite common. Young hogs are usually most greatly affected by mange. When hogs are seen vigorously scratching and rubbing, and lice are not present, they are probably infested with mange mites. The skin on the head, neck, and back becomes rough, scabby, cracked, and pimpled. The life history of the mange mite on hogs is the same as the variety on human beings.

A spray or dip containing lindane at concentrations of 0.05 to 0.06 will control hog mange. Animals should not be treated within 30 days of farrowing or 60 days of slaughtering. Pigs under eight to ten weeks old should not be sprayed or dipped.

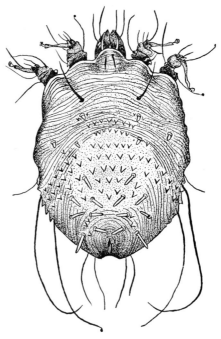

FIG. 15. A sarcoptic mange mite (female) greatly enlarged. (From Agricultural Research Service, U.S.D.A.)

Less effective insecticides are being replaced by use of lindane in control of horse mange. Two sprays should be applied with the second spray a week following the first one.

Sarcoptic mange of dogs may be treated with sulphur ointment, a solution of rotenone in alcohol or in a bland oil, or sprays or dips of lindane. Sarcoptic mange of dogs is not to be confused with follicular or demodectic mange. Follicular mange is very difficult to cure. Valuable animals should be placed under the care of a veterinarian as soon as follicular mange is discovered. Treating infected areas twice weekly with a rotenone solution, or sprays or dips of lindane are the most satisfactory treatments which may be prescribed for follicular mange.

Scab Mites. Scab or psoroptic mites attack sheep, goats, cattle, and other animals. Unlike the sarcoptic mites that burrow in the skin, the psoroptic mites live at the base of the hairs. The skin is pierced by the mouthparts producing an exudate which piles up, hardens, and forms a scab. Among the scabs all stages of the mites are found.

The sheep scab mite (*Psoroptes equi* var. *ovis*) is the most important of the group. The first symptom of sheep scab is tagging of the wool and the rough, matted appearance of the coat. Infested animals rub vigorously and indicate symptoms of severe itching. Females lay about 15 eggs each. The life cycle is extremely short, being about nine days in duration.

Sheep scab is subject to quarantine and its presence should be reported to the proper livestock official immediately. Treatment (spraying or dipping) with 0.06 percent lindane or 0.5 percent toxaphene will eliminate mite infestation. Animals in poor physical condition should not be treated.

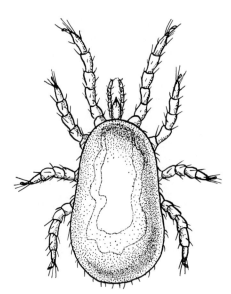

FIG. 16. The chicken mite (*Dermanyssus gallinae*) enlarged. (Redrawn from Herms, *Medical Entomology*, 1950. By permission of The Macmillan Company.)

The Chicken Mite (*Dermanyssus gallinae*). This is an important pest of poultry, particularly of chickens. The mite (Fig. 16) is widely distributed and it is most troublesome in the warm and dry regions. It feeds on the blood of its hosts and its capacity for harm is great. Young chickens and setting hens may be killed by the attacks. Chicken mites are $\frac{1}{30}$ to $\frac{1}{40}$ inch long, grayish or red in color. They hide almost everywhere—in cracks and crevices, under boards and litter, in dry manure and nests. Feeding upon poultry is chiefly at night. Only a relatively few mites will be found on the birds during the day.

Female mites deposit their white eggs in cracks, dry manure, and other similar places. Each female lays 25 to 35 eggs. Adults may live for several months. Only seven to ten days are required for a life cycle in warm weather, thus a large population may be built up in a relatively short time.

In mite control the first consideration is to clean the poultry house. Trash, litter and droppings should be removed prior to the application of insecticides. Co-Ral, malathion and sevin are recommended. The two latter compounds may be applied either as dusts or as sprays, and Co-Ral only as a dust.

Ticks

Ticks are of much economic importance as they suck the blood of their hosts and are vectors of a number of important human and animal diseases. Mammals, birds, and reptiles are attacked. Ticks may be distinguished from mites by their larger size, leathery skin, and spiracles located behind the third or fourth pair of legs.

Ticks are classified into two families, the *Ixodidae* and the *Argasidae*. The *Ixodidae,* or hard ticks, are characterized by a dorsal shield or *scutum,* a *capitulum* (a false or specialized head, anteriorly borne), and *spiracles* located on a *stigmal plate* behind each fourth leg. The scutum of the female is small and it is located directly behind the capitulum. In the male the scutum covers most of the dorsum which prohibits much distention and limits its size. This results in marked sexual dimorphism. The *Argasidae,* or soft ticks, are distinguished from the hard ticks by absence of the scutum, ventrally located capitulum, leg-like pedipalpi (palpi), and small stigmal plates behind the third pair of legs. Sexual dimorphism is not marked.

Mouthparts and accessory structures are borne by the capitulum (Fig. 17). A pair of *chelicerae* project forward from the basal part of the capitulum, the *basis capituli.* Distally the chelicerae are provided with digits bearing recurved teeth. The *hypostome,* bearing recurved teeth, lies in a median position below the chelicerae. On the side of each chelicera is located a four-segmented palpus. When the tick feeds, both chelicerae and hypostome are pushed into the skin of the host.

There are four stages in the development of ticks; namely, *egg, larva* (seed tick), *nymph* (yearling tick), and *adult.* Eggs are usually laid in protected places on the ground. The active six-legged larva seeks its host in different ways. When a host is found a succession of feeding and molting stages follows until the adult stage is reached. After feeding, the larva usually drops to the ground, molts, and becomes a nymph. The nymph has eight legs, as does the adult, but lacks the genital pore. The nymph now finds a new host, engorges, and generally drops to the ground and molts for the second time. A third host is found and the adult feeds to repletion.

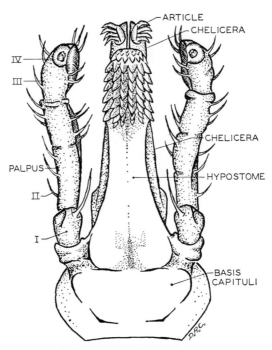

FIG. 17. Ventral view of the capitulum of the lone star tick (*Amblyomma ameri-canum*).

During this time the female is usually fertilized by the male. Following feeding and mating, the engorged female drops to the ground where it deposits the eggs and dies. The biology of the *Argasidae* differs from the above account in that there are several nymphal stages and the adult usually lives for a long while and feeds a number of times. Thus, more host animals are required for completion of the life cycle.

The life cycle of all species of ticks is similar; however, differences in the developmental cycle occur. Some species, such as the cattle tick (*Boophilus annulatus*), complete the life cycle on a single animal. These species are known as one-host ticks. In other species, such as the African red tick (*Rhipicephalus evertsi*), both larva and nymph develop on one host and the adult feeds on a second animal. They are two-host ticks. The lone star tick (*Amblyomma americanum*) and many other species require three hosts for development, leaving the host for each molt. They are referred to as three-host ticks. The fowl tick (*Argas persicus*) and most others of the Argasidae are many-host ticks as they require a number of hosts for the completion of the life cycle.

Family *IXODIDAE*. **The Cattle Tick** (*Boophilus annulatus*). The cattle tick once was not only the most common but the most important tick in the South. It has been eradicated in the United States with the possible exceptions of isolated areas in Florida and parts of Texas along the Mexican border. The cattle industry in the South was greatly handicapped until the cattle tick was eliminated.

The cattle tick is a vector of Texas fever, the causative organism of which is a protozoan (*Babesia bigemina*) which destroys the red blood cells of cattle. The tick obtains the organism in feeding. The parasite undergoes a developmental cycle in the tick and developing eggs of the female become infected. A larva hatching from an infected egg can transmit the disease organism to a new host. This is the first known record of transovarial transmission of a parasite and also the first record of a tick being the intermediate host of a protozoan parasite. Cattle are the principal hosts, but the tick also attacks horses, mules, sheep, goats, deer, and buffaloes.

The parasitic phase of the life cycle of the cattle tick is completed on only one host. Molting and copulation occur on the host animal. Following copulation and engorgement, the adult female drops to the ground and deposits eggs. Each female lays 3,000 to 5,000 or more eggs. The eggs normally hatch in about 30 days. Usually a month is required for the tick to complete its parasitic cycle and drop from the host. Thus, a generation may be produced in about two months. Unfed larvae may live for as long as eight months. Eradication of the cattle tick was feasible because it is a one-host tick and confines its attacks chiefly to cattle.

The Lone Star Tick (*Amblyomma americanum*). This tick (Fig. 18A) is readily recognized by a white spot on the posterior margin of the scutum of the female. It is widely distributed in the southeastern and south-central United States and occurs in greatest numbers in brush and wooded areas. This species shows little host preference. Both mammals and birds are attacked. Larvae, nymphs, and adults commonly attack cattle, horses, man, dogs, hogs, and other animals. Larvae and nymphs are found on small mammals, such as rodents, but adults rarely attack these animals. Birds of a number of species are common hosts of the larvae.

The lone star tick is quite important as a parasite and as a vector of human diseases. The tick is a predisposing factor in screw-worm infestations in cattle, particularly in Texas and Louisiana. The par-

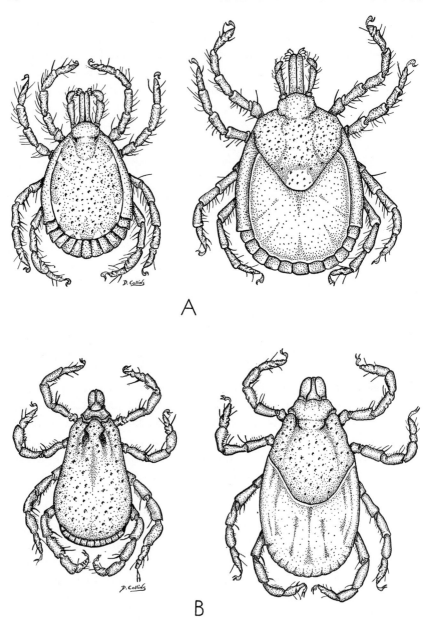

FIG. 18. **A,** The lone star tick *(Amblyomma americanum)*. Left, male; right, female.
B, The brown dog tick *(Rhipicephalus sanguineus)*. Left, male; right, female.

asite is a vector of Rocky Mountain spotted fever in Texas, Oklahoma, and probably other states. It transmits tularemia and is suspected of being a vector of American "Q" fever.

This is a three-host parasite and it normally completes one generation annually. The female lays 3,000 to 4,000 or more eggs. Nymphs and adults may live for more than a year without feeding.

The Brown Dog Tick (*Rhipicephalus sanguineus*). The brown dog tick (Fig. 18**B**) is probably the most cosmopolitan species. It is found in most tropical and temperate climates throughout the world. In 1912 this tick was reported only from South Texas. It is now widely distributed over the North American continent. The dog is the principal host; however other animals, such as cattle, horses, and occasionally man, are attacked. This three-host tick frequently becomes a serious pest in homes and kennels, where its reproduction may occur throughout the year. Females deposit 2,000 to 3,000 eggs and a generation of the tick may be completed in less than two months under favorable conditions. The brown dog tick is implicated as a vector in the transmission of several diseases.

The Gulf Coast Tick (*Amblyomma maculatum*). The Gulf Coast tick is found along the coast fom Virginia into Texas with its range usually extending inland for about 150 miles. It is also present in the West Indies, Mexico, and South America.

Adults parasitize large animals such as cattle, horses, dogs, sheep, goats, wolves, and others. Larvae and nymphs are found principally on birds, but they will also attack small mammals. In those regions where the tick is abundant it is an important pest of cattle. Attachment of the adults is chiefly inside the ears where the feeding of the ticks may produce suppuration and scabs. The Gulf Coast tick is an important predisposing factor in screw-worm infestations.

The Winter Tick (*Dermacentor albipictus*). The winter tick has a wide distribution in North America, but is most commonly found west of the Mississippi River. This is a one-host tick, attacking large animals such as moose, deer, elk, cattle, and horses. Ticks are found on the hosts only during the cooler parts of the year. The parasitic phase of the life cycle of the tick is completed in about six weeks after attachment of the larva to the host. Following copulation and engorgement, the female drops to the ground but it does not deposit its eggs until the next spring. Eggs hatch in three to six weeks. The larvae form a compact cluster and remain dormant during the warm season. With the first cool weather in autumn the larvae become active and attack their hosts.

The American Dog Tick (*Dermacentor variabilis*). This is a widely distributed North American species (Fig. 19). Larvae and

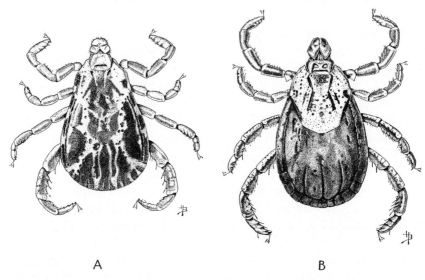

A   B

FIG. 19. The American dog tick (*Dermacentor variabilis*) . **A,** Male. **B,** Female. (From Agricultural Research Service, U.S.D.A.)

nymphs feed principally on rodents, such as mice; and the adults attack dogs, man, cattle, horses, and other large mammals. Females deposit 4,000 to 6,500 eggs. Larvae may live for 11 months, nymphs six months, and unengorged adults for more than two years without food. The American dog tick is an important vector of Rocky Mountain spotted fever in the East. This species also transmits tularemia.

Control of Hard Ticks (*Ixodidae*) on Animals

Arsenical dips, which were widely used in the past for the control of ticks on livestock, have been largely replaced by organic insecticides. As most organic insecticides are toxic to animals and methods of determining the concentration of the insecticides in dipping vats are not generally accurate, spraying is preferred to dipping. Too, spraying of livestock effects a considerable saving in time and labor. For control of ticks on beef cattle the following sprays are recommended: 0.5 percent toxaphene or 0.5 percent toxaphene combined with 0.03 percent lindane; 0.5 percent Co-

Ral, or 0.15 percent Delnav. As milk and other dairy products may become contaminated with these chlorinated hydrocarbons, their use is forbidden in the control of ticks on dairy cattle. Rotenone and pyrethrum sprays are recommended instead and repeated applications are necessary to reduce the tick population. Ticks on dogs may be controlled with rotenone, sevin, Delnav, or diazinon. Infested kennels should be sprayed with either of the two latter compounds.

Family *ARGASIDAE*. The Ear Tick (*Otobius megnini*). This tick (Fig. 20A) is found chiefly in the Southwest where it is a pest

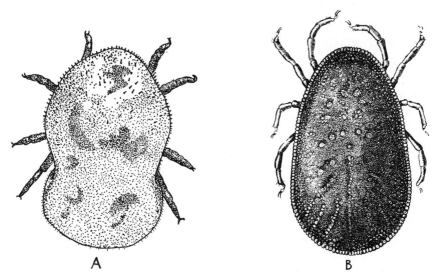

FIG. 20. **A,** The ear tick (*Otobius megnini*). **B,** The fowl tick (*Argas persicus*). (From Agricultural Research Service, U.S.D.A.)

of some importance. Domestic animals, particularly cattle and horses, are mostly attacked; however, wild animals sometimes are infested.

Larvae hatch from eggs which are laid on the ground. They are quite active and find their way into the deep folds of the ears of the host animals where they attach and feed. Seven to twelve days after attachment the larvae molt and become nymphs. There are two nymphal stages. Three weeks to several months following the first molt the second nymphal stage is completed, the ticks leave the host to molt into the adult stage. Adults do not feed, a characteristic which apparently does not exist in other species of ticks. Adults may live for more than a year. Each female lays an average of 800 to 1,000 eggs.

Lindane or Co-Ral formulations applied inside the ears are used in control. Only lindane is used on milk cows. Spraying with oil around salt and feed troughs will aid in elimination of the ear ticks in these breeding areas.

The genus *Ornithodoros* contains a number of species which transmit human and animal diseases. The American species are found chiefly in the Southwest where they are involved in the transmission of relapsing fever of man.

The Fowl Tick (*Argas persicus*). This important pest of poultry (Fig. 20**B**) is distributed in warm countries throughout the world. Chickens are the principal hosts; however, other domestic fowls such as turkeys, ducks and geese, and also wild birds are attacked. More than 600 eggs are laid by each female. Larvae remain attached to the host throughout this stage which is about five days in duration. Then they leave the host, molt, and become nymphs. There may be three nymphal stages. Nymphs and adults feed at night and hide underneath boards and other places of concealment during the daylight hours. Adults partake of several blood meals and the females deposit a batch of eggs following each engorgement. Under most favorable conditions, a generation may be completed in 30 days. Adults are reported to live for several years without food.

Malathion is recommended for control of the fowl tick in both the poultry house and other roosting places. The spray must be thoroughly applied wherever the pests are found. Sprays of chlordane or toxaphene may be employed outside the poultry house.

CLASS DIPLOPODA (MILLIPEDES)

The Diplopoda are represented by the millipedes or "thousand legs" which take the name from the large number of legs on the body. The common representatives of this class (Fig. 21) are cylindrical in form, and have the habit of curling into a close spiral when disturbed. This class is terrestrial and breathes by means of air tubes. A pair of antennae are found on the head. The body consists of a series of similar segments which bear two pairs of legs each, with the exception of the first three. Each of these segments bears only one pair of appendages. Millipedes normally feed on decaying organic matter, particularly manure. Occasionally plants are attacked. The poison bran bait as recommended for cutworm control provides

control of these pests if certain control measures should
be necessary.

CLASS CHILOPODA (CENTIPEDES)

The Chilopoda (Fig. 22),
as in the case of the Diplopoda,
are terrestrial, breathe by
means of air tubes, and bear a
pair of antennae on the head.
Unlike the millipedes, the
body of centipedes is somewhat flattened and each body
segment typically bears one
pair of legs. A pair of poison
claws, located on the first segment behind the head, is used
to paralyze insects and other
small animal life which constitute the principal source of
food. The class as a whole is
usually considered beneficial,
but some of the larger members are capable of inflicting
very painful bites upon man.
The house centipede (*Scuti-*

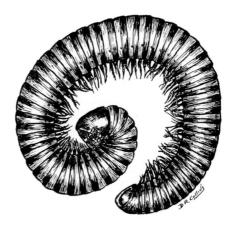

FIG. 21. A common millipede.

FIG. 22. A southwestern centipede.

gera, Fig. 23) is an interesting form with its long and fragile legs. It
feeds on flies and other insects.

FIG. 23. The house centipede (*Scutigera forceps*). (From Illinois Natural History
Survey. Drawn by C. O. Mohr.)

CLASS HEXAPODA (INSECTS)

This is the largest and most important class of the Arthropoda, with more than one-half million known species. We are chiefly concerned in this book with the study of this class. The insect body is divided into three distinct regions; the head, thorax, and abdomen. The thorax bears three pairs of legs and usually two pairs of wings. (See Fig. 24.) Respiration is by means of air tubes and, although living under a great diversity of conditions, insects must be classed as terrestrial animals.

FIG. 24. The eastern lubber grasshopper *(Romalea microptera)*. (From Department of Entomology, A & M College of Texas.)

See the table of General Characteristics of the Common Classes of Arthropoda on the next page.

General Characteristics of the Common Classes of Arthropoda

	Habitat	Breathe by	Body Divisions	Antennae	Legs
Crustacea (Crayfish, etc.)	Chiefly aquatic	Gills or body surface	Cephalothorax and abdomen, or head and body	Generally two pairs	Numerous, may be modified for swimming
Arachnida (Spiders, Mites, etc.)	Chiefly terrestrial	Air tubes, book lungs or body surface	Cephalothorax and abdomen	None	Eight on cephalothorax
Diplopoda (Millipedes)	Terrestrial	Air tubes	Head and body	One pair	Many, typically, 2 pairs per body segment
Chilopoda (Centipedes)	Terrestrial	Air tubes	Head and body	One pair	Many, one pair per body segment
Hexapoda (Insects)	Chiefly terrestrial	Air tubes	Head, thorax, and abdomen	One pair	Six on thorax

3

EXTERNAL ANATOMY
OF INSECTS

In addition to the general characteristics of the phylum *Arthropoda,* which are common to all of its classes, adult insects have: (1) three body divisions—head, thorax, and abdomen; (2) three pairs of legs borne on the thorax; (3) usually two pairs of wings attached to the thorax; (4) one pair of antennae; (5) compound and simple eyes; (6) respiration by means of air tubes; and (7) reproductive organs opening near the caudal end of the abdomen. (See Fig. 25.)

THE EXOSKELETON

A general knowledge of the anatomy of insects is essential in distinguishing groups and individual species and understanding their way of life. Insects are well protected by the exoskeleton which encases the individual like a suit of armor. Much of the success of these animals in competition with other forms of life must be attributed to this external skeleton. Protection is afforded against moisture, dryness, diseases, and natural enemies of many kinds. The exoskeleton protects the soft tissues within and serves as the place of attachment for the numerous muscles of insects. Leverage afforded by the exoskeleton is of the first class and is more efficient than that of animals with an endoskeleton. This superior leverage explains in part the remarkable relative strength of insects.

The exoskeleton is composed of three principal layers—*cuticula, hypodermis,* and *basement membrane.* (See Fig. 26.) The cuticula

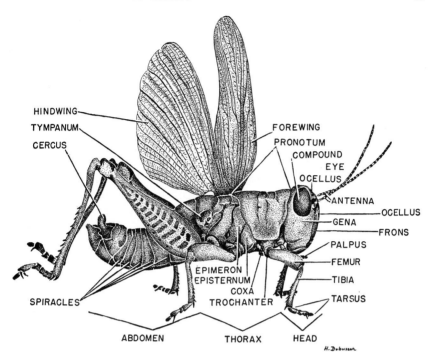

FIG. 25. Lateral view of a grasshopper (*Melanoplus differentialis*). (From Department of Entomology, A & M College of Texas.)

has a stratified appearance and consists of two distinct layers—an outer cuticula, *exocuticula,* and an inner cuticula, *endocuticula.* The exocuticula is covered on the outside by a thin layer about one micron in thickness known as the *epicuticula.* The most characteristic substance in the exocuticula and the endocuticula is chitin. This compound is a nitrogenous polysaccharide and is insoluble and resistant to the action of water, alcohol, and diluted alkalis

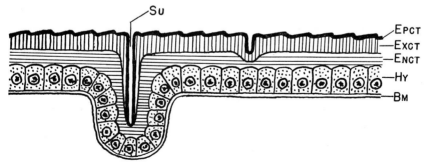

FIG. 26. Diagrammatic sketch of the body wall of an insect. Bm, basement membrane; Enct, endocuticula; Epct, epicuticula; Exct, exocuticula; Hy, hypodermis; Su, suture.

and acids. The epicuticula is nonchitinous in nature. It is composed of substances that protect insects from excessive dessication, humidity, and disease; thus, enabling them to live under a wider range of environmental conditions. The hypodermis consists primarily of a single layer of cells which secretes the cuticula. The basement membrane is a thin, noncellular membrane that forms the inner lining of the hypodermis.

The body wall of an insect is made up of plates or *sclerites* which are usually hardened or sclerotized. The sclerites are separated by lines, known as *sutures*. The sclerites and sutures have definite value in description and identification of insects. The surface of the body bears ridges, hairs, setae, spines, and scales. The body consists of three distinct regions—the *tergum* or dorsal portion, the *pleura* (singular *pleuron*) or sides, and the *sternum* or ventral region.

THE HEAD

The head is a heavily sclerotized capsule-like and unsegmented region which bears the *mouthparts, antennae,* and *eyes.* In the head of a generalized insect, such as the grasshopper (Fig. 27) the parts are fairly distinct; and for this reason the structures discussed here pertain to this insect. Among specialized insects some of these parts are greatly modified or lost through *fusion.* The *frons* or front extends from the region between the eyes to the *clypeus.* It bears the antennae and the median *ocellus.* A distinct suture separates the frons and the clypeus. The clypeus extends from the frons to the base of the labrum. The *genae* or cheeks are located on either side of the frons and below the eyes. The *vertex* is the highest point between the eyes. The *occiput* lies behind the vertex, eyes, and genae. Those parts that extend downward and back of the genae are known as the *postgenae.* The antennae, eyes, and mouthparts are the most important structures located on the head. They are discussed separately.

The Antennae

The paired antennae are located between and in front of the eyes. They vary much in form and size and have considerable value in identification of insects. The function of the antennae is sensory;

the sense of touch in particular is located here. In some instances at least, the senses of smell and hearing are located in the antennae also. The basal segment of the antenna is known as the *scape.* The second segment is the *pedicel,* and the remaining segments are col-

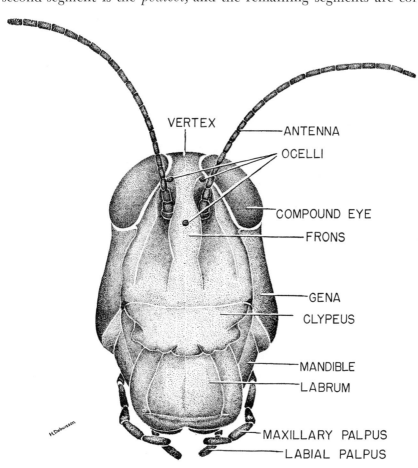

VERTEX

ANTENNA

OCELLI

COMPOUND EYE

FRONS

GENA

CLYPEUS

MANDIBLE

LABRUM

MAXILLARY PALPUS

LABIAL PALPUS

FIG. 27. Front view of the head of a grasshopper (*Melanoplus differentialis*). (From Department of Entomology, A & M College of Texas.)

lectively called the *flagellum.* A number of types of antennae are recognized (Fig. 28). The more common types are:

1. *Setaceous* (bristle-like); the antenna gradually tapers to a point distally;
2. *Filiform* (thread-like); the segments are quite uniform in size;
3. *Moniliform;* the segments are similar in size and bead-like in appearance;
4. *Serrate* (saw-like); the segments are somewhat triangular in shape and appear on one side like the teeth of a saw;

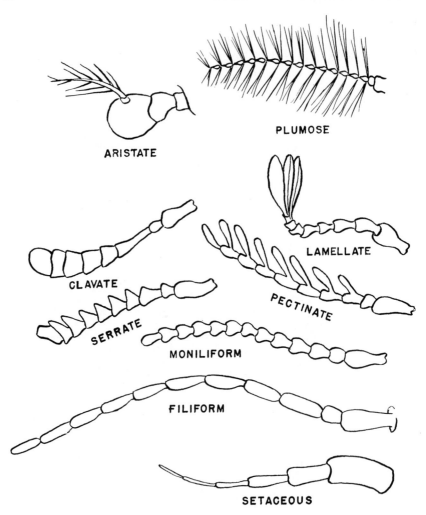

FIG. 28. The more common types of antennae. (Redrawn from various sources.)

5. *Pectinate* (comb-like) ; the antenna has the appearance of a comb;
6. *Clavate* (club-shaped); the segments are enlarged distally to produce a clubbed appearance;
7. *Lamellate;* the distal segments are expanded laterally to form thin plates;
8. *Aristate;* the distal segment is enlarged and bears a dorsal bristle;
9. *Plumose* (feather-like); most segments bear whorls of long hairs.

The Eyes

Typical adult insects have two types of eyes—*ocelli,* or simple eyes, and *compound,* or faceted eyes. When both are present there are two compound eyes and usually three ocelli. In more specialized groups both types may be absent or the number of simple eyes reduced. The ocelli are situated between the compound eyes on the front of the vertex. They are usually quite small and have a single lens for the entire eye. It is generally believed that these simple eyes or photoreceptors increase the insect's responsiveness to stimulation by light.

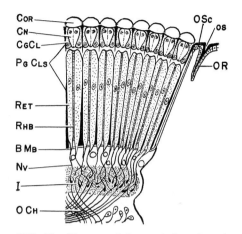

When a compound eye is examined under magnification, it is found to consist of a large number of hexagonal figures known as *facets* (Fig. 29). The number of facets varies from a few to as many as 50,000 in some insects. Each facet is the base of an inverted pyramid which is a functionally separate eye element known as an *ommatidium*.

FIG. 29. Diagram of the vertical section of a part of a compound eye. BMb, basement membrane; CgCl, corneagenous cell; Cn, crystalline cone; Cor, corneal lens; I, lamia ganglionaris; Nv, nerve; OCh, outer chiasma; OR, ocular ridge; Ret, retinula; Rhb, rhabdom. (Redrawn from Snodgrass, *Principles of Insect Morphology*, 1935, by permission of McGraw-Hill Book Co.)

The facet is the lens or cornea of an ommatidium. Behind the cornea is a crystalline cone which rests upon the *retinula*. Usually lying at the sides of the crystalline cone are two hypodermal cells from which the cornea is secreted. The retinula, the sensory part of the eye, is composed of seven or eight elongated pigment cells, the inner surfaces of which form the optic rod, the *rhabdom*. The ommatidium extends to the basement membrane. Nerve fibers from the cells of the retinulae form the optic nerve. Each ommatidium is surrounded by pigment cells.

Two types of vision may be explained on the basis of differences in structure of the ommatidia. Images may be formed by apposition or superposition. In most day-flying insects the ommatidia are so completely surrounded by pigmented cells that light is prevented from passing from one to the other. Hence, each ommatidium perceives only a small part of the object directly in front of it. The complete image is an apposition image.

In many nocturnal insects the ommatidia differ in morphological details from those of most diurnal insects. The ommatidia are more elongate. The retinulae are separated from the crystalline cones by a significant distance and the pigmented cells are concentrated forward between the crystalline cones. Hence, it is possible for a rhabdom to receive light rays from surrounding facets as well as from its own. Each elemental image is the result of the superposition of light from a number of facets. The compound image thus formed is known as a superposition image.

It is still not known how well insects can see. Their eyes cannot be moved or focused. Apparently insects are near-sighted and objects at some distance cannot be seen distinctly. Moving objects may be readily detected since a number of ommatidia would be successively stimulated. Insects can see color. Some have a perception of colors not visible to man, such as bands of ultraviolet rays. Certain insects are practically blind to red, while other insects can see this color.

The Mouthparts

As mouthparts of insects are of such fundamental importance, they deserve careful study. Insects feed on plants and animals in a diversity of ways, and their mouthparts have become modified for these purposes. This has resulted in the development of a number of types with much variation within each. Only representatives of the more important types of mouthparts can be considered here.

1. *Chewing type.* The chewing mouthparts, such as those of the grasshopper (Fig. 30), consist of the *labrum* (upper lip), a pair of *mandibles* (primary jaws), a pair of *maxillae* (secondary jaws), the *labium* (lower lip), the *epipharynx,* and the *hypopharynx* (tongue).

The *labrum* is a flap-like structure attached to the clypeus. The functions of the labrum are to close the front of the mouth cavity, protect the mandibles, and guide the food into the mouth. The *epipharynx* is not a well differentiated mouthpart in chewing insects; however it is an important structure in other types. In the grasshopper's mouthparts it is identified as a swollen area on the ventral surface of the labrum.

The two *mandibles* are the parts that chew and grind the food. They may also be used in cutting; tearing; fighting; and, by the honey bee, molding wax. The mandibles, together with the maxillae, move in a lateral manner and not as the jaws of higher animals.

The paired *maxillae* are more complicated than the mandibles, and consist of several parts. The basal segment, known as the *cardo,*

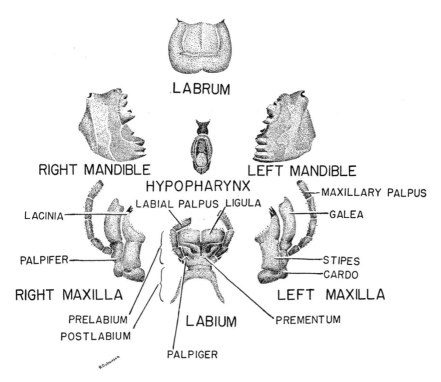

FIG. 30. The chewing mouthparts of a grasshopper (*Melanoplus differentialis*). (From Department of Entomology, A & M College of Texas.)

joins the maxilla to the head. This is joined to the central body of the maxilla, the *stipes.* On the outer side of the stipes is a more or less distinct sclerite known as the *palpifer* to which the palpus is attached. The *palpus* is an antenna-like appendage usually consisting of several segments which bear tactile hairs and also probably organs of smell or taste. The *galea,* a variously shaped segment, and the *lacinia,* which bears teeth, are found attached to the distal end of the stipes. The tooth-like parts of the lacinia may be employed in grasping, cutting, or chewing food.

The *labium,* or lower lip, closes the mouth cavity from below or behind. It has developed from two maxilla-like structures which have fused along the median line. The lower lip is composed of the basal *postlabium* and the distal *prelabium,* separated by the line of flexibility. The prelabium is composed of a large central part (the *prementum*), lobed structures (the *ligula*), and a pair of *palpi*.

The *hypopharynx,* or tongue, arises from the floor of the mouth cavity, and it is usually attached to the inner wall of the labium. Its size and form is quite variable, and it is more or less covered with hairs. The *salivary glands* open through it. These glands are significant in the transmission of diseases by certain insects and also in the production of silk by the silkworm.

2. *Rasping-sucking type.* Rasping-sucking mouthparts are unique in that they are intermediate in their position between the chewing and the piercing-sucking types. Thrips (*Thysanoptera*) have this type of mouthparts, which are used to rasp the surfaces of plants and suck the exuded sap. The cone-shaped beak is composed of the clypeus, labrum, elements of the maxillae, and the labium. Within the beak are found the maxillae, hypopharynx, and the left mandible. The right mandible is not developed. The maxillae and the left mandible are stylet-like in form. The food canal is between the labrum and the hypopharynx, and the saliva passes between the hypopharynx and the labium.

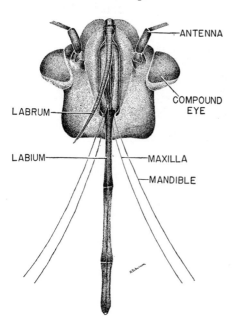

FIG. 31. Head and piercing-sucking mouthparts of a stink bug. (From Department of Entomology, A & M College of Texas.)

3. *Piercing-sucking type.* Piercing-sucking mouthparts are a very common and an extremely important type. The mouthparts have become greatly modified for puncturing the epidermis of plants or the skin of animals and sucking up the sap or the blood.

The type is divided into several subtypes. Mouthparts of the stink bug and the mosquito will be considered here for study.

Mouthparts of the Stink Bug. If the mouthparts of the stink bug (Fig. 31) are examined, a long four-jointed beak will be found lying between the legs when not in use. The main part of this beak is the labium. The labium has nothing to do with the actual sucking process. It acts only as a protective covering for the piercing-sucking organ lying within its folds. Its front surface is grooved throughout its entire length. Lying within this groove is a small, dark, needle-like structure which is responsible for the actual piercing and sucking. The labrum is an insignificant flap-like structure covering the groove of the labium at the base.

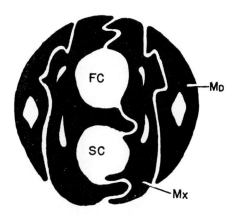

FIG. 32. Diagram of a cross-section of the mandibles and maxillae of the squash bug. Md, mandible; Mx, maxilla; FC, food canal; SC, salivary canal. (Modified from Tower.)

The needle-like structure is composed of four hair-like stylets fitted closely together. However, these stylets are not so firmly united but they may be separated. The outside pair of stylets are the mandibles, while the inner pair are the maxillae (Fig. 32). Although quite small, the maxillae are doubly grooved on their inner faces which, when brought together, form two small tubes extending their entire length. One tube is the food canal through which the liquid is taken. The second tube is the salivary canal through which saliva is pumped into the wound to facilitate the flow of food material.

Mouthparts of the Mosquito. Mouthparts of the mosquito (Fig. 33) consist of the *proboscis,* which is composed of the elongate labium within which are ensheathed six stylets. The stylets are composed of the labrum-epipharynx, the hypopharynx, the two maxillae, and the two mandibles. The food canal is found in the labrum-epipharynx. Located below the labrum-epipharynx is the hypopharynx which is traversed its entire length by the small salivary canal. At the base of the labium are the segmented maxillary palpi.

4. *Sponging type.* Mouthparts of the house fly (Fig. 34) are an excellent example of this type. The fleshy proboscis, which consists chiefly of the labium, projects downward from the head. The labium is grooved on its anterior surface. Within this groove lie the labrum-epipharynx and the hypopharynx. The margins of the convex labrum-epipharynx and the concave hypopharynx form the

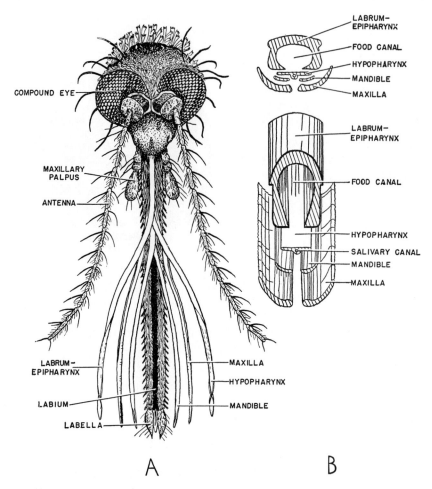

FIG. 33. The piercing-sucking mouthparts of a female mosquito. **A,** Front view of the head with the stylets pulled out of the labium. **B,** Cross-section of the mouthparts and an isometric view of their arrangement. (Redrawn from Metcalf, Flint, and Metcalf, *Destructive and Useful Insects,* 1951, by permission of McGraw-Hill Book Co.)

food canal. Within the hypopharynx is the small salivary canal. Mandibles are absent. Maxillae have disappeared except for the palpi. At the end of the proboscis are two sponge-like structures, the labella. The surfaces of the labella are traversed by capillary canals, *pseudotracheae,* which collect the liquid food and convey it to the food canal.

5. *Siphoning type.* This is the type of mouthparts (Fig. 35) found in moths and butterflies. The mandibles are absent, the labrum is greatly reduced and only palpi and a small basal part remain of the labium. The maxillae are represented by rudimentary palpi

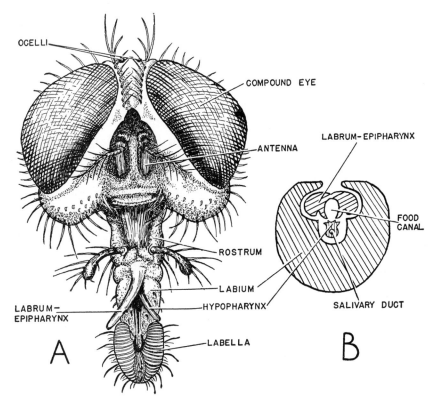

FIG. 34. The sponging mouthparts of the house fly. **A,** Front view of the head and mouthparts with the proboscis pulled out. **B,** Diagrammatic cross-section of the proboscis. (Redrawn from Metcalf, Flint, and Metcalf, *Destructive and Useful Insects,* 1951, by permission of McGraw-Hill Book Co.)

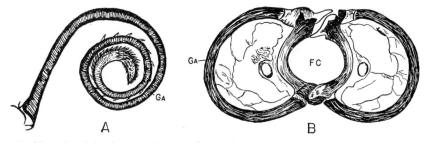

FIG. 35. The siphoning mouthparts of a moth or butterfly. **A,** Coiled proboscis; Ga, galea. **B,** Cross-section of the proboscis; FC, food canal. (Redrawn from *Report on Cotton Insects,* 1879, U.S.D.A.)

and the modified galeae. The two galeae are greatly elongated and joined on their inner concave surfaces to form the long hollow proboscis. When the proboscis is not in use it is coiled like a watch spring underneath the head. In feeding, the tip of the proboscis is dipped into the liquid and the food is drawn into the pharynx.

6. *Chewing-lapping type.* Chewing-lapping mouthparts (Fig. 36) are represented in the honey bee and bumble bee. The labrum and mandibles function as in the chewing type of mouthparts. The maxillae and labium are modified to form a proboscis. The glossa of the labium is greatly elongated and clothed with hairs. It forms a flexible tongue. A temporary food tube is formed by the galeae, labial palpi, and glossa fitting snugly together. Liquids are drawn up the tube by rapid movements of the glossa.

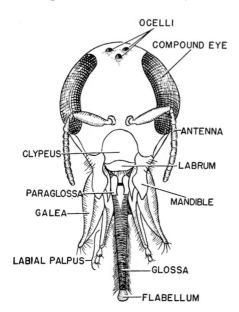

FIG. 36. Chewing-lapping mouthparts of the honey bee. (Redrawn and slightly modified from Metcalf, Flint, and Metcalf, *Destructive and Useful Insects,* 1951, by permission of McGraw-Hill Book Co.)

THE THORAX

Locomotion of insects is performed almost entirely by the thorax. Here are borne the legs and the wings (when present). The thorax is composed of three segments; the *prothorax, mesothorax,* and *metathorax.* Each segment bears a pair of legs. The first pair of wings arise from the mesothorax and the second pair is attached to the metathorax. The areas of the thorax are the *tergum* or *notum* (dorsal surface), the *pleura* (sides), and the *sternum* (ventral surface).

The thorax is quite specialized morphologically. In wingless orders the three segments are similar, but the mesothorax and the metathorax in wing-bearing orders have undergone marked modifications to accommodate functions of both legs and wings. The mesothorax and the metathorax are strongly united and form a compact body unit.

In the grasshopper the notum (tergal plate) of the prothorax resembles a sunbonnet and is known as the pronotum (Fig. 25). It almost completely covers the prothorax and extends over part of the mesothorax.

Each pleuron of the mesothorax and the metathorax of the grasshopper is composed of two sclerites. The anterior sclerite is the *episternum* and the posterior plate is named the *epimeron*. The two sclerites are separated by a slanting suture. Two pairs of spiracles are borne by the thorax: the mesothoracic spiracle, located between the prothorax and the mesothorax, and the metathoracic spiracle, found above the second pair of legs. The sterna of the thoracic segments are composed of broad flat plates. The morphological features of the thorax are essentially the same in different groups of insects; however, marked modifications may have occurred.

The Legs

The legs of insects are variously modified for the purposes for which they are used (Fig. 37). In walking or running insects they

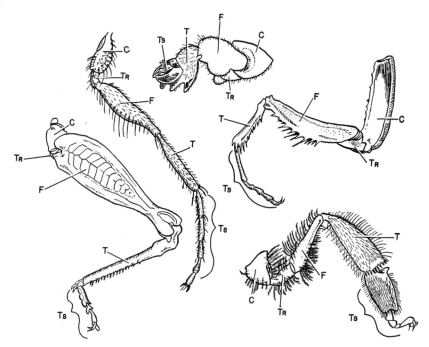

FIG. 37. Legs of insects showing modifications for different uses: C, coxa; Tr, trochanter; F, femur; T, tibia; Ts, tarsus. (Redrawn and modified from various sources.)

are usually quite similar, otherwise many modifications may be found. Regardless of modifications, five divisions of the leg are always present. These are, beginning with the division articulated with the body, the *coxa, trochanter, femur, tibia,* and *tarsus.*

The coxa frequently is found fitting in a cup-like depression of the body. It is generally freely movable. The trochanter is usually quite small and the femur is the largest and most powerful division. The tibia is usually slender, quite long, and provided with downward projecting spines which aid in climbing and maintaining a footing. The tarsus usually consists of several segments and generally terminates in a pair of claws with one or more pads or cushions at their base or between them. A pad between the claws is usually known as an *arolium,* and pads at their base are designated as *pulvilli.*

The Wings

Insects are the only animals with wings, other than birds and bats. While adult insects have a definite number of legs, the number of wings vary from two pairs to none. Certain primitive groups represented by silverfish and springtails have no wings and bear no evidences of a winged ancestry. Other groups, such as lice and

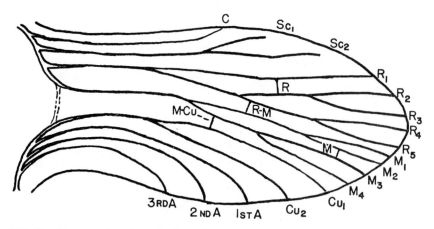

FIG. 38. Venation in a hypothetical wing. (See p. 51 for key to lettering.) (Based on Comstock, by permission of Comstock Publishing Associates.)

fleas, have lost their wings through the parasitic type of life they have followed. Flies and related insects have the second pair of wings modified into balancing organs known as *halteres.* As the wings vary much in their shape, size, and texture and are readily observed, the orders of insects are based on their characteristics.

A wing is an outgrowth of the body wall. It consists of two thin layers of the cuticula fused together except along certain lines where hollow rib-like structures known as veins are formed. They serve to strengthen the wing and give it rigidity. The veins are named and are widely used in the classification and identification of insects. Research has shown that the venation of the wings of all winged insects is basically the same. Similarity in the wing venation is evident when the more generalized types are compared, and particularly when the wing pads of nymphs and pupae are examined. Veins have developed around the tracheae (air tubes) of the wing pads. The names of the veins of a hypothetical type of wing and abbreviations designating them are listed below, beginning with the vein nearest the anterior margin. (See Fig. 38.)

Name of Veins	Abbreviation
Costa	C
Subcosta	SC
Radius	R
Media	M
Cubitus	Cu
First Anal	1st A
Second Anal	2nd A
Third Anal	3rd A

Wings of insects seldom have the number of veins of the hypothetical type. Indications are that fusion rather than loss accounts for the greatest disappearance of veins.

THE ABDOMEN

The abdomen usually consists of a series of ten or eleven ring-like segments which are quite similar with the exception of those on the posterior end which are modified. However, in many insects considerable reduction has occurred and only five or six segments are found. The female bears on the end of the abdomen an ovipositor which is adapted for egg deposition; cerci are present in the generalized groups. In the wasp-like insects the ovipositor has been modified into a sting. External genitalia of the males may also be found on the extremity of the abdomen, along with the cerci of the more generalized orders. In the immature stages of insects, particularly caterpillars of Lepidoptera, prolegs are located on the abdomen. Nymphs of mayflies (*Ephemeroptera*) and larvae of some of the neuropteroid insects are other examples of immature insects with appendages on the abdomen.

Each abdominal segment usually is composed of a dorsal plate (tergum or notum) and a ventral plate (sternum). Along the lower margins of the dorsal plates of the abdomen are a series of paired openings known as *spiracles* which lead into the tracheae of the respiratory system. Six to eight pairs of spiracles are usually found on the abdomen.

4

INTERNAL ANATOMY AND PHYSIOLOGY OF INSECTS

Although an insect may be very minute, its body organization and its ability to perform the essential functions of life are as perfect as those of man. Insects are unusual animals in many respects. Their life processes and behavior differ decidedly from those of higher animals in a number of ways. A brief study of the internal anatomy and some of the physiological processes of insects affords a much deeper insight into the life of insects and the problems which they present. Those students whose principal interest in the study of entomology is to learn how to control insect pests may obtain a wealth of fundamental information from this study which will be of aid in many practical problems.

The Digestive System

The alimentary canal (Fig. 39) is a tube extending through the body cavity from the mouth to the anus. It is divided into three

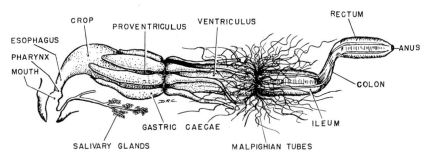

FIG. 39. Digestive system of a grasshopper (*Melanoplus differentialis*).

53

distinct parts—the foregut or *stomodaeum,* the midgut or *mesenteron (ventriculus),* and the hindgut or *proctodaeum.* A *cardiac
valve* between the foregut and the midgut, and a *pyloric valve* between the midgut and hindgut are usually present and regulate the
flow of food materials from one section of the digestive tract to another. The foregut and hindgut arise by invaginations of the body
wall and are lined with a thin layer of the cuticula. The ventriculus
is formed from the endoderm and lacks this lining of cuticula. As
the food of different species consists of most all kinds of materials,
many modifications of the alimentary canal exist.

The foregut is usually divided into the *mouth, pharynx, esophagus, crop,* and *proventriculus* (gizzard). The mouth is the anterior
opening of the alimentary canal, and the pharynx is the cavity in
which the food is received. Leading from the pharynx to the crop
is a simple tube known as the esophagus. The crop is usually a
simple dilation and its size is conspicuous in many insects, e.g., the
grasshopper. Behind the crop is the proventriculus or gizzard which
is usually present in those insects which feed on solid substances.
This structure is lined with sclerotized ridges or teeth that grind and
strain the food before it enters the ventriculus (stomach) through
the cardiac valve.

The midgut (ventriculus or stomach) is a relatively large simple
tube. Into its anterior region may open *gastric caeca,* blind-end tubes
of a glandular nature, the purpose of which is to secrete digestive
enzymes. Digestive enzymes are also secreted by the stomach walls.
Digestion is completed and most absorption of the food occurs in
the stomach. Some absorption, however, takes place in the ileum.
The walls of the stomach are not lined with cuticula, which permits
soluble food materials to be readily absorbed through the membrane. Insects which may ingest poisons with their food—those with
either chewing, sponging, or lapping mouthparts—are usually more
readily killed by way of the stomach than by the contact action
of insecticides on the body wall.

The remaining contents of the stomach pass through the pyloric
valve into the hindgut, which is ordinarily divided into three parts
—the *ileum, colon,* and *rectum.* The function of the ileum is absorption. The colon, which is often absent, is of doubtful function.
It contains indigestible matter. The rectum collects and expels the
waste.

Insects have salivary glands which in their simplest form are a
pair of blind-end tubes lying alongside the esophagus. They have

arisen as evaginations of the foregut. The saliva is discharged either into the mouth or into the host upon which the insect is feeding. The gastric caeca and the walls of the stomach secrete most of the digestive enzymes. All of the digestive enzymes present in higher animals are generally found in insects. But not all may be found in any one species. Also, specialized enzymes are found in some species that are not found in mammals. The types present are dependent upon the nature of the food of the particular insect.

The Malpighian Tubes

The Malpighian tubes function in insects as kidneys. They are long, slender, hollow, blind-end tubes of variable number which open into the ileum at its juncture with the stomach. They have arisen as evaginations of the hindgut. As blood flows over the tubes, wastes, chiefly nitrogenous, are taken up and discharged into the ileum. They are expelled from the body with the feces. Certain waste materials are deposited in the cuticula of insects. Silk is produced by the Malpighian tubes in larvae of neuropteroid insects, such as aphis lions.

The Respiratory System

Insects have a rather unique as well as a very efficient respiratory system (Fig. 40). Instead of oxygen being transported by the blood, it is carried directly to the tissues and cells by tubes known as

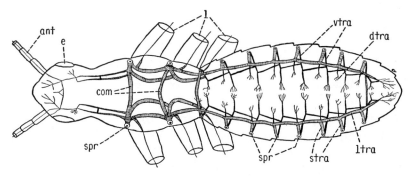

FIG. 40. Diagram of a horizontal section of an insect showing the arrangement of the principal tracheae. Ant, antenna; com, commissural tracheae; dtr, dorsal trachea; e, compound eye; l, legs; ltr, main longitudinal tracheal trunk; spr, spiracles; stra, spiracular tracheae; vtra, ventral trachea. (From Borror and DeLong, *An Introduction to the Study of Insects,* after Kolbe, by permission of Rinehart & Company and McGraw-Hill Book Co.)

tracheae, and most of the carbon dioxide is eliminated in the same way. Part of the carbon dioxide is carried by the blood and escapes through the body wall. Insects breathe through a series of small, paired openings along the sides of the body. These openings are known as *spiracles.* Some of the spiracles have valves by means of which they may be closed. Usually two pairs of spiracles are found on the thorax and six to eight pairs on the abdomen. The spiracles open into short transverse tracheae that connect to a large longitudinal trachea on each side. The tracheae divide many times and terminate in tracheoles. The tracheoles permeate the tissues and reach the cells where the oxygen is delivered and most of the carbon dioxide is removed. The large longitudinal tracheae of insects whose activities require relatively large quantities of oxygen are enlarged into air sacs. Tracheae arise as invaginations of the body wall and are lined with cuticula which takes the form of spiral thickenings, the *taenidia.* These spring-like spirals prevent the collapse of the tracheae and provide elasticity. The tracheoles lack taenidia; they are thin-walled and may contain fluids.

Respiration is effected largely through diffusion, and also by expansion and contraction of the abdomen, and body movements. Larvae of some aquatic insects, especially in the early stages of development, and a number of parasitic larvae respire through the body wall. Many nymphs and larvae of aquatic insects have tracheal gills. Some insects living in water come to the surface for air and others carry with them air bubbles clinging to special parts of the body.

Insects are cold-blooded animals. Within certain limits, their metabolism fluctuates with the temperature. Insect activity stops at about 40° F.; as the temperature increases, activity increases. The optimum temperature for insect activity is reached around 75° F. When the temperature is increased to about 95° F. or higher, activity decreases. These factors must be given consideration in insect control.

Contact poisons and fumigants enter the insect's body by way of the respiratory system or the body wall. Because body metabolism is slowed down at low temperatures, fumigants and contact poisons with residual toxicities of short duration, such as nicotine, should not be used. Furthermore, fumigants should not be employed at temperatures higher than 85° F., for above this point the gases become too volatile and unmanageable. Often attempts are made to kill insects with carbon monoxide gas. This gas kills animals by combining with the iron in the haemoglobin of the blood, destroying the capacity of the blood to carry oxygen. As insects obtain oxygen directly through the tracheal system this effect does not occur in them. The use of low temperatures and superheating in the control of insects is important and will be discussed later.

The Muscular System

Insects have a complicated muscular system. The muscles are distinctly cross-striated and the fibers are strong. They may be grouped into skeletal muscles and visceral muscles. The skeletal muscles are arranged to produce movements of the mouthparts, antennae, legs, wings, and body segments. Most insects require five sets of muscles for the operation of the wings alone. Two types of muscles move the leg; one type moves the leg as a unit, and the other moves individual segments. A layer of visceral muscles covers the digestive tract and produces wave-like movements. Also, bands of this type of muscle surround the heart and produce pulsations. Movements of insects may be quite rapid, as represented by the vibration of wings in flight; or slow, as in the walking of *Phasmidae* and certain beetles, e.g., *Zopherus* spp., and the crawling of larvae.

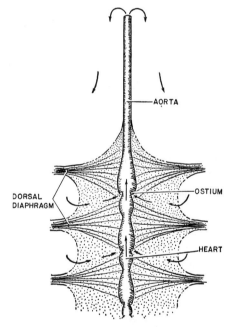

FIG. 41. The dorsal blood vessel and the dorsal diaphragm. (Redrawn from Snodgrass, *Principles of Insect Morphology*, 1935, by permission of McGraw-Hill Book Co.)

The Circulatory System

The circulatory system of insects is simple and quite incomplete. It consists of a tube (Fig. 41) lying close to the dorsal surface extending from the abdomen to the head. In the abdomen the tube is constricted, forming chambers. This constricted portion is known as the *heart*. The posterior end of the heart is closed; but a pair of openings *(ostia)*, through which the blood may enter, are found on the sides of each chamber. Valves prevent the blood from flowing out. Wave-like contractions force the blood or haemolymph forward through that part of the tube that is not chambered, and which is known as the *aorta*. The aorta may divide into several short branches in the head where the blood flows out into the body cavity.

As the pressure increases in the anterior region of the body cavity the blood flows backward, bathing the tissues. Food is picked up as it flows over the digestive tract and carried to the cells where it is needed. Wastes, chiefly nitrogenous, are taken up from the cells and are removed by the Malpighian tubes. Blood has only a secondary role in respiration. Haemoglobin is not known to be present in the plasma of insects except in a few midge larvae. However, the blood does aid in the transportation and exchange of oxygen and carbon dioxide in the cells, inasmuch as both gases are soluble in it. The blood is usually light amber, but its color may be brown, yellow, or green. Several different types of cells resembling leucocytes are found in the blood; they perform different functions. True red corpuscles are not present.

The Nervous System

The central nervous system of insects (Fig. 42) is found near the ventral surface along the median line of the body. It consists of cells grouped into bundles called *ganglia, connectives* or *commissures* which connect the ganglia, and nerve fibers leading from the ganglia to all parts of the body. Embryological studies indicate a ganglion of a paired nature for each body segment, but in the adult insect various degrees of coalescence are found.

The largest ganglion, the brain, is located in the head above the esophagus. Since it lies above the esophagus, it is also known as the *supraesophageal* ganglion. The brain innervates the eyes, antennae, and other structures of that part of the head. In addition, it serves as a coordinator for the other ganglia. An insect deprived of its brain may not die directly, but may lack coordination of its activities.

The other ganglia likewise supply nerves to those parts of the body where they are located. The ganglion below the esophagus is known as the *subesophageal* ganglion. In the more generalized insects a ganglion will be found in each thoracic segment. But, in some of the more specialized groups not only may the three ganglia have fused, but they may have included some of the abdominal ganglia as well.

A small *"sympathetic"* nervous system consisting of several elements is also present. It is concerned with the digestive system, heart, respiratory system, and sexual organs.

A number of insecticides kill by way of the nervous system. For example, nicotine paralyzes the ganglia, and thus causes death of the insect. DDT, BHC, and pyrethrum are examples of other insecticides acting upon the nervous system.

The Reproductive System

A general knowledge of the organs of reproduction (Fig. 43) and their processes is fundamental in understanding the reproductive potential and other phases of the biology of insects. Normally insects are of the two sexes, and mating is essential to reproduction; but among ants, bees, wasps, termites, and other groups sexually undeveloped individuals are found. It is usually the females, such as the worker of the honey bee, that are incapable of reproduction. Among some insects individuals known as gynandromorphs, which

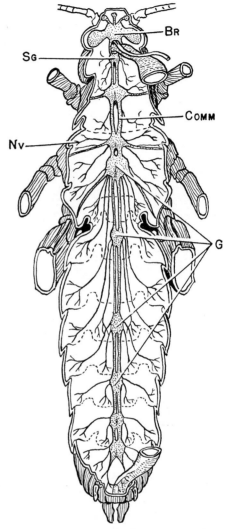

FIG. 42. Central nervous system of a grasshopper (*Dissosteira carolina*). Br, brain (supraesophageal ganglion); Comm, commissure; G, ganglia; Nv, nerve; Sg, subesophageal ganglion. (Modified from Snodgrass, *Principles of Insect Morphology*, 1935, by permission of McGraw-Hill Book Co.)

have characteristics of both sexes, are occasionally found. Some insects, e.g., aphids, may reproduce for a number of generations without fertilization. This is known as parthenogenetic reproduction or parthenogenesis. Although parthenogenetic reproduction is quite common among insects, it is not by any means the rule.

The paired *ovaries* of the female lie in the upper front region of the abdomen. An ovary consists of a number of tubes (*ovarioles*) within which the eggs are developed. The tubes of each ovary con-

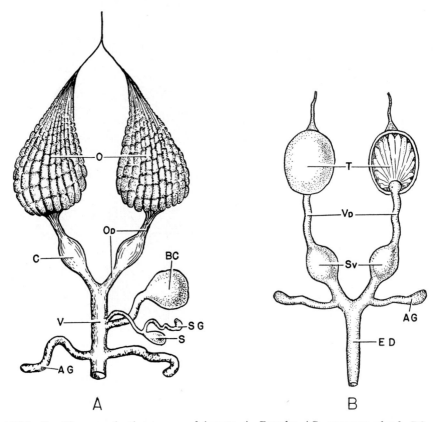

FIG. 43. The reproductive organs of insects. **A,** Female: AG, accessory gland; BC, bursa copulatrix; C, calyx; O, ovaries; Od, oviduct; S, spermatheca; SG, spermathecal gland; V, vagina. **B,** Male: AG, accessory gland; ED, ejaculatory duct; Sv, seminal vesicles; T, testes; Vd, vasa deferentia. (Based on Comstock, by permission of Comstock Publishing Associates.)

nect with the *oviduct* which extends downward and backward. The oviduct is joined with that of the opposite side to form the *vagina* or genital chamber. The vagina extends backward to its outer opening near the posterior end of the abdomen. A sperm receptacle (*spermatheca*) connects with the vagina. Here sperm is stored for the fertilization of the eggs. Accessory glands also open into the vagina. They secrete a substance for fastening eggs to objects, cementing them together, or forming a capsule over a mass of them.

A number of deviations from the above described system occur, chiefly in the number of ovarioles, and in the shape and arrangement of the ovaries, glands, and ducts.

The *testes* of the male are located in the body much as the ovaries of the female. Each opens into a seminal duct, the *vas deferens* (pl. *vasa deferentia*). The vasa deferentia are usually longer than the oviducts of the female and may be coiled or twisted. They pass downward and backward and unite below the digestive tract to form the *ejaculatory duct*. *Seminal vesicles* for the storage of sperm may be found either in the vasa deferentia or the ejaculatory duct. Also, various accessory glands associated with the ejaculatory duct may be present. The ejaculatory duct terminates within or on the *penis*.

Also, there are special external organs for mating and egg laying. The female bears an organ for use in egg deposition, the *ovipositor*. This structure is variously modified for specific purposes. In the stinging Hymenoptera it is associated with poison glands and modified into a sting. The external genitalia of the male consist of special clasping structures of some type, which are often quite complicated and complex in form.

5

GROWTH AND METAMOR-
PHOSIS OF INSECTS

Most insects undergo remarkable changes in form during the course of their development. The May beetle was once a grub; a butterfly developed from a caterpillar; and flies evolved from maggots. Knowledge of how insects grow and the changes (metamorphosis) through which they pass in attaining the adult stage is one of the basic essentials in the study of entomology, for this information enters into every phase of a study of the science.

Insects develop from eggs which are formed from primordial germ cells in the ovaries of the females. Eggs are usually laid, and hatching occurs after a variable length of time. Those insects that lay eggs are termed *oviparous*. In some cases the eggs are retained in the body of the female until hatched. Such insects are *ovoviviparous;* that is, living young are deposited instead of eggs. Rarely, mature larvae are produced, which is known to occur in a few flies such as the sheep ked and the tsetse fly. They receive nourishment from the body of the female, a condition suggestive of *viviparous* reproduction of mammals.

The eggs of insects are small; and, although they may vary considerably in size, shape, color, and markings, they are more alike than the insects that laid them. They are covered with a shell, the chorion, which is formed by the follicular epithelium of the tubes of the ovaries. Fertilization occurs at the time the eggs are being laid. The stored spermatozoa enter the eggs through the micropyle, located on the proximal end. The duration of the egg stage may vary from a few hours to several months or longer. In some insects, viz., aphids, embryonic development occurs without fertilization of the eggs (parthenogenesis).

Although insect eggs are much alike it is often possible to specifically identify them. This may be of much practical value in predicting outbreaks of certain pests, such as grasshoppers and the bollworm. In attempting to identify an insect in the egg stage several things should be noted—shape, size, color and sculpturation, host, places of deposition, and whether or not they are laid singly or in clusters.

Insects usually multiply rapidly. The rate of increase is governed by the number of eggs laid, the length of a life cycle, and the rapidity with which generations follow each other.

The number of eggs an insect lays is as variable as insect life itself. The true female of certain aphids may lay one overwintering egg. The moth of the corn earworm may produce as many as 3,000 eggs, and the cotton leafworm moth averages about 600 eggs, while the queen of the honey bee may lay 1,500 to 2,000 daily for several weeks without cessation. The average number of eggs laid by all insects would probably be 100 to 200. All the eggs may be laid at one time; they may be deposited in batches, which are produced at varying intervals; or they may be laid in small numbers daily over a considerable period of time.

Eggs are generally laid where the newly hatched young have ready access to suitable food. After the eggs are deposited the female usually pays no further attention to them and the young insects, upon hatching, must care for themselves.

Upon hatching from the egg, the young insect is usually quite unlike the adult into which it develops. The changes which occur during growth or development to the adult stage are termed *metamorphosis*. The young insect is quite small when it emerges from the egg. It feeds ravenously, but the extent of its growth is restricted by a rather rigid exoskeleton which encases the body. In order to continue to grow and develop the insect must periodically replace the exoskeleton with one of larger size. This is accomplished by a process of shedding the outer skin, called *molting*. Prior to the time of each molt feeding ceases and a molting fluid collects between the old and the newly formed cuticula. A slit in the old cuticula then appears, usually along the middorsal line of the head and thorax, through which the insect works its way out. The insect now has a soft elastic cuticula which is capable of further expansion to accommodate the increased size of the body. This new cuticula hardens after a lapse of several hours, and the growth of the insect is again definitely restricted. Thus the insect grows by a series of growing stages, called *instars,* and *molts.* The number of molts is variable but quite constant for any one species. Insects ordinarily molt five or six times.

METAMORPHOSIS

All insects do not develop into the adult stage by the same series of changes or type of metamorphosis. Metamorphosis is grouped into four types, namely:

1. *No Metamorphosis (Ametabolous Development).* Stages of development; (1) Egg, (2) Young, (3) Adult. Example, Silverfish.
2. *Incomplete Metamorphosis (Hemimetabolous Development).* Stages of development; (1) Egg, (2) Nymph, (3) Adult. Example, Mayfly.
3. *Gradual Metamorphosis (Paurometabolous Development).* Stages of development; (1) Egg, (2) Nymph, (3) Adult. Example, Stink Bug.
4. *Complete Metamorphosis (Holometabolous Development).* Stages of development; (1) Egg, (2) Larva, (3) Pupa, (4) Adult. Example, House Fly.

No Metamorphosis (Ametabolous Development)

When it hatches from the egg the young insect with ametabolous development looks exactly like the adult except in size and differences in armature of spines and setae (Fig. 44). The insect in

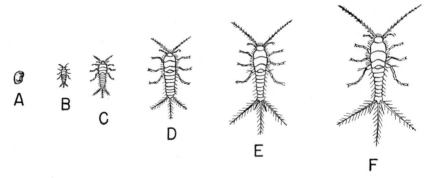

FIG. 44. No metamorphosis (ametabolous development). **A,** Egg. **B, C, D, E,** Stages of young. **F,** Adult. Example, silverfish.

each instar appears as in the preceding instar except for size and some minor differences. Some forms may molt after sexual maturity. In this respect they resemble the *Crustacea.* The young and adults live in the same environment, have the same types of mouthparts and feeding habits. This type of development is represented by the *Thysanura* (silverfish) and the *Collembola* (springtails). These groups of primitive insects are wingless, and there is no evidence to indicate that their ancestors possessed wings.

Incomplete Metamorphosis (Hemimetabolous Development)

Three orders of insects are characterized by this type of development—*Ephemeroptera* (mayflies), *Odonata* (dragonflies), and *Plecoptera* (stoneflies). (See Fig. 45.) The changes which occur during the development of the immature stages (called *nymphs* or

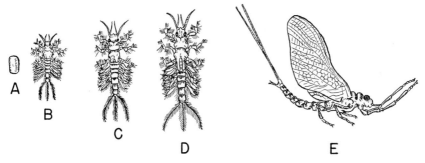

FIG. 45. Incomplete metamorphosis (hemimetabolous development). **A,** Egg. **B, C, D,** Nymphal stages. **E,** Adult. Example, mayfly.

naiads) of these insects are more pronounced than in the case of insects with gradual metamorphosis but are not nearly so great as the changes which occur in those forms which have complete metamorphosis. The immature stages of these insects are spent in water, while the adults are aerial. The nymphs breathe by means of tracheal gills and their bodies are variously modified for the type of environment in which they live. The immature forms have only slight resemblance to the adults into which they develop. They also grow by a series of instars (growing stages) and molts. Following the last molt the insects have fully developed wings fitted for an aerial life and a tracheal system for breathing oxygen from the air, together with other modifications of body structure.

Gradual Metamorphosis (Paurometabolous Development)

In those groups of insects with this type of metamorphosis the newly hatched individual resembles the adult in general body form, but lacks wings and the external genital appendages. (See Fig. 46.) The young insect (called a nymph) undergoes a series of feeding stages (instars), which in each case is followed by a molt. With each successive molt the nymph resembles the adult more than it did in the preceding stage. Thus, step by step the adult stage is

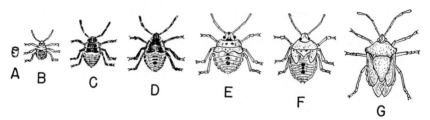

FIG. 46. Gradual metamorphosis (paurometabolous development). **A,** Egg. **B, C, D, E, F,** Nymphal stages. **G,** Adult. Example, stink bug.

reached. The wing buds appear in the latter instars and are externally developed. Both nymphs and adults have the same type of mouthparts, food habits, and occur in the same habitat. Grasshoppers, squash bugs, and aphids are examples of insects with gradual metamorphosis.

Complete Metamorphosis (Holometabolous Development)

Most species of insects undergo a complete metamorphosis, which includes four developmental stages; namely, *egg, larva, pupa,* and *adult.* (See Fig. 47.) The larva differs greatly in form from the

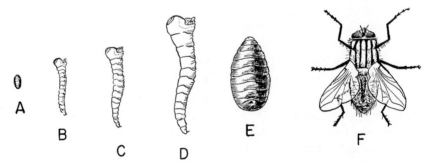

FIG. 47. Complete metamorphosis (holometabolous development). **A,** Egg. **B, C, D,** Larval stages. **E,** Pupa. **F,** Adult. Example, house fly.

adult into which it develops. It passes through a series of growing stages (instars) and molts, but, unlike insects with gradual metamorphosis, the larva does not resemble the adult any more closely following a molt than it did prior to the same, but remains worm-like or grub-like in form. The larval stage is primarily a growing stage. All larvae have chewing or modified chewing mouthparts. Various names are applied to the larvae of insects of different orders. Beetle larvae are known as grubs, butterfly and moth larvae as caterpillars, and the larvae of flies are known as maggots. The wing pads, and in those groups which have footless larvae, the legs develop internally and are everted at the time of pupation. Other changes are in the process of development also toward the close of the larval stage.

When the larva has attained maturity it ceases to feed and following a period of inactivity transforms to the pupa. In this stage the insect usually remains inactive, does not feed, but undergoes marked physiological and morphological changes. It is in this stage that the processes of changing a worm-like body into that of a moth, fly, bee, or beetle is completed.

In the case of many insects provisions are made by the larva for the protection of the helpless pupa. Some seek protection in the ground, others under the bark of trees, some spin cocoons as do moths, or pupate in the last larval skin like flies.

Following the lapse of a period of several days or months the adult emerges from the pupal stage. Special provisions are always made by nature to enable the adult to escape from the pupa. The primary function of the adult insect is reproduction. In many insects the eggs are laid and the adults die soon afterward. Others live for a longer period, and some, such as ants and certain beetles, live for a long time.

The active stages of insects with gradual or with no metamorphosis have identical mouthparts and feeding habits. In incomplete metamorphosis both the nymphs and adults have chewing mouthparts (vestigial in adult mayflies), but food habits and habitats are different. Those insects with complete metamorphosis may have entirely different types of mouthparts and food habits in the larval and the adult stages, or again, they may be similar. Larvae (caterpillars) of moths have chewing mouthparts and feed on a diversity of materials, while the adults have siphoning mouthparts and normally feed on nectar of plants. Boll weevil larvae and adults both have chewing mouthparts and feed upon the fruit of the cotton plant, while flea larvae feed on inert organic material with their chewing mouthparts and the adults suck the blood of their hosts.

DIFFERENT LARVAL TYPES

Larvae of different insects with complete metamorphosis vary considerably in form (Fig. 48). Many types of larvae exist, and some occur so commonly that names have been given them. Several of the most important types merit mention here.

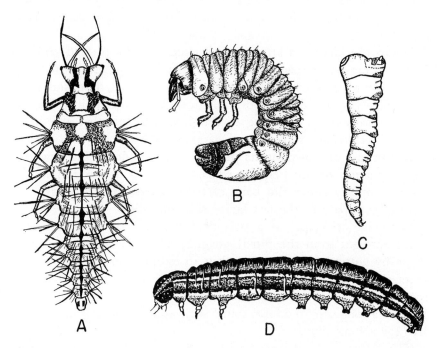

FIG. 48.   Common types of larvae. **A,** Campodeiform larva of a lacewing fly (*Neuroptera, Chrysopidae*). **B,** Scarabaeiform larva of a May beetle (*Coleoptera, Scarabaeidae*). **C,** Vermiform larva of a house fly (*Diptera, Muscidae*). **D,** Eruciform larva of a moth (*Lepidoptera, Phalaenidae*).

Scarabaeiform

The scarabaeiform type of larvae is grub-like. The white grubs of May beetles are the most common examples. They are almost cylindrical, curved, and bear short thoracic legs, but have no abdominal prolegs. Most of them are found in the ground, wood, or decaying organic matter. These larvae are sluggish and movement is slow.

Campodeiform

These larvae resemble certain members of the *Thysanura*. The body is elongate and flattened to some degree. Antennae and cerci are usually quite conspicuous and the legs are developed for running. Common examples are found among the *Coleoptera* and *Neuroptera*.

Eruciform

Most larvae (caterpillars) of *Lepidoptera* are the eruciform type. The body is cylindrical; short thoracic legs are present, and the abdomen is provided with prolegs.

Vermiform

Larvae of this type are maggot-like. The body is elongate and legs are absent. Representatives are found in the *Diptera, Hymenoptera, Coleoptera,* and other orders.

DIFFERENT PUPAL TYPES

Three types of pupae are readily recognized. They are the *coarctate, exarate,* and *obtect* types (Fig. 49).

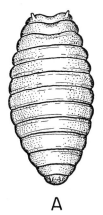

A   B   C

FIG. 49. Principal types of pupae. **A,** Coarctate type, such as pupae of flies. **B,** Exarate type, such as pupae of beetles. **C,** Obtect type, such as pupae of moths.

Coarctate

Coarctate pupae remain in the hardened larval skin (puparium), as with the pupae of most dipterous insects.

Exarate

Pupae of this type have the legs, wing pads, and antennae free. Most pupae of insects with complete metamorphosis, *Diptera* and *Lepidoptera* excepted, are exarate pupae.

Obtect

Pupae which have the legs, antennae, and wing pads glued to the body, such as pupae of *Lepidoptera*.

6

INSECT CONTROL

In broadest terms insect control includes the many and diverse factors which kill, repel, and interfere with feeding, propagation, and dispersal of insects in every way. Insect control is divided into two groups—natural control factors and artificial control measures. Natural control includes all factors which operate independently of man and over which he has no control. Artificial control includes mechanical and physical control measures, cultural control, use of chemical compounds, and other measures applied or influenced by man.

NATURAL CONTROL

The many and interrelated factors of nature tend to limit the numbers of all plants and animals, and keep them in proper balance. The influence of man and other agencies may bring about a disturbance of this natural equilibrium and cause an increase of some species at the expense of others.

The natural control factors that act as checks on insect populations, their distribution and activities include (a) climate—temperature, rainfall, and sunshine; (b) physical factors—mountain ranges, seas and other water barriers, and dominant plant and animal types; (c) predators and parasites indigenous to the country—insects, birds, mammals, reptiles, and fish; and (d) diseases naturally present—bacteria, viruses, and fungi.

Climate is the most important natural force in keeping insect populations in check, inasmuch as the factors of temperature, humidity, rainfall, and sunshine affect either directly or indirectly every phase of the life of an insect. When an attempt is made to evaluate the effects of any climatic factor upon an insect its natural habitat must be considered. A warm, moist environment is favorable for the development of most insects. Extremes of temperature are destructive to insect life. Cold, wet winter weather, especially when sharply fluctuating temperature changes occur, destroys many insects. This weather condition is particularly effective against those species of tropical origin. Conversely, hot, dry weather serves as a check on most insects.

The importance of air currents in the dissemination of insects is being more fully realized. The wind is an important factor in the spread of introduced pests, such as the pink bollworm. A number of species are known to drift northward from milder climates each season with the aid of air currents. For example, certain species of leafhoppers drift hundreds of miles from their breeding grounds; and several species of moths, such as the cotton leafworm moth and the fall armyworm moth, disseminate annually with the aid of the wind.

Physical factors play an important role in the distribution and abundance of insects. Mountain ranges and large bodies of water provide effective barriers to their spread. The soil type and its fertility determine the plant and animal life, which in turn tends to limit the number and type of species and their abundance. The physical characteristics of the soil may determine the presence or absence of soil-inhabiting species.

Every insect has its natural enemies, such as insect parasites and predators, birds, mammals, and reptiles. As an insect population increases, the natural enemies begin to increase since they have a larger food supply. This increase continues until most of the hosts are destroyed. Then their number in turn decreases, which provides the opportunity for the host insect population to build up again. The scales may tip first in one direction and then the other, and a balance within limits is maintained.

Insects, as do other groups of animals, have diseases of their kind. Infestations of chinch bugs are frequently eliminated by fungous diseases. Grasshoppers and house flies are also frequently attacked by fungi. Bacterial and virus diseases frequently wipe out great populations of insects, especially certain species of caterpillars. Protozoan diseases are present but are of less importance.

ARTIFICIAL CONTROL

Natural control is more important in keeping insect populations in check but cannot be depended upon at all times for the protection of crops and other products, and artificial measures must be employed. Artificial control measures may be grouped into five classes: (1) mechanical and physical control, (2) cultural control or farm and ranch practices, (3) biological control, (4) legal control, and (5) chemical control.

Mechanical and Physical Control

Certain mechanical and physical measures are important in eliminating or preventing the attacks of insect pests. The screening of houses is the most valuable of all mechanical controls. Screening to eliminate flies, mosquitoes, and other insects is now considered a necessary practice in civilized countries. The mosquito net or bar is a similar mechanical control device. Paper or tin collars are placed around small plants to protect them from cutworms. Fly traps are other commonly used mechanical control devices. Dust furrows are of value in checking the migration of chinch bugs. In proper construction of building foundations termite damage may be prevented. Hand picking may be employed in the protection of a few plants against certain insects. A number of other mechanical control measures could be mentioned.

As previously stated, insects in nature are killed by high and low temperatures. Temperature may be used quite effectively in artificial control. Insects cannot survive long at temperatures of 140° to 150° F. Heating cereals, beans, peas, and other food products will destroy all stages of insects which may be present; and the resultant drying of the products lessens the chances for future infestations, since a certain amount of moisture is necessary for development.

Low temperatures are not so effective as high temperatures in the destruction of insects. Some insects in hibernation withstand temperatures of 30° F. or more below zero. However, insect feeding stops around 40° F. Transferring wheat in an elevator from one bin to another in cold weather results in its being chilled sufficiently to check weevil damage. Cold storage vaults for furs and other clothing operate at temperatures around 40° F. Although this temperature may not kill insects, it definitely prevents feeding.

Many different kinds of insects are readily attracted to bright lights. Light traps for practical control of insects have never been found to be satisfactory. Although many insects may be collected, some are beneficial and most of them of no economic importance at all. Red and yellow lights attract fewer insects than white or blue lights. Yellow lights are popular for porch and outdoor purposes.

The use of male-sterile insects is a new and fundamentally sound approach in insect control as exemplified in screw-worm eradication programs. Irradiation to achieve sterility is physical control. Yet rearing and releasing the insects is biological; so the method is in part both.

Cultural Control, or Use of Farm and Ranch Practices

Cultural control involves the use of ordinary practices on the farm and ranch in such a way as to eliminate or, in most cases, to reduce populations of injurious insects. These practices are usually based on some weak point in the seasonal history, or environmental or host adaptation of an insect. When research has determined an effective practice, often all that is necessary to put it into effect is to vary the time and performance of some routine practice in crop and livestock production. These are the cheapest of all control measures and often cost nothing. In the production of some crops of low acreage value cultural practices are the only control measures that the operator can afford.

Farm and ranch practices are of many types. Crop rotation, destruction of crop residues, weeds and debris, proper cultivation, use of fertilizers, time of planting, improved varieties of plants or types of animals, drainage, sanitary measures, and the proper timing of certain operations in livestock production are the more important cultural controls. There are others of less importance or more specialized in nature.

Crop rotation is one of the most valuable farm practices. The number of insects that feed on most all kinds of plants is relatively small. Host plants of most insects are usually rather restricted. For example, a number of insects feed on grain and legume crops, but serious pests feeding on both crops are relatively few. So a rotation of these crops will prove helpful. Factors to be considered in the effectiveness of rotation against restricted feeders is their power of migration and rate of reproduction. Rotation is most effective against those pests which migrate the least and have a long life cycle. Some insects quickly move into other fields and reproduce in sufficient numbers to produce serious damage. Although rotation cannot be depended upon for the protection of crops against these insects, the infestations will be later, lighter, and the injury less.

The destruction of crop residues, weeds, and debris aids in the control of a number of pests. Burning is not advised unless the vegetation cannot be disposed of by plowing under, composting, or other means. Many insects continue to feed on plants following harvest. Cull fruits harbor a number of pests. Volunteer plants may carry over pests from one season to the next. A number of common pests reproduce in large numbers on weeds and later migrate to fields. Trash of all types affords hibernation quarters for many crop pests. Proper and timely cultivation is of value particularly in the control of those insects which spend part of their life cycle in the soil. Fall and winter plowing is recommended if it is advised for other purposes.

All factors which tend to produce healthy growing crops that produce and mature as early as possible are of aid in reducing losses due to insects. Time of planting is very important. In some crops early planting is advised; in others delayed planting is advantageous. The best suited varieties should be grown. Results are being obtained in breeding varieties of plants resistant to some insects. In animal husbandry the imported Brahman cow is known to be more resistant to insects than other breeds. Its desirable qualities have been used in the production of another breed. Proper fertilization produces more vigorous and heavier fruiting plants and more profitable crops. Drainage of certain soils may change the environment of a soil-infesting insect and bring about its elimination, while flooding may be a means of control of other species.

The performance of certain operations on the ranch at the proper time will prevent many screw-worm cases in livestock. Castration, branding, dehorning, docking, and earmarking should be done when the screw-worm flies are absent or in fewest numbers. Wounds from all causes should be carefully avoided during the warm weather when the flies are abundant. In those southern regions where the pest is most severe, animals should be bred so that the young are dropped during the fly-free season.

Biological Control

Biological control is frequently defined as "sicking one bug on another." Insect parasites, predators, and diseases have been discussed as important factors in natural control. When man introduces these beneficial forms and releases them in new areas, or propagates them for liberation, this effort is known as biological control. Many of our most important insect pests are introductions from foreign countries. One of the factors accounting for the extensive damage they produce is that they do not have their natural checks in this new location. The attempt is made then to restore "nature's balance" by searching out these natural checks in their native home and releasing them here. Much good work has been accomplished in this field.

Combinations of types or classes of control measures are found. In the new male-sterile method of insect control the rearing and releasing of the insects is biological; yet the sterilizing irradiation is physical. Indications are that chemicals which produce sterility in insects may be developed soon. As these compounds would be used as insecticides the method would be chemical-biological control.

Legal Control

In early days all products of commerce moved freely without thought of the insect pests which they might harbor. This practice resulted in many serious pests becoming widely disseminated over the earth. Early experiences in this country, particularly with the San Jose scale and the grape phylloxera in Europe, aroused people to the necessity of quarantine laws. The first quarantine act in the United States was passed in 1905. Since that time more adequate laws have been enacted and amended as needed. Today both state and federal governments have laws in effect designed (1) to prevent the introduction of foreign pests, (2) to prevent the spread of established pests in this country, (3) to enforce the application of control measures for established pests, and (4) for the prevention of adulteration and misbranding of insecticides, and to limit the amount of insecticides that can remain on a raw agricultural crop.

A large part of the insect damage in this country today is caused by introduced pests. The purpose of foreign quarantine measures is to prevent the entrance of others. Although not wholly successful, quarantines do prevent the entry of most and may delay the introduction of others for many years. The goal of domestic quarantines is to prevent the spread of certain pests already here through shipment of materials. Such measures will not stop the dispersal of the pests, but will check their spread and may prevent infestations in some parts of the country for many years. Regulations are also in force for the application of control measures for established pests. These include cleanup measures, planting and plow-up dates of crops, and the application of insecticides.

Legislation has been enacted to protect the public in the purchase of insecticides and against harmful residues on foodstuff. The sale of insecticides is carefully regulated. Federal laws regulate interstate marketing, and most states have laws regulating insecticide sales within their borders. Packages of insecticides must be properly labeled and their contents accurately stated. The label also must not bear false and misleading information. The purpose of pesticide residue laws is to assure the production of high quality foods without hazard of harmful residues to the consumer. The amount of an insecticide allowed to remain on a specific crop is established for different poisons.

7

INSECTICIDES

Although natural control factors, cultural, mechanical, and physical, legal and biological methods are most important in keeping in check populations of arthropods, they are usually insufficient to prevent appreciable losses as a result of their activity. To produce the quantity and quality of food demanded, and to protect the health of man and his domestic animals, the use of insecticides is imperative.

Insecticides are poisonous compounds and the recommended precautions need be followed in their use. Instructions on labels must always be carefully heeded. Only an insecticide recommended for a particular purpose should be selected, and the user must comply with the recommended dosage, and manner and time of application of the pesticide. If instructions are complied with and precautions heeded, the use of insecticides is safe.

There are both federal and state pesticide laws enacted for the protection of the public. Most state laws are similar to the federal statutes. Federal regulation pertaining to insecticides and fungicides was first initiated under the Insecticide Act of 1910. The Act provided means to prevent misbranding and adulteration of those products marketed in interstate commerce. It was superseded in 1947 by the Federal Insecticide, Fungicide and Rodenticide Act. This Act expands the protection formerly afforded the public in the Act of 1910. All products subject to the Act are required to be registered with the U.S. Department of Agriculture before they may be marketed through the channels of interstate commerce. Furthermore, each product is required to bear a label which includes the name and address of the manufacturer, name brand or trademark, net contents, and proper ingredient statement. Products highly toxic to man must bear a poison label in red and the skull and crossbones. A statement of an antidote is required of such products. Adequate directions and necessary precautions must be provided. The product is guaranteed by the manufacturer to comply with the Act. Claims for the pesticide must be in conformity with the registration, and proof must be supplied before registration can be effected. False or misleading statements may lead to court action.

The Federal Food, Drug and Cosmetic Act of 1938 contains provisions for regulation of pesticidal residues in food; but during this time there were relatively few pesticidal chemicals, and the residue control was effected through informal and unofficial tolerances. As

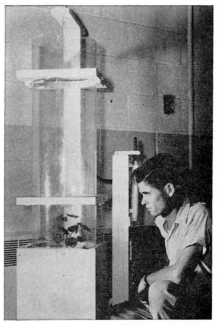

FIG. 50. Science is continually searching for more satisfactory insecticides. (From Texas Agricultural Experiment Station.)

the number of pesticides greatly increased, and large quantities of these products were being used on crops, supplemental legislation was deemed necessary. Consequently in 1954 the Miller Amendment to the Food, Drug and Cosmetic Act was enacted as Public Law 518. This amendment provides the Food and Drug Administration with the authority to establish the amounts of pesticide residues which will be tolerated on raw agricultural products marketed in interstate commerce. Presently, tolerances have been established for a large number of pesticides but not all of them. Tolerances, given in parts per million (ppm), may vary for different crops and are subject to modification from time to time. When tolerances are established they are published in the Federal Register. Some pesticides require no tolerance, as rotenone and oils. Others have zero tolerance because a safe level in the food of man and animals has not been determined or because of serious physiological effects.

A knowledge of the relative toxicity of insecticides is quite necessary in their study and use. Due to the multiplicity of factors involved this information may not be quite exact, but it does establish reasonably well the toxicity of a compound in relation to other products. The most satisfactory criterion for acute toxicity of liquid and solid insecticides is the Median Lethal Dose (LD_{50}) determined on rats or other test animals. This dosage is the amount of the toxicant required to kill 50 percent of the test animals and is expressed in milligrams per kilogram of body weight. In fumigants the LD_{50} is most satisfactorily expressed as vapor concentration on the basis of milligrams per liter and multiplied by length of the exposure. But it is generally given in parts per million (ppm) which will produce a given response in a stated time. Chronic toxicity is usually determined by feeding test animals a measured quantity of a toxicant in diet and determining the maximum level which does not produce harmful symptoms or death.

The development of resistance of arthropods to insecticides poses most serious problems in their control. The occurrence of resistance of arthropods to chemical compounds is not new to entomologists, as this phenomenon has been known for more than 50 years. In 1945 only 13 species of insects and ticks were known to have developed resistance in at least some segments of their populations. Since this time, large quantities of synthetic compounds have been used and the number of resistant strains of harmful species has been greatly increased. Presently more than 130 resistant strains of insects, ticks, and mites are known. Resistance has developed through the selective action of an insecticide killing off susceptible members of a population through a number of generations. This resistance is an inherited characteristic. The problem can be dealt with only in changing to insecticides to which the strain is susceptible while searching for new and more satisfactory compounds, and the development of other types of control measures.

CLASSES OF INSECTICIDES

Insecticides may be grouped for study in various ways. They are commonly classified as stomach poisons, contact poisons, and fumigants. The grouping is based upon the mode of entry of the toxicant into the insect's body and may have no significance as to its mode of action. Another classification may be based upon the chemical nature of the insecticides, as inorganic poisons, organic compounds derived from plants, and synthetic organic compounds. The inorganic compounds are generally effective only as stomach poisons. Insecticides of plant origin act as contact poisons mainly, but may also kill as stomach poisons and even as fumigants. The synthetic organic compounds are predominantly contact poisons, but they usually function as stomach poisons also, and some may even have fumigating or systemic poisoning properties. When overlapping occurs the pesticide is discussed in the class in which it chiefly functions. Perhaps the most logical grouping of insecticides would be on the basis of their physiological mode of action. It would hardly be possible to attempt such a classification at this time without more knowledge and study.

For purposes of presentation of insecticides to beginners, a classification of stomach poisons, contact poisons, systemic poisons, and fumigants is satisfactory. Attractants, repellents, and synergists or activators also need brief mention.

Insects with chewing, sponging, lapping or siphoning mouthparts often may be more readily destroyed by poisoning their food than by other means. As the insecticides so employed are ingested and absorbed through the digestive tract they are known as stomach poisons.

Contact poisons are employed primarily in the control of insects with piercing-sucking mouthparts; however, these poisons will kill insects with all types of mouthparts except some of the more highly resistant forms. The insect must come in direct contact with these insecticides to be killed. This may occur by direct application to the body or by the residual effect of the poisons upon the surface where the insect crawls or rests.

There are both plant and animal systemic poisons. In plants these compounds may be taken up either from the soil or plant surfaces. Those used on animals are either absorbed through the skin or by way of the digestive tract. When they have been introduced, they may be transported to other parts of the plant or animal. The future of systemic poisons in the program of insect control is very promising.

Fumigants are released as gases in enclosures like warehouses, mills, grain bins, ships, and fumigation vaults and under tarpaulins. Sometimes they are used to destroy insects in the soil and in wood. Fumigation is a very effective means of killing insects when the enclosures are sufficiently airtight and the fumigants are properly applied.

Attractants, repellents, and activators and synergists too are of much importance in combating insects. Considerable research is being conducted in the fields, and these factors probably will play a still more significant role in the future.

STOMACH POISONS

Lead arsenate is the best known and has been the most widely used of all arsenical insecticides. Industry produces both an acid and a basic form of the insecticide, but it is the acid preparation ($PbHAsO_4$) which has had such a large usage, and it is the product referred to here. The compound is only slightly soluble in water, is quite stable, has good storage qualities, and contains about 21 percent elemental arsenic.

The chief uses of lead arsenate has been to protect fruit, shade and forest trees, ornamental plants and truck crops from injury by chewing insects. It is still employed in the control of these pests but the quantity used has been greatly reduced in recent years.

The insecticide is generally considered as being non-phytotoxic, but the foliage of stone fruits and legumes is quite susceptible to injury as well as that of some other plants under certain weather conditions. In spraying such plants, the recommended precautions must be taken to prevent injury. Either sprays or dusts are used, but mostly the former. The dosages vary, but 3 pounds of powdered lead arsenate mixed with 100 gallons of water is the usual recommendation for sprays. Dusts may be applied undiluted or mixed with diluents.

Lead arsenate is a safe and satisfactory insecticide when used properly. A tolerance of 7 ppm of combined lead is established for most products. The acute oral LD_{50} to mammals is 10 to 50 mg/kg.

Although *calcium arsenate* has other uses, it has been employed primarily for the control of the boll weevil and other chewing insects attacking the cotton plant. It was the principal insecticide employed in combating these pests for many years until the chlorinated hydrocarbons and the organic phosphorous compounds largely superseded its use.

Calcium arsenate is not the standardized product such as lead arsenate. The exact chemical nature of the insecticide is not very well understood. The presence of a basic calcium arsenate, $3Ca_3(AsO_4)_2 \cdot Ca(OH)_2$, is indicated by phase-rule studies, which compound is unstable below 35° C. Carbon dioxide decomposes commercial grades of calcium arsenate with the formation of calcium carbonate and dicalcium hydrogen arsenate, the latter compound being quite soluble in water. It is therefore unstable and has a tendency to injure foliage, and consequently should be used only on plants with hardy foliage. The arsenic content of the product is not less than 26 percent expressed as metallic.

Undiluted calcium arsenate dust is recommended for use on cotton, usually at the rate of 10 to 15 pounds per acre. When mixed with diluents, the dust is occasionally used for the control of other pests.

A tolerance of 3.5 ppm of combined As_2O_3 is established for a number of products. Mammalian toxicity is relatively high by ingestion, the LD_{50} being 35 to 100 mg/kg.

In contrast with commercial products which contain an excess of lime, "lime-free" calcium arsenate mixtures are being manufactured for use on cotton. The advantages in their use are that they are compatible with parathion, benzene hexachloride and other organic poisons; and also that they may be used as sprays.

Sodium arsenite is a highly soluble and a very toxic compound. It has been considered as sodium meta-arsenite ($NaAsO_2$) but is now regarded as reactants in a solid solution rather than as a fixed compound. It has long been used as a weed killer and in poison baits. However, its most important use was as the killing agent in arsenical cattle dips employed in the eradication of the cattle tick in the South. It is also an excellent soil poison in termite control but it is too toxic to both plants and animals for general use. Every precaution must be taken if it is used. The acute oral LD_{50} to mammals is 10 to 15 mg/kg.

Chemically *Paris green* is copper aceto-arsenite $(CH_3COO)_2Cu \cdot 3Cu(AsO_2)_2$. Although employed in the control of many pests years ago its present use is limited probably to the preparation of a few poison baits. This stomach poison is violently toxic to mammals and is also very phytotoxic.

Sodium fluoride (NaF) had a very wide usage for many years in the control of cockroaches and poultry lice. The product is efficient in control of these pests but synthetic products have largely superseded its use. Occasionally it is employed in the preparation of poison baits. This water-soluble white powder is marketed preferably colored as a warning of its toxicity. The lethal dose of this insecticide to man is 75 to 150 mg/kg.

Sodium fluosilicate (Na_2SiF_6) is less soluble than sodium fluoride, but it is still too phytotoxic for use on plants. Because of its cheapness, it has been used considerably in preparation of poison baits. Soluble fluosilicates are among the compounds used in mothproofing fabrics. The acute LD_{50} of sodium fluosilicate to rabbits is 150 to 200 mg/kg.

Cryolite (sodium aluminum fluoride, Na_3AlF_6) is practically insoluble in water and may be applied with safety either as a dust or spray on most plants. Lime must not be mixed with it as fluorine and alkaline compounds are incompatible. Cryolite is primarily a stomach poison but has some contact action, a characteristic in common with other fluorine compounds. The pesticide is of low acute toxicity to mammals, but fluorine in drinking water may cause mottling of teeth at concentrations of 2 to 3 ppm. Chronic poisoning may be produced in some species of animals with daily dosages ranging from 15 to 150 mg/kg. A tolerance of 7 ppm of combined fluorine has been established for cryolite and other fluorine compounds for a number of products. The use of this insecticide presently is rather limited, being confined principally to vegetable crops.

CONTACT POISONS

Oils are old insecticides and records indicate that the ancients made use of both mineral and vegetable oils, and tars. Fuel oil fractions are employed in mosquito control and are used as solvents for other insecticides.

More oil of the kerosene fraction is used in insect control than any other petroleum product. Large quantities of this fraction are used annually in household sprays as a solvent and a base for pyrethrum, DDT, chlordane, and other insecticides. A deodorized type of oil is recommended for this use.

Summer oils are higher fractions (light to medium) than kerosene and are used in water emulsion sprays for control of scale insects, whiteflies, mealybugs, mites and other pests of trees, shrubs and ornamentals. These oils are highly refined and the unsulfonatable residue is usually in excess of 90 percent. Plants vary in susceptibility to injury by these sprays, but tender foliage may sustain some damage under almost any conditions. Dependent upon circumstances, spray concentrations vary from $\frac{1}{4}$ to 2 percent of oil. Occasionally these oils are used in combination sprays.

Heavy and less refined oils are employed in the preparation of dormant sprays. They are available in emulsifiable form with concentrations usually varying from 85 to 99 percent of actual oil. Diluted sprays containing 2 to 5 percent oil are applied to shade and fruit trees, and to shrubs during the dormant season for control of scale insects, mealybugs, aphids, certain mites and other pests. The sprays should not be used when there is danger of freezing.

Oils are of low toxicity to animals, but kerosene fractions are poisonous if taken internally in quantity. No tolerances are established for use on growing crops.

Sulphur is primarily a contact poison, but it may be burned to serve as a fumigant. However, this practice is no longer recommended.

For insecticidal purposes sulphur is applied chiefly as a finely ground dust. It is recommended primarily for the control of certain spider mites, and as a diluent for some insecticidal dusts. It is also used in control of chiggers. The average dose of sulphur as a dust is about 15 pounds per acre. Wettable sulphur has had a wide usage as a spray in the control of spider mites and as a fungicide on stone fruits. Six to 10 pounds per 100 gallons of spray is recommended. Sulphur is not toxic as commonly used other than being irritating to the eyes.

Lime-sulphur is made by boiling lime and sulphur together in water. Several chemical compounds are formed; those of most insecticidal value found in this mixture are the polysulphides—calcium pentasulphide (CaS_5) and calcium tetrasulphide (CaS_4).

Lime-sulphur has been employed widely as a dormant spray, primarily for the control of the San Jose scale, and also as a foliage spray for mites. The product is also a very good fungicide and it is used in a number of combination sprays. Both liquids and dry forms are available. The product is listed as a safe insecticide by the Pure Food and Drug Administration and no tolerances are established in its use.

Nicotine ($C_{10}H_{14}N_2$) is the principal alkaloid found in tobacco. It is marketed chiefly as nicotine sulphate containing 40 percent of the alkaloid. Free or alkaloidal nicotine is also available. The chemical may act as either a contact poison, a fumigant, or as a stomach poison, but principally as a contact poison. The chief use of nicotine is in the control of plant lice and other soft-bodied insects. Both sprays and dusts are available. Nicotine sulphate dip is efficient in control of sheep scab. It may be painted on roosts in control of lice and mites of poultry. The alkaloidal form is still used to some extent as a greenhouse fumigant. Fixed nicotines have a limited use. A tolerance of 2 ppm has been established for a long list of products. Vegetables should not be harvested for at least three days following application. The acute oral LD_{50} to rats is 50-60 mg/kg. The dermal LD_{50} to rabbits is 50 mg/kg applied in a single application.

Rotenone occurs in the roots of certain leguminous plants which grow in tropical regions. Derris (*Derris elliptica*) and cube (*Lonchocarpus* spp.) are the commercial sources of this insecticide. Associated with rotenone are several other closely related compounds which account for part of the toxicity of the pesticide. The powdered roots of these plants are usually marketed with a rotenone content of 4 to 5 percent.

Rotenone acts as both a stomach and a contact poison, but chiefly as the latter. It is employed in the control of a number of vegetable pests and several animal parasites. Vegetable dusts should contain 1 percent rotenone. The same percentage of rotenone in dusts for the control of lice and fleas on pets is recommended, but a higher concentration is needed for satisfactory results for ticks on dogs. It is the only insecticide presently recommended for control of cattle grubs on dairy animals. A dust containing 1.5 percent rotenone is recommended for this purpose. Too, sprays containing 7.5 pounds of derris per 100 gallons of water may be used. It is also employed for control of lice and ticks on these animals.

Rotenone is a relatively safe insecticide and is exempt from tolerances with only one day required between the last application and harvest of vegetables. The acute oral LD_{50} to rats is 132 mg/kg.

Pyrethrum is derived from the flowers of *Pyrethrum cinerariaefolium*. Chief commercial source of the product is Kenya, Africa. The insecticidal properties of this product are due to four esters; namely, pyrethrin I, pyrethrin II, cinerin I, and cinerin II. These esters are unstable, being hydrolized by alkali and decomposed by sunlight. This is a contact insecticide with a rapid "knockdown" action, but it has little residual effect. Pyrethrum is usually mixed with other insecticides and synergists, and is employed in the control of household and certain vegetable and livestock pests, and as protectant for certain food commodities. Formulations of dusts, aerosols, solutions and emulsions are available. The pyrethrin content of most preparations ranges from 0.05 to 0.10 percent.

The insecticide is of low toxicity to warm-blooded animals in the concentrations used, but it may cause dermatitis to some people. Pyrethrum is exempt from tolerance on growing crops and livestock. Tolerances of 1 to 3 ppm have been established for many stored food products. When administered orally to mammals the acute LD_{50} is listed to be 200 mg/kg.

Allethrin is a synthetic pyrethrin-like compound. Chemically it is similar to the pyrethrins, but it is more stable. As a contact poison, it is as effective as pyrethrins in house fly control but not as efficient in control of cockroaches and other insects. It also exhibits less synergism with piperonyl butoxide than the pyrethrins. Toxicologically it is similar to the pyrethrins. Tolerances of 2 or 4 ppm have been established for postharvest applications on a number of food products.

Sabadilla is a product of the seeds of plants of the genus *Schoencaulon* which contains several alkaloids. Dusts of this insecticide satisfactorily control certain hemipterous insects. The pesticide is of low toxicity to mammals. No tolerances have been established in its use, but the dusts are irritating to the applicator.

Ryania has been recommended in control of the European corn borer, sugarcane borer and several other pests. The source of the insecticide is stems and roots of *Ryania speciosa*. Ryanodine is the most important toxic principle and is effective as both a stomach and a contact poison. The product is of low toxicity to mammals and is exempt from tolerances.

Several compounds of the *dinitrophenol* group have commercial value as insecticides. *Dinitro-o-cresol* (DNC or DNOC) is employed as an ovicide in dormant sprays for aphids and mites. The product is very phytotoxic and thus has properties as a weed killer. It is highly toxic to mammals both as an acute and as a chronic poison. The acute oral LD_{50} to rats is given as 40 to 65 mg/kg. A zero tolerance is established for the product. *Dinitro-ortho-cyclohexylphenol* (DNOCHP, Dinex), a related compound, is employed primarily for spider mite control on apples, walnuts, citrus fruits, vegetables and other crops. Foliage injury may result if the product is not correctly applied. It possesses considerable toxicity to mammals and the acute oral LD_{50} for mice and guinea pigs is in the range of 50 to 125 mg/kg. A tolerance of 1 ppm is established for a long list of fruits and some vegetables. *Dinitroanisole* is of very low mammalian toxicity and as it has ovicidal properties it was used in louse powders during the first years of World War II.

There are several insecticides of commercial importance among the *thiocyanates*. *Lauryl thiocyanate* is used in sprays under both greenhouse and field conditions for control of aphids, whiteflies, spider mites, thrips, mealybugs and scale insects. The *lethane* compounds are used as contact insecticides in fly, cattle and industrial sprays. These compounds are not very toxic, but adequate ventilation and other recommended precautions should be taken when they are used.

Sevin ($C_{12}H_{11}NO_2$) is a carbamate; it is a white crystalline solid, and the technical product is not less than 95 percent pure. The insecticide is slightly soluble in water but quite soluble in most organic solvents. It is stable to hydrolysis under normal conditions, has good residual properties, and is compatible with most sprays except those with a strong alkaline reaction. It is reported to have contact-poison, stomach-poison, and some systemic action. The product is recommended for control of a wide variety of field, vegetable, and fruit pests. It is also approved for use in control of mites and lice of poultry. Formulations of emulsifiable concentrates, wettable powders and dusts are employed. Dosages per acre for row crops range from 0.5 to as high as 4 pounds, dependent upon the crop and pest. Amounts per 100 gallons of spray used on fruit trees vary from $3/4$ to $1\frac{1}{2}$ pounds.

A number of tolerances ranging from 0 to 25 ppm have been established for the insecticide. The acute LD_{50} to rats by ingestion is 560 mg/kg.

THE CHLORINATED HYDROCARBONS

The discovery of DDT as an insecticide was of considerable importance itself, but of greater significance was the interest and research in pesticides it stimulated. These have resulted in the development of a large number of other effective poisons. New methods of application and the improvement of old ones have tended to keep pace with the insecticidal development.

As a result of these developments insects are being controlled to a degree and on a scale that was formerly thought impossible. However, challenging problems have arisen, particularly the development of insecticidal resistance in insects and residues on raw agricultural products.

This group of compounds are chiefly contact poisons, but they also act as stomach poisons, and some have action as fumigants as well. The more representative of the group are discussed below.

DDT ($C_{14}H_9Cl_5$) was first synthesized in 1874, but its insecticidal value was not discovered until 1939 by Muller. The pure product is a white crystalline compound which has a melting point of 108-109° C. The compound is practically insoluble in water, fairly solvent in most organic solvents, and highly soluble in aromatic hydrocarbons, such as velsicol, xylene, and the naphthas. The pesticide is quite stable under most conditions and deposits remain insecticidally active for relatively long periods.

DDT is widely used in the control of pests of man and crops. It is primarily a contact poison but also acts as a stomach poison. The insecticide acts slowly, and hours or even days may be required for it to kill. Solutions containing 1 to 5 percent DDT are in common use for household pests; the DDT content of aerosols is 3 percent. These sprays usually contain pyrethrum and/or other insecticides. For field-crop pests a dosage of 1 to 2 pounds of technical DDT per acre is usually required. Either dusts or sprays may be employed. In controlling pests of trees 1 to 2 pounds of the active ingredient per 100 gallons of spray is commonly recommended.

Even though a number of arthropods, such as house flies, certain mosquitoes, ticks, and fleas, have developed resistance to DDT, and curtailments have developed in its use because of residues, it is still widely employed in control of a number of pests.

The extensive safe use of DDT and laboratory tests with the compound would indicate it to be a relatively safe insecticide. The acute oral LD_{50} to man is estimated to be 250 mg/kg. There is little evidence that chronic toxicity is high. But DDT is stored in the body fat of animals and is excreted in milk. This indeterminate hazard to the health of man has resulted in its elimination for use on meat and milk animals and in dairy barns. Also it must not be used on feed or forage crops which may be fed to dairy cattle or to animals being prepared for slaughter. A tolerance of 7 ppm has been established for a large number of products.

Methoxychlor ($C_{16}H_{15}Cl_3O_2$), an analog of DDT, is a white solid with a slightly fruity odor and a melting point of 89° C. The compound is insoluble in water, somewhat soluble in petroleum oils, and readily soluble in most aromatic hydrocarbons. The insecticide is resistant to oxidation, stable to heat, and has a prolonged residual effectiveness.

Methoxychlor is recommended in the control of a number of legume, grass, vegetable, fruit, and livestock pests, killing both as a stomach and a contact poison. Its order of toxicity to insects is not as high as that of DDT, and it has fewer hazards in use. Formulations of emulsions, wettable powders, and dusts are available. The pesticide is safe for use on plants with the exception of some cucurbits. In field-crop pest control dosages ranging from ½ to 1¾ pounds of the active ingredient per acre are recommended. Sprays for fruit trees should contain 1 to 1½ pounds of the pesticide per 100 gallons of water.

This is one of the few insecticides which may be used on dairy cattle, and then only as a 50 percent dust sprinkled on the back, neck and flanks with a dosage of one tablespoonful per animal at intervals of three weeks. It may also be employed for fly control in dairy barns and milk rooms. On beef cattle methoxychlor is recommended in control of horn flies and lice in a spray containing 0.5 percent of the toxicant. In control of lice on sheep and goats, a spray of 0.5 or a dip of 0.25 percent is used.

The acute oral LD_{50} to rats ranges from 5000 to 7000 mg/kg. There is little tendency for this insecticide to collect in animal tissues.

A tolerance of 14 ppm has been established for vegetable crops, 100 ppm for forage, 0 for milk, 2 for grain and 3 for fat of meat.

BHC ($C_6H_6Cl_6$) was first prepared in 1825; however, its insecticidal properties were not discovered until World War II. The crude product contains not less than five isomers; namely, alpha, beta, gamma, delta and epsilon. Also small quantities of hepta- and octa-chlorocyclohexanes may be present. The insecticidal properties of the product are due almost entirely to the gamma isomer. The commercial product is a light-brown powder with a persistent musty odor. The pesticide is insoluble in water but soluble in a large number of organic solvents. BHC acts as a contact or a stomach poison and also to some extent as a fumigant. It does not have the residual properties of DDT, but in protected places it may persist for several weeks. The insecticide is available as a dust, emulsion, and wettable powder.

BHC is effective in the control of many insects, but its use is restricted, as it may impart a musty odor and flavor to many foods. Recommendations are for aphid control on certain fruit and nut crops in amounts of 0.2 to 0.4 pound per 100 gallons of water. On cotton the insecticide may be used for the control of a number of insects. The amount of the gamma isomer per acre recommended is usually 0.3 to 0.45 pound. A tolerance of 5 ppm has been established for a large number of fruits and vegetables. The acute oral LD_{50} to rats of the gamma isomer is 125 mg/kg. The product is stored in animal tissues, but with the exception of the beta isomer, it has a low order of cumulative toxicity.

Lindane ($C_6H_6Cl_6$) is the name applied to the refined gamma isomer of benzene hexachloride in at least 99 percent pure form. This refined compound is practically free of the musty odor and does not accumulate in the fat of animals to any marked extent, since it is metabolized quite rapidly.

This insecticide is a white crystalline substance with a melting point of 112° C. General chemical characteristics are as BHC. Wettable powders, emulsions, and dusts are used.

The chief uses of lindane are against pests of vegetable crops and livestock. Some use is made of the product in household and fruit sprays. On vegetable crops a dosage of $\frac{1}{4}$ pound per acre is recommended. One-fourth to $\frac{1}{2}$ pound of the toxicant per 100 gallons of spray is required for use on fruit trees. Lindane is the principal active ingredient in the screw-worm smear, E.Q. 335. Sprays containing 0.03 percent lindane for louse control and 0.025 percent for ticks are used on beef cattle. This spray is not to be used on dairy cattle. Similar sprays for control of lice, and ticks on sheep and goats, and lice on swine are recommended. It also has a use in control of flies inside and outside of barns, and the control of chiggers and ticks in infested areas.

Tolerances of 4 to 7 ppm of lindane are established for fat of animals and 10 ppm for a wide variety of vegetable and fruit crops. The LD_{50} administered orally to rats is 125 mg/kg.

The empirical formula of *toxaphene* is commonly given as $C_{10}H_{10}Cl_8$, but the exact chemical nature of the compounds of which it is composed is not known. This product is a yellow waxy solid with a mild chlorine-camphor odor. The insecticide has a melting point in the range of 65° to 90° C.; it is insoluble in water but readily soluble in a number of organic solvents, including petroleum oils. This is both a contact and a stomach poison with considerable residual action, but it is decomposed by heat, sunlight, and certain catalysts and alkalies. Formulations of wettable powders, emulsions, dusts and granules are available.

The insecticide is employed in combating a wide range of pests of field crops, range and pastures, vegetables and livestock. In treatment of feed crops, care must be exercised in its use so there will be no excess residues in fat of meat and milk resulting from feeding of these products to animals. For field-crop pests, 2 to 3 pounds of the toxicant per acre is usually required. Livestock sprays are recommended at a strength of 0.5 percent on beef cattle and 0.25 percent in dips for sheep and goats. It may be used in fly control outside of barns and on infested areas for ticks.

A tolerance of 7 ppm has been established for most products. The acute oral LD_{50} to rats is 60 mg/kg and the insecticide also possesses chronic toxicity to animals.

The commercial form of *chlordane* contains a number of related compounds with a chlorine content of about 64 to 66 percent. It is insoluble in water but quite soluble in most organic solvents. The product is both a contact and a stomach poison with some fumigating action and considerable residual effectiveness. Formulations of dusts, emulsions, solutions, wettable powders and granules are available for use.

Chlordane is used primarily in control of grasshoppers, many soil insects including termites, ants, nonresistant cockroaches and other household insects, flies outside of barns, and chiggers and ticks in infested areas. In grasshopper control, dosages of $3/4$ to $1\frac{1}{2}$ pounds of the toxicant per acre are employed. In treatment of areas infested with chiggers 2 to 4 pounds per acre are recommended. Two to 5 pounds per acre are recommended for control of soil insects. A 5 percent dust, or a 2 percent solution or emulsion is suggested for the control of the harvester ant. Household sprays usually contain 2 percent chlordane.

A tolerance of only 0.3 ppm is established for fruits and berries and a number of vegetables. The acute oral LD_{50} to rats is about 500 mg/kg. Although the acute oral toxicity is low, it may be absorbed through the skin and repeated doses in diets may produce toxic symptoms and death of the animal, dependent upon the animal and the dosages. Foods must not be contaminated by it and skin contact avoided.

Aldrin ($C_{12}H_8Cl_6$) contains 95 percent of the pure compound and 5 percent insecticidally active related products. The insecticide is insoluble in water, but moderately soluble in mineral oils and quite soluble in acetone, xylene, and benzene. Formulations of wettable powders, emulsions, dusts and granules are available. This insecticide possesses some fumigating action as well as being a contact and stomach poison. It has considerable residual effectiveness.

Aldrin has a wide usage for grasshopper and soil insect control and it is recommended for the control of a number of cotton insects. Dosages vary from $1/8$ to 2 pounds per acre, the amount varying with crop and the pest.

Established tolerances vary from 0 to 0.75 ppm, depending upon the product. Toxicity to man and animals is high, and the insecticide should not be used on animals, around food products, or in buildings. The acute oral LD_{50} to rats is about 50 mg/kg. Skin contact and inhalation are to be avoided.

Commercial grades of *dieldrin* ($C_{12}H_8Cl_6O$) are buff to light brown color and about 85 percent pure. This insecticide exhibits both stomach- and contact-poison properties and possesses marked residual effectiveness. Solubility is similar to that of its related compound, aldrin. Formulations of wettable powders, emulsions, dusts and granules are in use. Dieldrin is highly toxic to man and animals, and if it is applied to forage crops, its use is limited to those applications which will leave no residue at the time of harvesting or feeding. In cockroach control within the home, it should be used only as a residual spray in spot treatment.

This pesticide will control a wide variety of insects. It is recommended chiefly for the control of grasshoppers, ants, cockroaches, plum curculio, many soil insects including termites and certain cotton pests. Recommended dosages in the field are comparable with those of aldrin. In fruit sprays about $\frac{1}{4}$ pound of the toxicant per 100 gallons of spray is used.

Established tolerances are about the same as those of aldrin. The acute oral toxicity to rats is 100 mg/kg and it can be absorbed through the skin and by inhalation.

Technical *endrin* ($C_6H_8Cl_6O$) is a light tan powder of not less than 85 percent purity. It is practically insoluble in water, slightly soluble in alcohols and petroleum oils and moderately soluble in benzene and acetone. It is stable to ordinary alkaline reagents. Emulsions, dusts and granules are in use.

This insecticide has a rather wide usage in control of field and vegetable crop pests. If used on forage crops, no residue must be present at time of harvest or feeding. This highly toxic product should be applied only by a trained operator and should never be used on livestock. Usual dosages are about $\frac{1}{4}$ pound per acre. Zero tolerances are established on all products upon which it is used. This pesticide is more toxic than dieldrin to warm-blooded animals and strict care in handling is essential. The acute LD_{50} to rats by ingestion is 10 to 12 mg/kg. It has considerable chronic effect. Most occupational hazard is by absorption through the skin.

Technical *heptachlor* ($C_{10}H_5Cl_7$), a soft, waxy solid, contains about 72 percent of heptachlor with the remainder related compounds. The pesticide is practically insoluble in water, and soluble in ethyl alcohol and kerosene. It is a very stable product and is prepared as dusts, granules, emulsions and wettable powders. As the product is dangerously poisonous, it must be used with care.

The insecticide is recommended for control of grasshoppers, soil insects including termites, and cotton insects. Dosages per acre are 1 to 2 pounds for soil insects, $\frac{1}{4}$ to $\frac{3}{4}$ pound for cotton pests, and 2 to 3 ounces for grasshoppers.

Tolerances of 0 are established for a number of products. The LD_{50} to rats by ingestion is 130 to 135 mg/kg. Heptachlor epoxide is formed in the decomposition of this product. This epoxide in turn is toxic which intensifies the toxicity problem of the pesticide. The chronic toxicity of heptachlor is probably higher than that of chlordane.

PHOSPHOROUS COMPOUNDS

The development of organic phosphorus insecticides had its origin in Germany. A number of these compounds have now been developed and are available for use for almost every type of insect control as contact, stomach, and systemic poisons; and too, a few have some fumigating action. These insecticides are as a whole very efficient, acting as nerve poisons and being cholinesterase inhibitors. Some are so dangerously poisonous to man and animals that they should be applied only by trained applicators, while others are quite safe for use by the public with usual precautions. Only the more representative phosphorus insecticides can be discussed here.

The technical grade of *parathion* ($C_{10}H_{14}NO_5PS$) is a brown to yellow liquid with the odor of garlic and contains about 80 percent of the pure compound. It is only slightly soluble in water and petroleum oils, but miscible in common organic solvents. Hydrolysis is rapid in alkaline solution.

Parathion kills insects and mites as a contact and stomach poison, and also to some extent as a fumigant. The insecticide is available for use as a wettable powder, dust, emulsion, and as an aerosol.

Parathion is highly effective in the control of a wide range of insects and mites of field, vegetable and fruit crops, and pests of the greenhouse. For use on field and vegetable crops recommended dosages are $\frac{1}{8}$ to $\frac{1}{2}$ pound of the technical material per acre. Dosages for fruit pests range from $\frac{1}{8}$ to $\frac{1}{2}$ pound of the toxicant per 100 gallons of water. Aerosols containing parathion are employed chiefly in greenhouses. The required interval between the last application of the insecticide and harvesting is usually 7 to 21 days, dependent upon the crop and uses of the product.

A tolerance of 1 ppm has been established for a very long list of food products. The acute LD_{50} by ingestion to female rats is 6 mg/kg. and to males 15 mg/kg. Parathion is also highly toxic to mammals through dermal absorption and inhalation. The poison is a powerful cholinesterase inhibitor. This highly toxic insecticide should never be used around the home and on livestock. It should be applied only by a trained applicator who should wear the recommended clothing and equipment and follow all the rules in its use.

Commercial *methyl parathion* ($C_8H_{10}NO_5PS$) is a light to dark tan liquid which crystallizes around 29° C. It is only slightly soluble in water but soluble in most of the organic solvents. Chemical characteristics are similar to those of parathion, but the rate of hydrolysis by alkali is 4.3 times higher. This pesticide kills arthropods in the same way as parathion and is used in dusts and sprays.

The insecticide is recommended on small grains for greenbug control at the rate of 1/4 pound of the toxicant per acre. For cotton pests it is used chiefly in control of the boll weevil, aphid, leafworm, thrips, and spider mites. One-fourth to 3/4 pound per acre of the active ingredient should be applied on this crop and at least one day must elapse from last application to hand harvest. It has the same tolerances on agricultural products as parathion. The acute oral LD_{50} to rats is 9 to 25 mg/kg. It is also toxic through dermal absorption and inhalation but less so than parathion. Chronic sublethal doses continue to lower the cholinesterase level as with parathion. The same precautions are recommended in its use as are recommended for the latter.

Technical *malathion* ($C_{10}H_{19}O_6PS_2$) (95 percent) is a dark-brown liquid with the odor of garlic. It is slightly water-soluble, of very limited solubility in petroleum oils but miscible with most organic solvents. The residue on crops disappears rather rapidly. The insecticide is marketed as wettable powders, dusts, emulsions, solutions, and aerosols.

Since it is not as toxic as most other organic phosphorus compounds, it has a wide usage. Malathion is recommended for a number of diverse pests of field crops, vegetables, fruits, livestock, stored products and of the home. On most crops recommended dosages are from 3/4 to 1 1/4 pounds of the active ingredient per acre. In fruit sprays 1/2 pound of the toxicant per 100 gallons of water is required.

Malathion is one of the few insecticides which may be used on dairy cattle in fly control. Two ounces of a 4 percent dust may be sprinkled on the neck, flanks and back at intervals of three weeks. Sprays and dips must not be used on these animals. A 0.5 percent spray may be applied on beef cattle for fly, louse and tick control; on sheep and goats for lice, keds, and ticks; and on swine for lice. It also may be used in baits inside and outside of barns for fly control. Sprays and dips for lice, ticks and fleas on cats and dogs are used at concentrations of 0.25 to 0.50 percent of the toxicant. Household sprays for control of cockroaches and other pests are in common use. Such sprays are in combination with other insecticides as chlordane and pyrethrum. Because of odor, the most completely deodorized products are employed here.

Tolerances established for most agricultural products are 8 ppm. There is a zero tolerance for milk and eggs, and 4 for meat and meat by-products. Acute oral toxicity in corn oil is 479 mg/kg to white rats. The product is of low chronic toxicity to mammals.

Diazinon ($C_{12}H_{21}N_2O_3PS$), the technical product (90 percent pure), is a brown liquid. It is only slightly soluble in water but miscible in

FIG. 51.   The intelligent use of insecticides greatly increases crop yields. (From Texas Agricultural Experiment Station.)

alcohol, xylene, acetone, and soluble in petroleum oils. The insecticide has considerable residual effectiveness. Dusts, emulsions, wettable powders, oil solutions and baits are formulated. The insecticide is employed in the control of a number of pests of vegetables, fruits, cotton, and flies in and around barns. Dosages for field crop pests are $\frac{1}{4}$ to as much as 2 pounds of the toxicant per acre. Fruit tree sprays contain $\frac{1}{4}$ to $\frac{1}{2}$ pound per 100 gallons of water. For house fly control, both dry and liquid baits are formulated.

Tolerance of 0.75 ppm has been established for a long list of vegetables and fruits. The acute LD_{50} by ingestion for rats is 100 to 150 mg/kg and 82 mg/kg for mice.

The technical grade of *Delnav* ($C_{12}H_{26}O_6P_2S_4$) is a brown liquid

(70 percent pure) insoluble in water but soluble in a number of organic solvents. It is stable in water emulsions, but is hydrolized by heating and by alkali. It is marketed as a wettable powder and an emulsion. Tolerances have been established for use of the insecticide on meat animals, grapes and citrus. Chief use at this time is for control of lice and ticks on beef cattle, fleece worms, keds, and ticks on sheep and goats at concentrations of 0.15 percent. It is also employed as a spray against fleas, lice and ticks on dogs with concentrations as above and for treatment of premises infested with fleas and ticks with sprays of 0.5 percent of the toxicant.

A tolerance of 1 ppm is established for fat of meat of cattle, hogs and sheep; 2.1 ppm for grapes and 2.8 ppm for citrus fruits. The acute LD_{50} to albino rabbits is 107 mg/kg.

Guthion ($C_{10}H_{12}N_3O_3PS_2$) is a solid compound with a melting point of 73 to 74° C. It is very insoluble in water but soluble in most common organic solvents. Dusts, emulsions and wettable powders are employed in control of a number of insects and certain species of mites on vegetable, fruit and cotton crops. Dosages usually range from $1/4$ to $1/2$ pound of the toxicant per acre for field crops and $1/2$ pound per 100 gallons of spray is recommended for fruit trees.

Tolerances of 2 ppm are established for a number of fruits and vegetables and 0.5 ppm for cottonseed. The acute oral toxicity to female rats is 16.4 mg/kg, and for male guinea pigs 80 mg/kg. As this is a highly toxic insecticide, great care must be exercised in its use.

Dylox or *Dipterex* ($C_4H_8Cl_3O_4P$) is a white or pale yellow crystalline solid, soluble in water, ether, chloroform, and benzene but insoluble in petroleum oils, and it is unstable to alkali. It is marketed as soluble powders, dusts, and bait formulations. It is recommended for use in combating certain pests of alfalfa, sugar beets, and cotton. Dosages range from 0.25 to 1.5 pounds of the active ingredient per acre. It is recommended for use in poison baits for house fly control. Experimentally, the insecticide is promising in controlling a number of livestock pests, but is not approved at this time.

SYSTEMIC PHOSPHORUS INSECTICIDES

The technical grade of *demeton* (Systox $C_8H_{19}O_3PS_2$) is a light yellow oily liquid with a distinct mercaptan odor. The product is slightly soluble in water but soluble in most of the organic solvents. This is a systemic poison with contact and some fumigating action.

It is prepared as an emulsifiable concentrate, and also combined with activated charcoal for seed and soil treatment.

This dangerously toxic insecticide is widely used in aphid and phytophagous mite control. Dosages range from 2 to 8 ounces of the toxicant per acre for field crops and ordinarily 4 ounces per 100 gallons of water for spraying fruit trees.

This insecticide is too toxic for use around homes and livestock. It should be applied only by a trained operator who must wear recommended clothing and equipment. It is a dangerous cholinesterase inhibitor.

FIG. 52. Crop dusting with an airplane. (Courtesy of Shell Chemical Corporation. Photographer, Bob Taylor.)

A tolerance of 0.75 ppm is established for a number of vegetable and fruit crops, and for nuts; 0.3 ppm for beans; 1.25 ppm for grapes and hops; 5 ppm for fresh alfalfa and clover, and almond hulls. The acute LD_{50} for rats is 6-12 mg/kg by ingestion. Also there is a high acute toxicity by dermal absorption and inhalation.

Among other plant systemics are products such as *Phosdrin, phorate* or *Thimet,* and *Di-Syston.* Phosdrin has a short residual effectiveness and is useful in treatment of edible products near harvest. Thimet and Di-Syston are employed in seed treatments to protect the young plants from aphids, mites, and thrips.

There are two grades of *ronnel* ($C_8H_8Cl_3O_3PS$); Trolene is the drug grade, and Korlan the technical form. This insecticide is practically insoluble in water but readily soluble in most organic solvents.

Formulations of wettable powders, emulsions, smears and boluses are in use. The uses of this systemic and contact insecticide are in control of pests of livestock and house flies. It must not be applied on dairy cattle. In cattle grub control, ronnel (Trolene) is administered in two ways: 0.275 percent in feed daily for 14 days or as a 40 percent bolus. In the control of other pests of livestock such as horn flies, lice, and screw-worms, a 0.5 percent spray of the Korlan grade is generally used. A 5 percent smear of Korlan is recommended also in screw-worm control. House flies both inside and outside of barns may be controlled with a 0.5 to 1 percent spray.

This insecticide is of low acute toxicity to mammals. The acute LD_{50} to rats by ingestion is 1740 mg/kg, and by skin absorption 2000 mk/kg. A zero tolerance has been established for meat of cattle.

Technical *Co-Ral* ($C_{14}H_{16}ClO_5PS$) is composed of brownish crystals which are practically insoluble in water, with slight solubility in light petroleum but readily soluble in most of the common organic solvents. Wettable powders and dusts are formulated for use. This is a systemic poison which also has contact action. It is widely recommended for control of animal pests, particularly cattle grubs, lice, ticks, keds, screw-worms, poultry mites, and horn flies. Sprays of 0.25 to 0.50 percent strength are generally used. Co-Ral should not be used with pyrethrins, allethrin or synergists. As with ronnel, the product can not be used on dairy cattle. Tolerances of 0 in milk and eggs, and 1 ppm in meat and fat have been established. The acute LD_{50} to rats by ingestion is given as 90 to 110 mg/kg.

Ruelene ($C_{12}H_{19}ClNO_3P$) is a systemic insecticide which is promising in control of cattle grubs. It may also provide at least a measure of control for lice and horn flies when employed in sprays. A formulation is available for drenches, and sprays are prepared from an emulsifiable concentrate. Sprays containing 0.5 percent of the toxicant are recommended to be applied to the backs of the cattle with a volume of 3 quarts per animal. Treatment is not employed until after heel fly activity has ceased. The oral acute LD_{50} of the insecticide for white rats is about 1000 mg/kg. No tolerances have as yet been established for the product.

FUMIGANTS

Hydrocyanic acid or *Hydrogen cyanide* (HCN) is a colorless gas with the odor of peach kernels. It is soluble in water, alcohol and ether. The product is marketed chiefly in cylinders as a liquid under pressure and in pressure containers absorbed in porous material. Some calcium cyanide and sodium or potassium cyanide are also used. The gas is slightly lighter than air and not inflammable at concentrations generally employed.

Hydrocyanic acid has been widely employed in fumigating warehouses, mills, households, ships, and citrus trees. The amount of gas liberated per 1000 cubic feet of space is 6 to 8 ounces except in the fumigation of citrus for which purpose a much lower dosage is required.

Several tolerances are established which range from zero in fresh fruits and vegetables to 250 ppm in other products as spices, sage and pepper. Hydrocyanic acid is one of the most poisonous substances known. It should be applied only by a trained applicator wearing an approved gas mask. The lethal dose for man taken orally is 50 mg. which is about 0.8 mg/kg. Inhalation in high concentrations causes death immediately. A concentration of one part in 500 is fatal. Also in high concentration, the gas is absorbed by the skin; so gas masks are not completely effective.

The commercial grade of *carbon disulphide* (CS_2) is a slightly yellow liquid about $1/4$ heavier than water and with a disagreeable odor due to the presence of impurities. The liquid volatilizes readily when a large surface is exposed, forming a gas 2.63 times heavier than air and thus has excellent penetrating properties. It is an efficient fumigant for the protection of bulk grain from insect damage and has been widely used in the past. The fumigant is highly inflammable and is explosive when mixed with air in a wide range of proportions. Lighted cigarettes, sparks from electric switches and static electricity may ignite it. Also the gas may be ignited without the presence of a flame at 297° F. or above. Because of attendant hazards, a non-inflammable mixture of one part of carbon disulphide and four parts of carbon tetrachloride is recommended for use on stored grain. Two to five gallons of this mixture per 1000 bushels of grain are required. The recommended dosages vary with the type of bin and also the kind of grain which is being fumigated. Germination of grain may be affected if the seed is not reasonably dry or if the fumigant is applied directly upon it.

This fumigant is exempt from tolerances for grains as corn, wheat, rice, rye, oats and sorghum. Vapors are poisonous to mammals and recommended precautions should be followed.

Ethylene dichloride ($C_2H_4Cl_2$) is a colorless liquid with the odor of chloroform. The liquid has about the same specific gravity as carbon disulphide. Its vapors are about 3.5 times heavier than air, and so the fumigant has good penetrating properties.

This is an effective stored-grain fumigant. If the grain is reasonably dry there is little danger of affecting its germination. As the product has flammable and explosive properties, a mixture of three volumes of it with one volume of carbon tetrachloride is used to eliminate these hazards. Three to six gallons of the mixture per 1000 bushels of grain are recommended. Emulsions of ethylene dichloride are also used in the control of the peach tree borer. The fumigant is exempt from tolerances when used on wheat, corn, barley, rye and similar grains. It is of low mammalian toxicity.

Ethylene dibromide ($C_2H_4Br_2$) is a non-inflammable and stable product. It is marketed in solution in an inert solvent for use in soils and mixed with carbon tetrachloride for warehouse and mill fumigation. Its recommended uses are as a grain fumigant, and against certain soil insects and nematodes. Dosages of mixtures for grain fumigation are two to four gallons per 1000 bushels. In its effect on the germination of seed, it is moderately safe if the grain is reasonably dry.

Established tolerances (as inorganic bromide) range from 5 to 7.5 ppm. The acute oral LD_{50} to male rats is 146 mg/kg. Skin irritation and blisters may be produced on prolonged contact.

Methyl bromide (CH_3Br) is an important fumigant in commercial work. The product is a gas at ordinary temperatures, and is 3.3 times heavier than air. At temperatures of 40.1° F. or lower, it is a colorless, odorless, and volatile liquid. The fumigant is marketed in cans or cylinders of various capacities. Small amounts of chloropicrin may be added as a warning agent.

Methyl bromide is widely employed in the fumigation of many products—milled flour and feed, dairy products, dried fruits, beans, sweet potatoes, Irish potatoes, fresh vegetables of many kinds, and nursery stock. It also may be used in the fumigation of bulk grain where the bins are equipped with aeration systems. The use of this gas provides the most satisfactory control for the leaf-cutting ant. The compound is also an efficient soil fumigant for nematodes, wireworms, and other pests. Germination of seed may be impaired by this fumigant.

Since a tight enclosure is essential for successful fumigation, the use of an atmospheric fumigation vault is usually recommended. The dosage and the length of exposure depend upon the temperature and the nature of the materials being fumigated. A dosage of three pounds per 1000 cubic feet for two hours at 70° F. has proved effective for most purposes. The gas should be introduced into the chamber from the outside. The fumigant is toxic to human beings and the safe upper limit is set at 17 ppm. In the air above this concentration, respirators should be worn. Only experienced operators should use the fumigant. A wide range of tolerances has been established for the product.

Paradichlorobenzene ($C_6H_4Cl_2$) is a white crystalline substance which has the appearance of ice-cream salt. Upon exposure it volatilizes slowly into a gas 5.1 times heavier than air. The chemical has a characteristic though not unpleasant odor. Paradichlorobenzene is used in peachtree borer control; the usual dosage is one ounce per tree. Applications should be made in the fall in the form of a ring around the tree base, and then covered with soil. Considerable quantities of the crystals have been employed in the control of clothes moths and carpet beetles by simply sprinkling the layers of stored clothing or fabrics. From two to four pounds per 100 cubic feet of space is recommended.

Naphthalene ($C_{10}H_8$) is a white crystalline substance available as flakes or as the familiar "moth balls." The product volatilizes slowly, forming a gas with a characteristic pungent odor. Naphthalene is employed chiefly in the protection of fabrics from the depredations of clothes moths and carpet beetles. The dosage is the same as that of paradichlorobenzene. The flake form is the more efficient for use.

Several *soil fumigants* are commercially available for use in the control of nematodes and certain soil-inhabiting insects. The best-known products are *D-D mixtures* (composed of *dichloropropane* and *dichloropropene*), *ethylene dibromide,* and *methyl bromide.* Fumigation of the soil with these compounds is expensive, but the cost is not prohibitive for seedbeds, small home gardens, and certain truck crops where the income per acre is large.

The soil should be well prepared and free from clods and debris. It should be neither too dry nor too wet, but suitable for cultivation, and the soil temperature should not be below 50° F. The operator should follow the recommendations of the manufacturer in the application and the proper dosages of these fumigants.

ATTRACTANTS

Insects are attracted to many substances through olfactory stimulation, the chief types of which are concerned with sex, oviposition and food. Attractants have long been used to induce insects to feed upon poison baits and to lure them into traps. They are valuable in actual control, and also in determination of distribution and population densities of specific pests. Adults of the Japanese beetle are trapped in large number with an attractant consisting of a mixture of *geraniol* and *eugenol. Methyl eugenol* is an effective oriental fruit fly lure. A *protein hydrolysate bait* spray is very attractive to fruit flies and was employed successfully in eradication of the Mediterranean fruit fly in Florida during 1956 and 1957. Extracts of the female gypsy moth are of practical value in locating new infestations of the insect as the males are strongly attracted to the odor. *Metaldehyde* acts to lure snails and slugs to poison baits. *Keratin* is attractant to sheep blow flies, and low concentrations of *formaldehyde* attract house flies. *Terpinyl acetate, anethol* and *isoamyl salicylate* are other commonly known attractants.

REPELLENTS

A large number of materials have at least some repellent effect on insects. Even many of the common insecticides possess repellent properties in addition to their positive toxic value. Such common materials as road dust, lime and talc are well known for their repellent characteristics. *Creosote, pentachlorophenol* and *trichlorobenzene* are employed commercially for protection of buildings and timbers of various kinds and uses from termites and other wood-feeding insects. *Pine-tar oil* is an example of a repellent which prevents an insect (screw-worm fly) from laying its eggs. *Bordeaux mixture* is a repellent to plant-feeding insects. *Sulphur* prevents chigger infestations. *Moth balls* and *cedar oil* are employed to protect fabrics. *Oil of citronella* and *oil of pennyroyal* have been used for many years as repellents to be applied to the skin. More recently, compounds have been discovered which are much more efficient than oil of citronella which was the best previously known. These materials include *dimethyl phthalate, dimethyl carbate, indalone* and *diethyl-meta-toluamide.*

JOINT ACTION OF INSECTICIDES

Joint action refers to the response obtained when two or more insecticides are applied in combination. Studies of this phenomenon have increased during the last ten years with the introduction of many different insecticides and mixtures of insecticides on the market.

Several types of joint action of insecticides have been defined by research workers. The two most common classifications of joint action include:

1. Similar joint action is when the poisons act independently but similarly. The poisons applied separately produce a common response and produce the same response when applied jointly. Equivalent amounts of one poison may be substituted for the other in the mixture without altering the toxicity.

2. Synergistic action is when the application of a mixture of poisons produce a total response greater than the sum of the component poisons used separately. The toxicity of the mixture in this case is greater than the additive effects of the component poisons.

Results of studies on joint action have had important bearings on insect control. In many cases the addition of relatively nontoxic materials such as *piperonyl butoxide* to *pyrethrum* has increased its effectiveness greatly. An outstanding case of synergism is the mixture of the *cyclodiene*-type compounds (as *toxaphene*) with *DDT* which has extended the usefulness of the cyclodienes for control of resistant boll weevils. Some authorities believe that the use of insecticide mixtures which exhibit independent joint action may tend to prevent the development of insecticide resistance in insects.

8

THE CLASSIFICATION
OF INSECTS

In the preceding chapters a brief account has been given of the systematic position, morphology, physiology, and types of development of insects together with general methods of control of harmful species. With this information as a background, it is now essential to consider the classification and biologies of insects. In science, as in all other progressive enterprises, some logical system of grouping or classifying according to the types, quality, or the needs of the materials concerned is necessary. A natural system of classification is followed in the science of biology, of which entomology is a part. It is believed that in the world of living things all animals and plants had a common origin—that they have evolved into the present-day forms and complexities of development through the processes of evolution. The chief factors of evolution are variations, mutations, natural selection, and heredity.

Since the days of Aristotle many able biologists have devoted much time to the study and classification of plants and animals. The greatest of these early biologists was Linnaeus, a Swedish naturalist. He proposed the present-day system of classification based upon the natural relationships among living organisms. The names used to designate the different forms were Latin, a dead language. This was a fortunate procedure as the language is not subject to change and is the basis of a number of our present-day languages. At present these Latin names are in general use, so that either animal or plant forms may be recognized by name designation throughout the scientific world. Common names of insects usually are not known except locally. Although Latin names are of little value to the layman, they are indispensable to the scientific worker who must identify species, conduct research, and compile and disseminate information pertaining to them.

Several times more species of insects exist than all other animal forms combined. Upwards of a million species are believed to exist. The number is so great that insects must be studied largely as groups because no one has the time nor the mental capacity to learn all of them. Other than common species he must content himself with recognizing the order, family, and perhaps the genus to which an insect belongs. If a worker is sufficiently conversant with the characteristics and general biologies of these groups, oftentimes he has most of the essential information needed regarding an insect.

As mentioned earlier, insects constitute the largest class of the phylum *Arthropoda,* the *Hexapoda.* When Linnaeus classified the insects he established the orders of insects on the basis of wing characteristics and named them accordingly. For example, all two-winged insects (flies) were named *Diptera*[1] and those insects with the first pair of wings consisting of horn-like, veinless wing covers, beetles, were designated as *Coleoptera.*[2] This proved to be a very desirable system of classification as it facilitated the identification of an insect to the order, and made the names easier to learn. This system of naming the orders has been continued as far as possible to the present time.

Linnaeus assigned the insects to only seven orders which he named *Aptera* (wingless arthropods), *Hemiptera* (true bugs), *Neuroptera* (net-veined insects), *Coleoptera* (beetles), *Lepidoptera* (scale-winged insects), *Diptera* (flies), and *Hymenoptera* (bees, wasps, and others). Inasmuch as little was known concerning the biologies and the morphology of the arthropods at that early day dissimilar groups naturally were placed in the same order. As an example, the Linnaean order, *Aptera,* contained not only all wingless insects, but crustaceans, arachnids, millipedes, and centipedes as well. The crustaceans, arachnids, millipedes, and centipedes certainly belong to different classes on the basis of anatomical characteristics. Such a great diversity of morphology, method of development, and habits exists among the wingless insects that it was necessary to divide this group into several orders. Thus reclassification necessarily has occurred and a number of new orders has been established. Twenty-five orders are recognized for the purposes of

---

[1] *Dis,* two; *pteron,* wing.
[2] *Coleos,* sheath; *pteron,* wing.

this text. Some of these orders are of only slight importance and will be treated very briefly.

The class *Hexapoda* may be naturally divided into two subclasses, the *Apterygota* (those insects without wings) and *Pterygota* (those insects with wings). The subclass *Apterygota* is made up of those primitive insects, such as silverfish and springtails, which are primitively wingless; that is, there is no evidence that their ancestors ever had wings. Conversely, the members of the *Pterygota* bear wings, or in case of the absence of wings, as with bed bugs or animal lice, there is evidence that they descended from a winged ancestry. The wingless condition of these groups is the result of a parasitic way of life.

The subclasses and orders of insects as considered here are as follows:

1. Subclass *Apterygota*. Primitive wingless insects, there is no indication that they developed from winged ancestors.
    Order *Thysanura*—The Silverfish.
    Order *Collembola*—The Springtails.
2. Subclass *Pterygota*. Winged and wingless insects, if wingless the condition is an acquired one.
    Order *Ephemeroptera*—The Mayflies.
    Order *Odonata*—The Dragonflies and the Damselflies.
    Order *Plecoptera*—The Stoneflies.
    Order *Orthoptera*—The Cockroaches, Grasshoppers, Katydids, and others.
    Order *Isoptera*—The Termites.
    Order *Dermaptera*—The Earwigs.
    Order *Embiidina* or *Embioptera*—The Embiids.
    Order *Zoraptera*—The Zorapterons.
    Order *Corrodentia*—The Psocids.
    Order *Thysanoptera*—The Thrips.
    Order *Mallophaga*—The Chewing Lice.
    Order *Anoplura*—The Sucking Lice.
    Order *Hemiptera*—The True Bugs.
    Order *Homoptera*—The Aphids, Scales, and others.
    Order *Coleoptera*—The Beetles.
    Order *Strepsiptera*—The Stylopids.
    Order *Neuroptera*—The Corydalis, Aphis Lion, and others.
    Order *Mecoptera*—The Scorpionflies.
    Order *Trichoptera*—The Caddisflies.

Order *Lepidoptera*—The Moths and Butterflies.
Order *Diptera*—The Flies.
Order *Siphonaptera*—The Fleas.
Order *Hymenoptera*—The Wasps, Bees, and others.

KEY TO ORDERS OF COMMON INSECTS (ADULTS)

1. Functional wings present   2
   Wings absent or vestigial   27
2. With one pair of wings   3
   With two pairs of wings   5
3. Wings net-veined; halteres absent; mouthparts vestigial
   (Certain Mayflies)   **Ephemeroptera**, p. 119
   Wings with veins but not net-veined; halteres present; suck-
   ing or vestigial mouthparts   4
4. Wings with reduced venation; caudal filaments present;
   minute, delicate insects (Males of *Coccidae*)   **Homoptera**, p. 198
   Wings with longitudinal and a few cross veins; caudal
   filaments absent (Flies)   **Diptera**, p. 382
5. Front and hind wings unlike in texture   6
   Front and hind wings similar in texture, membranous   12
6. Front wings reduced to slender clubs; hind wings large,
   triangular in form, folding fanlike; very small parasitic
   insects (Stylopids or Twisted-wing Parasites)   **Strepsiptera**, p. 287
   Both front and hind wings normally developed   7
7. Front wings thickened at base, membranous and usually
   overlapping apically; piercing-sucking mouthparts (True
   Bugs)   **Hemiptera**, p. 172
   Front wings of same texture throughout   8
8. Front wings horny, veinless sheaths (elytra)   9
   Front wings parchment-like or leathery   10
9. Front wings usually covering abdomen; abdomen without
   movable forceps-like caudal appendages (Beetles)
                                                           Coleoptera, p. 228
   Front wings short, not covering end of abdomen; abdomen
   with movable forceps-like caudal appendages (Earwigs)
                                                           Dermaptera, p. 153
10. Hind wings folded fan-like; chewing mouthparts (Cock-
    roaches, Grasshoppers, and others)   **Orthoptera**, p. 131
    Hind wings not folded fan-like; piercing-sucking mouth-
    parts   11
11. Beak arises from anterior ventral portion of head (Certain
    True Bugs)   **Hemiptera**, p. 172
    Beak arises from posterior ventral portion of head (Cicadas,
    Leafhoppers, and others)   **Homoptera**, p. 198

12. Wings with many longitudinal veins and cross veins; net-veined, at least basally ... 13

Wings with branching veins and with relatively few cross veins ... 19

13. Front and hind wings approximately equal in size ... 14

Front and hind wings unequal in size ... 17

14. Head prolonged into a trunk-like beak (Scorpionflies) **Mecoptera**, p. 294

Head not prolonged into a trunk-like beak; mouthparts in normal position ... 15

15. Each wing with a joint-like structure, the nodus, near the middle of each front margin; tarsus with 3 segments (Dragonflies) **Odonata**, p. 123

Nodus absent on middle front margin of wings; tarsus with 4 or 5 segments ... 16

16. Front and hind wings long, narrow, and similar with venation weakly developed except in costal and anal areas; wings held flat over body; tarsus with 4 segments; colonial insects (Termites) **Isoptera**, p. 147

Wings large, leaf-like, strongly veined, held roof-like over the body; 5-segmented tarsus (Aphis Lions, Dobsonflies, and others) **Neuroptera**, p. 289

17. Front wings larger than hind wings; 2 or 3 long, many-segmented filamentous caudal appendages on abdomen (Mayflies) **Ephemeroptera**, p. 119

Hind wings larger than front pair and folded in plaits when not in use ... 18

18. Front and hind wings of same texture; body depressed and elongate, sides subparallel; nymphs develop in water (Stoneflies) **Plecoptera**, p. 128

Front wings parchment-like and somewhat thicker than hind pair; body variable in form but when depressed sides not subparallel; terrestrial insects (Grasshoppers, Cockroaches, and others) **Orthoptera, p. 131**

19. Wings fringed with long hairs or covered with long hairs or scales ... 20

Wings without long hairs or scales ... 23

20. Wings usually completely covered with scales; mouthparts adapted for sucking (Moths and Butterflies) **Lepidoptera**, p. 298

Wings fringed with long hairs or covered with long hairs ... 21

21. Base of abdomen constricted and joined to the thorax by a narrow segment (certain minute parasitic wasp-like insects) **Hymenoptera** (in part), p. 440

Base of abdomen not constricted; broadly joined to the thorax ... 22

22. Wings and body usually clothed with long hairs, wings held roof-like over the body; mouthparts vestigial; tarsus with 5 segments and with claws (Caddisflies) **Trichoptera**, p. 296

Wings long, narrow with 1 or 2 veins or none, and fringed
with long hairs; tarsus with 2 segments without claws and
terminates in a retractile bladder-like structure; minute
insects (Thrips)   **Thysanoptera,** p. 158

23. Piercing-sucking mouthparts enclosed in a sheath-like beak,
which arises from posterior ventral portion of head
(Cicadas, Aphids, and others)   **Homoptera,** p. 198
Mouthparts adapted for chewing, or chewing and lapping,
arising from normal position   24

24. Tarsus with 4 or 5 segments; front pair of wings larger than
the hind pair (Bees, Ants, and others)   **Hymenoptera,** p. 440
Tarsus with 2 or 3 segments   25

25. Cerci absent; wings held roof-like over body; veins prominent but somewhat reduced (Psocids)   **Corrodentia,** p. 156
Cerci present; small frail insects, body less than 3 mm in
length   26

26. Wings subequal in size; tarsus with 3 segments (Embiids)
                                                   Embiidina, p. 154
Hind wings smaller than front wings; tarsus with 2 segments (Zorapterons)   **Zoraptera,** p. 156

27. Abdomen with one or more anteriorly located ventral appendages; mouthparts usually retracted with only the
tips visible   28
Abdomen with anteriorly located ventral appendages absent; the only abdominal appendages consisting of posteriorly located cerci and genitalia   29

28. Abdomen with no more than 6 segments; collophore or
ventral tube usually present on ventral surface of first abdominal segment; spring-like structure usually present
on ventral surface of fourth abdominal segment; cerci
absent (Springtails)   **Collembola,** p. 117
Abdomen with 10 or 11 segments terminating in a pair of
many-segmented cerci or unsegmented forceps-like appendages; styli situated on ventral side of abdomen (Silverfish, Bristletails)   **Thysanura,** p. 115

29. Sedentary, scale-like, attached to host; usually covered with
waxy secretions (Scale Insects)   **Homoptera,** p. 198
Not sedentary, not scale-like; capable of locomotion   30

30. Mouthparts modified for chewing   31
Mouthparts modified for sucking   40

31. Head terminating in broad deflexed beak (Scorpionflies)
                                                   Mecoptera, p. 294
Head not terminating in a deflexed beak   32

32. Base of abdomen constricted and joined to thorax by a
narrow stalk (Ants, Gall Wasps, and Velvet Ants)
                                                   Hymenoptera, p. 440
Base of abdomen not constricted; broadly joined to thorax   33

33. Abdomen with movable forceps-like caudal appendages
    (Earwigs) **Dermaptera,** p. 153
    Abdomen without movable forceps-like caudal appendages 34
34. Hind legs enlarged for leaping or jumping (Wingless Katy-
    dids and Crickets) **Orthoptera,** p. 131
    Hind legs not so modified 35
35. Small, louse-like in form; usually flattened and leathery 36
    Size variable but not louse-like; usually not flattened 37
36. Antenna with 5 or fewer segments; parasitic on birds and
    mammals (Chewing Lice) **Mallophaga,** p. 164
    Antenna with 9 or more segments; not parasitic (Book Lice)
    Corrodentia, p. 156
37. Tarsus with 2 segments (Zorapterons) **Zoraptera,** p. 156
    Tarsus with 3 to 5 segments 38
38. First segment of front tarsus greatly enlarged; tarsus with
    3 segments (Embiids) **Embiidina,** p. 154
    First segment of front tarsus normal; tarsus with 3 to 5 seg-
    ments 39
39. Small, soft-bodied, stocky; live in colonies usually in soil or
    wood (Termites) **Isoptera,** p. 147
    Exoskeleton heavily sclerotized, body elongate or oval; large
    insects not in colonies (Cockroaches, Walkingsticks)
    Orthoptera, p. 131
40. Body compressed laterally; legs long and stout, modified for
    jumping (Fleas) **Siphonaptera,** p. 433
    Body not compressed laterally; legs not modified for jump-
    ing 41
41. Tarsus without claws, terminating in a retractile bladder-
    like structure; very small insects (Thrips) **Thysanoptera,** p. 158
    Tarsus with well developed claws 42
42. Antenna concealed in a pit, not visible from dorsal view
    (Pupipara) **Diptera,** p. 382
    Antenna exserted dorsally, visible 43
43. Mouthparts retractile; tarsus with 1 claw (Sucking Lice)
    Anoplura, p. 167
    Mouthparts form a beak; tarsus with 2 claws 44
44. Beak arises from anterior ventral portion of head (Bed
    Bugs) **Hemiptera,** p. 172
    Beak arises from posterior ventral portion of head (Aphids
    and others) **Homoptera,** p. 198

An order of insects is based on three primary characteristics:

1. **Wings present or absent; if present, the type and structure.**
2. **Type of metamorphosis.**
3. **Type of mouthparts.**

In addition, one or more minor characteristics are given which aid in readily identifying the insect to the order. As an example, the order *Coleoptera* is characterized by the horny, veinless wing covers that usually meet in a straight line down the back when the insect is at rest. Coupled with this major characteristic most all beetles are stout-bodied. This combination of characters readily places the insect in the order *Coleoptera*.

Most insects may be identified to an order on sight. When the order to which an insect belongs is recognized, the type of mouthparts and the type of metamorphosis are known. This knowledge is of basic value as it provides information regarding the type of feeding and the stages of the insect that may be involved. A knowledge of the general biology of the order supplies still further information. If the family of the insect is known, some information concerning such points as life history, feeding habits, hosts, and reproduction may be available. For example, consider the boll weevil. A brief observation identifies the insect as belonging to the order *Coleoptera*. The mouthparts throughout this order are of the chewing type regardless of the presence of the snout. The metamorphosis is complete. The stages of development are then known to be egg, larva, pupa, and adult—larva and adult being the active stages. The larva is known to have the same type of mouthparts and generally feeds upon the same hosts as the adult. The boll weevil belongs to the family *Curculionidae*. Parenthetically speaking all family names of animals end in *-idae;* thus, the family names may be readily recognized anywhere. Members of the *Curculionidae* are provided with snouts for use in feeding primarily within the tissues of the host plants. Hence, they are as a group specialized in their feeding habits. This immediately suggests that the insect may be poisoned with some difficulty by the application of insecticides. The *Curculionidae* not only have specialized feeding habits but they are usually specialized with respect to food plants as well. For all practical purposes the boll weevil may be considered as restricted to cotton as its source of food. The plum curculio feeds upon peaches, plums, apples, and related hosts and never feeds upon cotton. The acorn weevil breeds in acorns and the hickory weevil attacks hickory nuts and pecans.

The green stink bug may be taken as another example. The presence of four wings with the front pair thickened at the base, with the apical portions membranous and overlapping while the insect is at rest, and the large triangular scutellum on the broad flat back identifies the insect as belonging to the order *Hemiptera*. When the order is recognized the mouthparts are known to be of the piercing-sucking type and the nature of feeding indicated. The stages of development are known to be egg, nymph, and adult—the nymph having the same type of mouthparts and feeding habits as the adult. This insect belongs to the family *Pentatomidae*. If the biology of the family is adequately known, one may surmise the number of generations produced annually; perhaps also the overwintering stage and other pertinent information.

A knowledge of the orders of insects and the characteristics of each provides more information than any other basic facts of the science of entomology. Knowledge of the families is also of great value. However, there are so many different families of insects that one can become acquainted with comparatively few in a general course of entomology.

A family is subdivided into genera and species. The scientific name of an animal or a plant consists of the name of both the genus and species. This practice of naming insects is known as the *binomial system of nomenclature*. The scientific name of the boll weevil is *Anthonomus grandis* Boh. Here the first word of the combination is the genus name which should always begin with a capital letter; the second word is the species name and the first letter is never capitalized. The abbreviation *"Boh."* (for Boheman) is the name of the describer of the species and, excepting technical discussions, this name is usually omitted. Scientific names are either italicized or underscored.

9

SUBCLASS APTERYGOTA

The Apterygota are primitively wingless insects, and there is no morphological or biological evidence to indicate that they descended from a winged ancestry. Another primitive feature of this subclass is the presence of rudiments of abdominal appendages, particularly the styli in the Thysanura (bristletails). The members of this order are therefore of special interest as they furnish some evidence to the ancestry of insects.

FIG. 53. The silverfish (*Lepisma saccharina*). (From Agricultural Research Service, U.S.D.A.)

Apterygota are generally small insects, some being only ½ millimeter long; however some of the larger forms are known to approach 50 millimeters in overall length. The insects in this group develop with only slight morphological changes, and they are considered as having no metamorphosis (ametabolous development). The mouthparts are formed for chewing. In some forms the mouthparts are almost concealed by the overlapping folds of the cheeks. About 2,500 species of Apterygota are known to science.

Order THYSANURA[1]

Bristletails, Silverfish, Firebrats

The chief characteristics of the members of this order are:

1. **Primitively wingless or without evidence of a winged ancestry.**
2. **Mouthparts formed for chewing.**
3. **Development without metamorphosis, the adult stage attained by the young with little change in body form except size.**
4. **Abdomen composed of ten or eleven segments, terminating in a pair of many-segmented cerci or unsegmented, forceps-like appendages.**
5. **Styli situated on the ventral side of the abdomen.**

Insects of this order are commonly referred to as bristletails because of the presence in most species of either two or three long filamentous appendages at the tip of the abdomen. The paired appendages are called cerci. When a third, median, appendage is present it is a prolongation of the eleventh abdominal segment. In certain species of bristletails the cerci are not jointed filamentous appendages, but are much shorter and stouter, and are forceps-like structures.

The Thysanura are considerably larger than the other members belonging to this subclass. The abdomen is composed of ten or eleven segments. The latter bear on the ventral surface slender two-segmented appendages known as styli. These are believed to be vestigial abdominal legs. The number of styli varies in different species and they are also present on the ventral side of the thorax in certain forms. The eyes of the insects of this order may be perfect, degenerate, or entirely absent. In some species the body is covered with scales.

The life history of bristletails is imperfectly known. Upon hatching from the egg the young resembles the adult except in size and in some other minor details. The silverfish and firebrats are known to molt in a manner similar to other insects. In fact, they may molt a large number of times and may continue to molt after attaining sexual maturity.

Only two members of Thysanura are of much economic importance in the United States. They are the silverfish or "slicker," and the so-called firebrat.

---

[1] *Thysanos,* tassel; *oura,* tail.

Silverfish (*Lepisma saccharina*).　Silverfish are soft-bodied insects about ½ inch in length with three long tail-like appendages at the apex of the abdomen (Fig. 53). These insects are covered with scales which give them a uniform silvery or gray color. The presence of these scales and the feeding habits have probably suggested the name "fish-moths" which is frequently applied to them. These insects are nocturnal in habit and prefer to secrete themselves in dark places. They are rarely seen until disturbed. When disturbed they are very active and quickly dart to safety, usually eluding capture.

In homes silverfish may be found from the basement to the attic. They feed upon materials with a high starch or sugar content, such as wallpaper, book bindings, pastes, and paper sizing (Fig. 54).

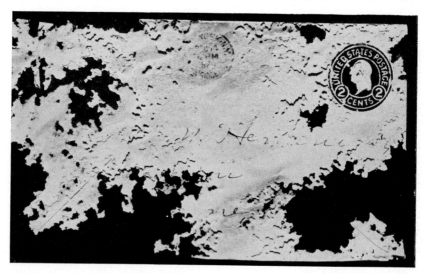

FIG. 54. An envelope almost destroyed by silverfish. (From Agricultural Research Service, U.S.D.A.)

They may seriously damage starched clothing and lace curtains. Sometimes these insects also attack such thin fabrics as rayon. Perhaps the most extensive injury done by these insects is in loosening wallpaper from the walls and eating holes in it.

Eggs of the silverfish are laid in cracks, crevices, or folds of the food materials. The eggs are not glued to any object but roll freely as those of a flea. Egg to adult development may occur in seven to nine months in tropical regions, but about two years are required to complete the life cycle in temperate climates.

Although silverfish and bristletails produce but few eggs and develop slowly, they may maintain a relatively high population since the mortality rate is low and the life span protracted.

Firebrat (*Thermobia domestica*). The firebrat closely resembles the silverfish in general appearance, but the body above is mottled with light and darker spots. This insect thrives best under conditions of relatively high temperatures and is usually found in heated basements, about furnaces, and in bakeries. Its food and biology are similar to that of the silverfish.

Control measures for silverfish and firebrats should be applied primarily in those parts of a building where the insects are developing in the largest numbers—usually the basement or the attic. If this is not done reinfestations will continue in other parts of the building.

DDT or chlordane sprays or dusts will control both pests. To be effective the insecticide should be applied on baseboards, in closets, bookcases, and other places where the insects hide or will be forced to crawl over the deposit. A solution of DDT or chlordane in refined kerosene is recommended for use in the home. The spray should be applied so that the surfaces treated are thoroughly moistened. The residual deposit will remain effective for a considerable length of time. When infestations occur in places where a fire hazard exists DDT or chlordane dust may be used. Control measures may not produce immediate noticeable results, but a gradual reduction of the pests may be expected when insecticides are thoroughly applied.

Order COLLEMBOLA[2]

The Springtails

The chief characteristics of this order of insects are:

1. **Primitively wingless or without any evidence of winged ancestry.**
2. **Mouthparts of the chewing type but only the tips of the mandibles are visible.**
3. **Metamorphosis is slight or absent as in the Thysanura.**
4. **Abdomen composed of not more than six segments.**
5. **Collophore or ventral tube usually present on the ventral surface of the first abdominal segment.**

[2] *Colla,* glue; *embolon,* bolt, bar. The name is derived from the presence of a collophore.

The common name "springtail" has been applied to members of this order because of a spring-like structure which is usually present on the ventral side of the fourth abdominal segment. This springing organ is called the *furcula*. When the furcula is suddenly released against the surface upon which the insect is resting the insect is propelled through the air. On the ventral aspect of the third abdominal segment there is usually a pair of appendages forming a structure known as the catch or *tenaculum,* which holds the fur-

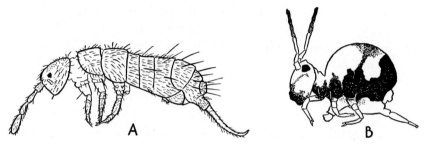

FIG. 55. Springtails *(Collembola)*. **A,** *Isotoma andrei.* **B,** *Sminthurides lepus.* (Courtesy of H. B. Mills and the Iowa State College Press.)

cula when not in use. A *collophore,* or ventral tube, is usually present on the ventral surface of the first abdominal segment. It is provided with two eversible sacs which secrete a sticky substance. This substance enables the insects to cling to smooth surfaces.

Springtails are minute insects, rarely more than ⅕ inch long (Fig. 55). Although seldom observed by the layman, they may occur in enormous numbers on the surface of stagnant water, in decaying vegetable matter, in mushroom houses, or other damp places.

In general, springtails are not considered to be of much economic importance. However, they may do serious injury to tender leaves of garden crops and mushrooms. Dusting with rotenone or malathion provides satisfactory control of these insects.

10

SUBCLASS PTERYGOTA

ORDERS EPHEMEROPTERA, ODONATA AND PLECOPTERA

Most insects belong to the Pterygota. This subclass is composed of all insects which bear wings in the adult stage. Also certain wingless insects such as lice and fleas are included here, since biological and morphological studies clearly show that these forms have descended from a winged ancestry. These apterous insects have lost their wings by degeneration.

Morphologically and biologically, the Pterygota are a diverse group. Incomplete, gradual, and complete metamorphosis occur among the members. The mouthparts may be formed for chewing, sucking, sponging, or lapping, with various modifications or adaptations depending upon the type of food consumed. The only abdominal appendages present are cerci and genitalia. These differences, among others, are so great that the members of Pterygota must be studied under a number of separate orders.

Order EPHEMEROPTERA[1]

Mayflies

The Ephemeroptera are characterized by:

1. **Two pairs of membranous wings, triangular in shape and net-veined; the hind pair (sometimes absent) always much smaller than the front pair.**
2. **Mouthparts of the adults vestigial, fitted for chewing in the nymphs.**
3. **Incomplete metamorphosis.**

[1] *Ephemeros,* lasting but a day; *pteron,* wing.

4. **Two or three elongate, many-segmented, filamentous appendages at the tip of the abdomen.**

Mayflies are commonly found in the vicinity of ponds, lakes, or streams. The adults are readily recognized by the rather large net-veined triangular shaped front wings and their frail bodies (Figs. 56 and 57). The hind wings are smaller and absent in some species.

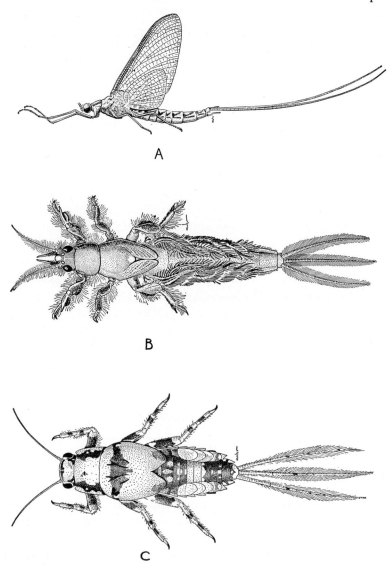

FIG. 56.   Mayfly adult and nymphs. **A,** Adult of *Hexagenia limbata*. **B,** Nymph of *H. limbata*. **C,** Nymph of *Ephemerella argo*. (From Illinois Natural History Survey. Drawn by C. O. Mohr.)

They are soft-bodied, with inconspicuous antennae and bear at the tip of the abdomen two or three long, many-segmented filamentous appendages. These insects are attracted to lights and at times huge numbers are found around street lights in towns and cities located near large bodies of fresh water.

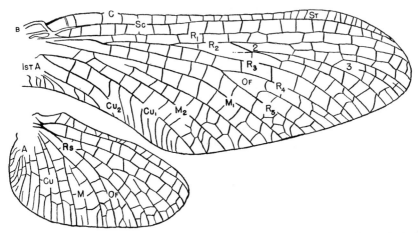

FIG. 57. Front and hind wings of a mayfly (*Siphlonurus berenice*) showing principal veins. (Based on Needham *et al.*, by permission of Comstock Publishing Associates.)

KEY TO THE FAMILIES OF EPHEMEROPTERA

Adults

1. Veins M and Cu_1 of front wing diverging strongly at base with M_2 bent strongly toward Cu_1 basally; outer fork of hind wing wanting, hind tarsus with 4 segments (Fig. 57)
   Ephemeridae

   Veins M and Cu_1 of front wing not diverging basally to any extent with fork of M more nearly symmetrical; outer fork of hind wing present or absent; hind tarsus with 3 to 5 segments   2

2. Hind tarsus with 5 segments; cubital intercalaries in 2 parallel pairs, long and short alternately; venation never greatly reduced   **Heptageniidae**

   Hind tarsus with 3 or 4 segments; cubital intercalaries not in parallel pairs as above; venation at times greatly reduced
   Baetidae

Nymphs

1. Mandible with forward projecting external tusk, visible from dorsal view   **Ephemeridae**

   Mandible with no tusk as above only in rare exceptions   2

2. Head decidedly depressed; eyes dorsal   **Heptageniidae**
   Head not decidedly depressed; eyes lateral   **Baetidae**

Mayflies attract the attention especially of scientists and fishermen. Scientists are interested in the short life span of the adult, which may not extend more than a day or two, and the molting habits and the biology of the various species; whereas the fisherman's interest has been aroused by the feeding of fish upon them. Vainly have fishermen tried to use the adults as bait, but their bodies are too fragile for this purpose. A number of artificial lures resembling mayflies, fashioned out of feathers, wire and silk are used by fishermen.

The swarming and mating flights of mayflies have been described by several writers. These flights consist only of males and usually occur at twilight. The cloud of insects rises and falls in the air in endless repetition. Females dart into the swarm, are seized by the males and the pairs fly away together to a nearby bush or other resting place. Soon after mating the females return to the water, lay their eggs, and die.

The various species swarm at different times. Some swarm only at a certain time, while swarms of others may be seen several times during the season. The swarming flights usually occur between sundown and dark.

The nymphs of mayflies live in relatively clean water. All species are found in an aquatic environment for which they are adapted. Typical immature forms are elongate and bear on the end of the abdomen two or three caudal filaments. In these characteristics they resemble the adults. The nymphs usually have paired tracheal gills located along the sides of the first seven abdominal segments. These are provided with numerous tracheae which obtain oxygen from the water. The gills vibrate in a shuttle-like manner. The nymphs have functionally chewing mouthparts and they feed on decaying vegetable matter and small plant life. They may molt a number of times, and as many as 27 molts have been observed in at least one species.

The life history of mayflies is imperfectly known. Certain species are thought to have two generations annually while the period of development of others is longer. Probably most species produce one generation a year. These insects hibernate as nymphs. When the nymphs reach maturity they float to the surface of the water, cast their skins, and the winged forms quickly fly away and alight on some nearby object. This is not a true adult or *imago;* it is known as a *subimago.* Shortly thereafter the subimago molts. This is the only winged insect that molts as an adult. The mouthparts of the adult are vestigial and they probably do not partake of any food. The digestive tract is filled with air which gives the insect added buoyancy in flight. Soon after the final molt the females mate and then return to the water to oviposit. The number of eggs laid may range from several hundred to several thousand.

The life of a mayfly is fraught with many dangers. The nymphs are fed upon by fishes, water beetles, frogs, and other enemies. The subimago may be devoured as it emerges from the water. Birds, spiders, dragonflies, frogs, and other enemies feed upon them on land; and as the females dip into the water in the process of egg-laying many are eaten by fish before this final mission of life is accomplished.

Mayflies are important in the economy of fresh waters. Much organic matter which, otherwise, would pollute streams, lakes, and ponds is destroyed by the nymphs. They constitute an important source of food for a number of animals, especially fish. They are the most abundant insects in some waters.

Several families and more than 500 species of mayflies are now recognized from North America. The nymphs of certain species of mayflies serve as intermediate hosts of nematode parasites of fish, frogs, and salamanders.

Order ODONATA[2]

Dragonflies and Damselflies

Members of the order Odonata are recognized by:

1. **Four net-veined, membranous wings; the hind pair as large or slightly larger than the front pair; and a nodus or notch near the middle of the front margin of each wing.**
2. **Well developed chewing mouthparts.**
3. **Incomplete metamorphosis.**
4. **Adult usually with large head and large eyes, and long slender body.**
5. **Antennae short, awl-shaped, and inconspicuous.**

[2] *Odous,* tooth.

Dragonflies and damselflies are known to practically everyone and are generally of interest to the layman. They are commonly found

in the vicinity of lakes, stock tanks, and streams, where the eggs are laid and the immature stages develop. However, the dragonflies are strong fliers and may frequently be found considerable distances from water.

The Odonata are divided into two distinct and readily recognizable suborders, the *Anisoptera* (dragonflies) and the *Zygoptera* (damselflies). The dragonflies are much larger and are strong flying and soaring individuals (Fig. 58). When at rest the wings are held horizontally and at a right angle to the long axis of the body. The head is large, broad, subglobose, and concave posteriorly. The compound

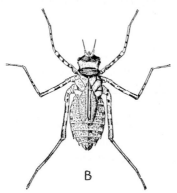

FIG. 58. **A,** An adult dragonfly (*Platythemis lydia*). (From Department of Entomology, A & M College of Texas.) **B,** Nymph of a dragonfly (*Macromia magnifica*). (From Kennedy.)

eyes often cover the greater surface of the head, each of which in certain species may contain more than 30,000 facets. Due to the curvature of the surface of the head the large eyes enable the insects to see in almost every direction. The damselflies are rather delicate insects, and are weak fliers. When at rest their wings are held parallel over the long axis of the body. The head is transverse with prominent compound eyes borne on lateral prolongations.

Odonata have three ocelli; antennae are short and awl-like, and the mouthparts are strongly mandibulate. The insects are predaceous and catch their prey in flight. The modified legs are held in such a way that a basket is formed into which the food is scooped.

KEY TO SUBORDERS AND COMMON FAMILIES OF ODONATA

ADULTS

1. Wings held horizontally and at a right angle to the long axis
   of the body when at rest; stout-bodied (Dragonflies)

   Suborder **Anisoptera**, 2

   Wings held parallel over the long axis of the body when at
   rest; rather frail insects (Damselflies)   Suborder **Zygoptera**, 4

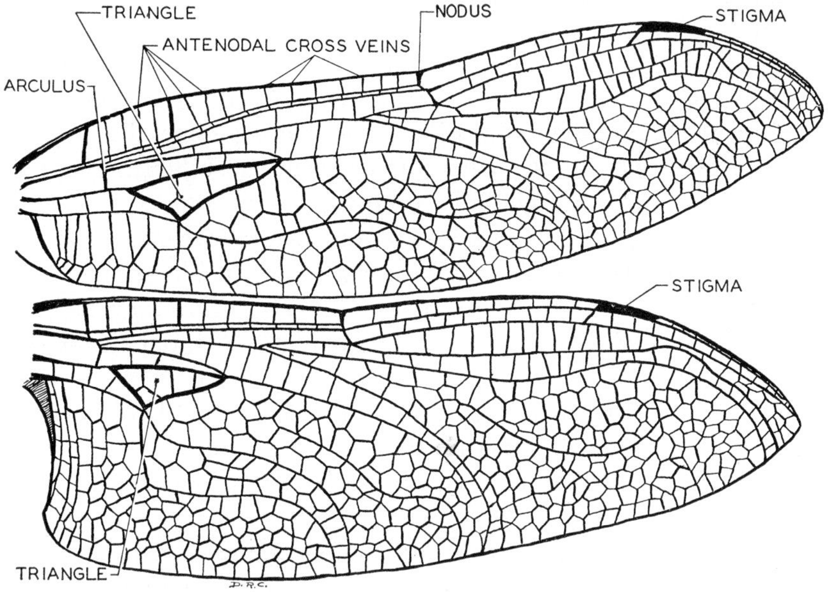

FIG. 59. Front and hind wings of a dragonfly (*Anax junius*), showing wing characters used in the key (p. 125).

2. Triangle of hind wing nearer arculus than in front wing and
   shaped differently (Fig. 59)   **Libellulidae**

   Triangle about equidistant from arculus in both front and
   hind wings and of similar shape   3
3. Eyes meeting on top of head   **Aeschnidae**
   Eyes widely separated on top of head   **Gomphidae**
4. Wings not stalked; numerous antenodal cross-veins   **Agrionidae**
   Wings stalked; only 2 antenodal cross-veins   **Coenagrionidae**

NYMPHS

1. No leaf-like gills on posterior end of abdomen

   Suborder **Anisoptera**, 2

   Three leaf-like gills on posterior end of abdomen

   Suborder **Zygoptera**, 4

2. Labium spoon-shaped or mask-shaped   **Libellulidae**
   Labium flat or nearly so   3
3. Antenna with 4 segments   **Gomphidae**
   Antenna with 6 or 7 segments   **Aeschnidae**
4. Labium widely and deeply cleft along the median line; basal
      segment of antenna quite long   **Agrionidae**
   Labium undivided or almost so; basal segment of antenna
      short   **Coenagrionidae**

The dragonflies are also known as mosquito-hawks and devil's darning needles. The name mosquito-hawk is naturally derived from the habit of the adults feeding on mosquitoes and similar small insect life. Superstition is responsible for the name of devil's darning needle, as the impression exists among some that the insects may sew up the eyes and ears of sleeping children. Needless to say, these insects are perfectly harmless.

Damselfly is quite an appropriate and descriptive name for the members of this beautiful and delicate group of insects that flits and flutters over the water surface (Fig. 60). However, they are also known as snake-doctors by many because of the superstition that they administer to ill or injured snakes. Country boys are often admonished in killing snakes to thoroughly macerate their heads or else a snake-doctor will stitch up the wounds and nurse the serpents back to health. These insects have long slender bodies and are often beautifully colored.

With the exception of one group, odonates mate during flight. A peculiarity of the order is that the copulatory organs of the male are found on the ventral side of the second and third abdominal segments. Prior to mating the seminal fluid is transferred to a cavity located here. In mating the male grasps the female by the prothorax or head with its clasping organs and the female bends its abdomen around to reach the copulatory organs of the male. United dragonflies flying over water are commonly seen. Eggs are laid in the stems of aquatic plants, logs, or directly in the water.

The eggs hatch into immature forms known as nymphs which have little resemblance to the adults. They are found on the bottom of the bodies of water, in the mud, on submerged plants, or in debris. The nymphs feed upon aquatic insects as well as other small animal life including young fish. The labium is greatly elongated and jointed, bearing hooks at the apex. It is used in reaching out and capturing the prey. When not in use it folds backward and conceals the mandibles, thus forming a mask-like structure over the

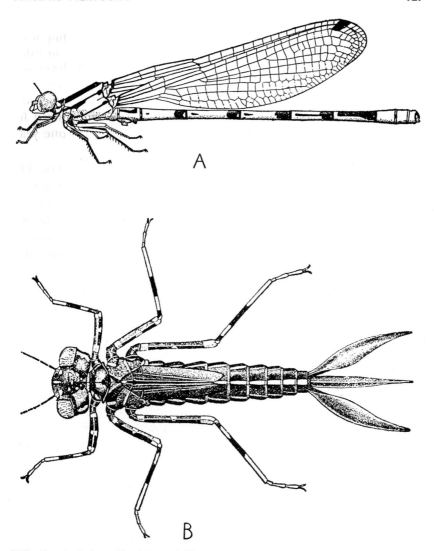

A

B

FIG. 60. **A,** A damselfly (*Argia vivida*). **B,** A nymph of a damselfly (*Argia emma*). (From Kennedy.)

face. Damselfly nymphs respire through three leaf-like tracheal gills located at the end of the abdomen. These tracheal gills also are used in swimming. In dragonflies the rectum of nymphs is modified into a tracheal gill. Its walls are thin and abundantly supplied with tracheae and tracheoles. Water is drawn into this chamber and alternately expelled. If the water is expelled forcibly, the recoil carries the insect forward thus providing a means of locomotion.

Few life history studies have been made of the odonates. The nymphs molt a number of times; and when fully grown they leave the water and attach themselves to a weed stem, tree trunk, or other object for the final molt from which the adult with fully developed wings emerges. The cast skins of emerged dragonflies are common objects in and around the water's edge. Some species may have more than one generation annually. In others more time is required for a life cycle. It is thought that the usual life cycle requires one year. The winter months are usually spent in the nymph stage.

The Odonata are generally considered as beneficial insects. The adults feed on all forms of small insects. They will prey on any insect that is not too large for them to overcome. Larger species of dragonflies may feed on honey bees and become pests of some importance around apiaries. Nymphs are quite beneficial in feeding upon noxious insects breeding in water, and they are of some value as a source of food for fish. Conversely, however, they prey upon small fish. Fish produce so many young, however, that this habit of feeding upon them could not be considered of any importance except possibly in hatcheries.

More species of Odonata exist than is commonly realized. Upwards of 5,000 species have been recorded. They occur in greatest numbers in warm climates. Certain species are intermediate hosts of flukes, which attack waterfowl, poultry, frogs, and other animals.

Order PLECOPTERA[3]

Stoneflies

Members of the Plecoptera may be characterized by:

1. Usually 2 pairs of membranous wings exceeding length of body; hind pair much larger than front pair and folded in plaits when at rest; a number of cross-veins usually present.
2. Mouthparts mandibulate but frequently vestigial in the adult.
3. Incomplete metamorphosis.
4. Antennae and cerci long.

Stoneflies are soft-bodied insects, small to moderate in size, and generally drab in appearance; the predominant colors are gray, black, brown, and green (Fig. 61). In build the body is elongate, and flattened with parallel sides. Members of the order are poor fliers and are usually found near their breeding places. The adults

---

[3] *Plecos,* plaited; *pteron,* wing.

usually have poorly developed mouthparts and probably do not partake of any food, but some species have well developed mandibles and are known to cause injury in feeding on buds and leaves. Two pairs of membranous wings are usually present which lie flat on the body when not in use. The hind wings are generally broader than the front pair, and fold in plaits over the abdomen when at rest.

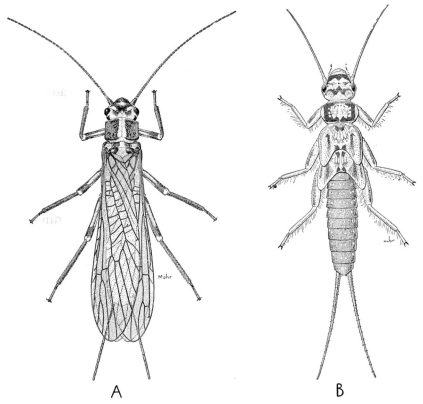

A B

FIG. 61. A stonefly *(Isoperla confusa)*. **A**, Adult. **B**, Nymph. (From Illinois Natural History Survey. Drawn by C. O. Mohr.)

They have a moderate number of veins but a number of cross-veins may be present.

Eggs, often several thousand in number, are dropped in a mass by the female in the water. Here they hatch into nymphs which live under stones, logs, or masses of debris in swiftly running or other well aerated water. Most of the nymphs feed on vegetable matter, but some feed on insects and other aquatic invertebrates.

The nymphs have the general body conformation of the adults and are usually somewhat more brightly colored. Respiration is generally effected by means of tracheal gills which are usually located at the base of each leg. However, the nymphs of some of the smaller species respire through the thin body-wall of the ventral surface. The nymphs leave the water when fully grown and attach themselves to nearby objects where the final molt occurs. Their cast skins are commonly observed around the breeding places. The adults may live for several weeks. The life history of stoneflies is not very well known. The smaller species complete a life cycle in one year, while the larger forms require more time.

Stoneflies are of little economic importance. Most nymphs feed on organic material of vegetable origin and are thus of some value as scavengers; others are predators on small aquatic animal life. They constitute a source of food for fresh water fish which is of some importance.

Some 1,500 species of stoneflies are known, but less than 300 of these occur in North America.

CHAPTER

II

ORDERS ORTHOPTERA
AND ISOPTERA

Order ORTHOPTERA[1]

Cockroaches, Grasshoppers, Crickets, Katydids, and Others

Members of the Orthoptera are characterized by:

1. Two pairs of wings, sometimes absent or vestigial; front wings more or less parchment-like with distinct venation, hind pair membranous and folded fan-like when at rest.
2. Mouthparts of a typically chewing type.
3. Gradual metamorphosis.
4. A pair of cerci present.

The order Orthoptera contains some of the more common and better known insects, such as grasshoppers, katydids, crickets, and cockroaches. It is one of the larger orders of insects, comprising more than 30,000 species of which about 2,000 occur in North America. Some of the more important pests, such as grasshoppers and cockroaches (Fig. 62), belong here as well as katydids and crickets, those major contributors to nature's orchestra of the long summer evenings.

This group of insects is so diverse in morphology and habits that it is difficult to cite specific characteristics. There is some justification in the tendency to subdivide the order. Mouthparts of all members are mandibulate. The grasshopper's mouthparts are usually selected for study of a generalized chewing type. Metamorphosis is

[1] *Orthos,* straight; *pteron,* wing.

131

gradual, with the nymphs and adults feeding on the same materials and occurring in the same general habitat. With the exception of a single family, the *Mantidae,* the members of which are predaceous, the Orthoptera are mostly all feeders on plants or plant products.

Members of the Orthoptera typically bear two pairs of net-veined

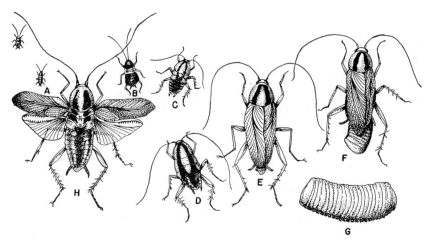

FIG. 62.   The German cockroach (*Blatella germanica*). **A, B, C, D,** Nymphs. **E,** Adult. **F,** Adult female with egg case. **G,** Egg case (ootheca). **H,** Adult with wings spread. (From Agricultural Research Service, U.S.D.A.)

wings. The two pairs of wings differ in structure. The front wings (known as tegmina) are more or less thickened and parchment-like. The hind wings are somewhat thinner and are usually broader in the anal areas and are folded fan-like when at rest. In some species the wings of the adult are small or wanting. The nymphs of short-winged grasshoppers, katydids, and crickets may be readily separated from the adults because their wing pads are inverted, with the hind pair on the outside and with the outer surfaces corrugated. The males of those families composed of grasshoppers, katydids, and crickets have modifications on their wings for making sounds of a more or less musical nature. These insects are sometimes called the musicians of the insect world. The sounds are made for the purpose of attracting the opposite sex. Grasshoppers produce sound by rubbing the two pairs of wings together in flight, or by rubbing the hind femora against the front wings when the insect is at rest. Their auditory organs are located on the first abdominal segment. In the common cricket each front wing (tegmen) bears near its base a file, a scraper (a hardened area) and vibrating areas (tympana). The file of one wing scrapes on the hardened area of the other and sets the tympana in vibration. The auditory organs are found on the front tibiae. The sound-making organs of the katydids are similar to those of the crickets, but only one functional file is present in common representatives of the family, and this is on the left tegmen. As with the crickets, the auditory organs of katydids are located on the front tibiae.

Orthopterous insects have several biological characteristics in common. Most members have only one generation annually in the more temperate climates. Exceptions are found, particularly in certain species of cockroaches. Most Orthoptera overwinter in the egg stage, but cockroaches may overwinter in all stages if conditions permit. Many lay their eggs in packets or capsules; some deposit their eggs singly.

KEY TO COMMON FAMILIES OF ORTHOPTERA

1. Jumping insects; hind femur stouter and much longer than
    middle femur; tarsi with less than 5 segments   2
   Running or walking insects; hind femur hardly, if at all,
    stouter and longer than other femora; tarsi almost always
    with 5 segments   4
2. Antenna short; tarsi with 3 segments; ovipositor short (Grass-
    hoppers)   **Acrididae,** p. 139
   Antenna as long as or longer than body (except in mole
    crickets and sand crickets); tarsi with 2 to 4 segments; ovi-
    positor long (except in mole crickets and sand crickets)   3
3. Tarsi 4-segmented; ovipositor sword-shaped (Katydids and
    Meadow Grasshoppers)   **Tettigoniidae,** p. 143
   Tarsi with 2 or 3 segments; ovipositor usually spear-shaped
    (Crickets)   **Gryllidae,** p. 145
4. Body oval, depressed; head almost completely covered by
    pronotum; rapidly running insects (Cockroaches) **Blattidae,** p. 133
   Body long and slender; head free; legs slender; walking insects   5
5. Front leg fitted for grasping prey; cerci segmented (Praying
    Mantids)   **Mantidae,** p. 137
   Front leg not fitted for grasping prey; cerci not segmented
    (Walkingsticks)   **Phasmatidae,** p. 138

Family *Blattidae* (Cockroaches)

Cockroaches are known to practically everyone and a description of them is scarcely necessary. The body is oval and depressed. They are brown or brownish-black in general color; however green cockroaches are known. The head is bowed downward and almost completely covered by the pronotum as viewed from above. The mouth-parts project backward between the front legs. The antennae are long and slender and are of much use as tactile organs. Two pairs of fully developed wings are usually present; however in some cases they may be short or entirely lacking. In some species the female is wingless or has vestigial wings, but fully developed wings are present in the male.

Cockroaches thrive best in tropical or subtropical climates. More than 2,000 species are recorded in the world, of which about 70 different kinds are known to occur in the United States, and most of these are found in the southern states. Only a few native species occur in the northern part of the United States. This is a very ancient group of insects. Fossil remains indicate that they were most abundant in the Carboniferous Age (more than 200,000,000 years ago).

Cockroaches prefer a warm, dark, and humid environment. They are secretive and feed during the night. Certainly the ancients were acquainted with their feeding habits as they called them *lucifuga,* meaning light-fleeing. The name cockroach is derived from the Spanish, *Cucaracha.*

Only a few species of cockroaches have taken up their abode in the habitations of man and thereby have become pests. They are practically omnivorous feeders. Their food consists of most kinds of plant and animal products—the foods of man, garbage, sewage, binding and sizing of books, and wallpaper paste. They are not only destructive through their feeding activities, but their fetid odor may be imparted to foods over which they crawl. Their filthy habits suggest the probability of spreading diseases, such as dysentery and typhoid, although positive proof is lacking. Some cockroaches may serve as intermediate hosts of certain parasitic worms of birds and mammals.

A wood cockroach (*Cryptocercus punctulatus*) found in the southeastern states is of interest because it has developed a type of true social life and is capable of digesting cellulose as termites do, with the aid of certain Protozoa in their digestive tracts. A colony consists of several generations of individuals living together in decaying logs where they feed on the rotten wood.

The most important domestic species of cockroaches (Fig. 63) are the American cockroach (*Periplaneta americana*), the Australian cockroach (*Periplaneta australasiae*), the Oriental cockroach (*Blatta orientalis*), the brown-banded cockroach (*Supella supellectilium*), and the German cockroach or croton bug (*Blattella ger-*

manica) (Fig. 62). All of these species originally came from the tropics and have been introduced into the United States through channels of commerce.

Most cockroaches deposit their eggs in brown bean-like capsules (*oothecae*). The oothecae are usually carried for several days protruding from the abdomen of the female and are then secreted in

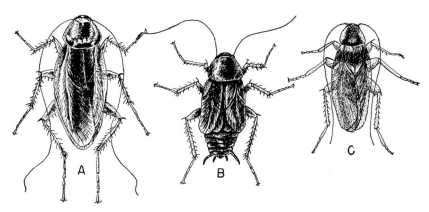

FIG. 63.   Common cockroaches. **A,** The American cockroach (*Periplaneta americana*). **B,** The Oriental cockroach (*Blatta orientalis*). **C,** The brown-banded cockroach (*Supella supellectilium*), relatively enlarged to show markings. (From Agricultural Research Service, U.S.D.A.)

a secluded spot. The German cockroach differs from the other common species in carrying its ootheca until almost time for the eggs to hatch.

The American cockroach attains a length of about 1½ inches, is reddish-brown with a light brown band around the lateral and posterior margins of the pronotum. The length of the life cycle from egg to adult requires from a year to 1½ years. Adults may live for longer than a year. During this time females will deposit 50 or more egg capsules which normally contain 16 eggs each. This species has migratory habits. It may come into the home on its own volition from stores, garbage dumps, and sewer lines. In the southern states it is capable of rather long flights.

The Australian cockroach is of less importance than the American cockroach but this cosmopolitan species may become locally abundant. It may attain approximately the size of the American cockroach. The general color pattern is similar but it can be distinguished by the presence of a yellow mark extending about one-third the length of the front wing along the costal margin.

The Oriental cockroach is shining black, occasionally dark reddish-brown, and about one to 1¼ inches long. The male has fully developed wings and is capable of flight, while the wings of the female are greatly reduced in size and are nonfunctional. The species has about the same life cycle as the American cockroach. A seasonal cycle is suggested by the emergence of a preponderance of adults in the spring. This insect is considered the filthiest of cockroaches.

The German cockroach is one of the most common pests of the home, grocery, and cafe. It measures about ½ inch in length and is light brown with two dark stripes on the pronotum. This form is known as the water bug and also the croton bug. Due to its small size it is frequently brought into the home with groceries. Migrations from nearby infested places also occur.

Unlike other common species, the female of the German cockroach carries the ootheca until the eggs are about ready to hatch. It is quite prolific and under conditions of high temperatures three or more generations may be completed annually. Adult females may live for about nine months.

The brown-banded cockroach is a comparatively recent introduction into the United States, where it is now quite widely distributed. It first was rather confined to the southern part of the country but later it spread northward and became established in heated buildings. It has the general appearance of the German cockroach but is slightly smaller. The sexes differ in that the male is longer, narrower, and has fully developed wings; while the female is darker, broader, and has short, nonfunctional wings. Two light transverse bands are present across the back. These markings are more distinct on the nymphs than on the adults.

Unlike the German cockroach, the brown-banded cockroach does not tend to confine itself to the kitchen and bathroom, but may be found throughout the home. This species is often found in elevated situations such as shelves in closets and behind pictures and molding. Egg capsules may be deposited in almost any secluded spot, often among linens and clothing. The female life span averages about 200 days, and there may be two generations annually.

Cleanliness and guarding against infestations is the first step in the control of roaches. Proper protection of foods and disposal of food scraps and garbage should be practiced. Also, care should be exercised to prevent the introduction of the pests in bags of groceries. Cracks or other entrances around plumbing should be sealed.

Cockroaches may be controlled by treating with chlordane,

dieldrin, or malathion the dark corners, cracks, and crevices underneath sinks, and other hiding places where cockroaches congregate or frequent in search of food. Numbers of cockroaches frequently congregate in basements and underneath buildings. These places may need proper insecticidal treatment before the pests can be eradicated from the buildings. With heavy infestations of the American cockroach the use of yellow phosphorus paste may be advisable as a supplemental control measure.

Family *Mantidae* (Praying Mantids, Devil's Horses)

Mantids (Fig. 64) are common insects, particularly in the South. They constitute the only family of *Orthoptera* which is beneficial, since all of the members are predaceous on other insects. They are

FIG. 64. The Carolina mantid (*Stagmomantis carolina*). (From Illinois Natural History Survey. Drawn by C. O. Mohr.)

even cannibalistic and readily eat each other. These large to medium sized insects are readily recognized by the elongate prothorax on which is borne the first pair of grasping legs. The ventral side of both femur and tibia of each front leg is armed with spines and the tibia is capable of being folded back on the femur, thus forming an efficient grasping organ. The second and third pairs of legs are long and similar, and are used for walking.

Mantids, like cockroaches, are found in largest numbers in tropical and subtropical regions. More than 600 species are known, but only about two dozen are found in North America. These insects are green or brown or with a mixture of the two colors. Wings may be fully developed, abbreviated, or wholly absent. In some the wings simulate the leaves of plants.

The common name of praying mantid has been applied to this insect because of the habit of holding its grasping front legs in a pious attitude while waiting for prey. This attitude has suggested the name of a common species, *Mantis religiosa*. Superstition has it that the brown saliva of mantids will cause blindness to man and

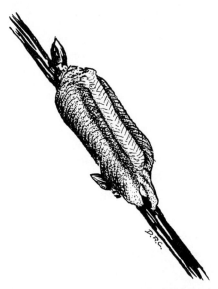

kill a mule, and that the dead insects, when eaten in hay, will kill mules and horses. The common walking-stick is implicated also in the latter superstition.

Eggs are laid in a mass (*ootheca*) arranged in a definite pattern of rows and glued together (Fig. 65). These brown oothecae are rather commonly observed glued to branches of trees, fence posts, or other objects. The eggs are often destroyed by a hymenopterous parasite which emerges soon after the time the young mantid should have emerged.

FIG. 65.   Egg capsule (ootheca) of a mantid.

The winter season is spent in the egg stage. Only one annual generation of the insects has been observed.

Family *Phasmatidae* (Walking-sticks)

The common name applied to these insects aptly describes them (Fig. 66). They usually simulate in both body conformation and general color a twig of a tree or a stem of grass upon which they

FIG. 66.   A walking-stick (*Diapheromera femorata*). (From Illinois Natural History Survey.)

are commonly found. Nature has done such an excellent job of camouflaging their presence that they are usually passed by unseen. Their movements are very slow and deliberate.

Only one North American species has wings. Some of the tropical forms are broad and resemble the leaves of the trees upon which they are found. About 700 species of walking-sticks are known, and occur mostly in the tropics. One species found in the East Indies and Borneo measures nearly 13 inches in length and is thought to be the world's largest insect. Walking-sticks feed entirely on vegetation. They have been known to become so numerous as to defoliate trees, but such occurrences are rare.

No provisions are made for the protection of the eggs. The females drop eggs at random to the ground, where they remain through the winter months and hatch the next season. Parthenogenesis is common. Only one generation is produced each year.

Family *Acrididae* (Grasshoppers, Locusts)

Members of this family are commonly known as grasshoppers. The term locust is most frequently applied to the migratory forms. Grasshoppers are readily recognized by the antennae usually shorter than the body, tarsi of three segments, auditory organs located on the first abdominal segment, and the presence of a short stout ovipositor.

Among the grasshoppers are found some of the most important pests of mankind. They have destroyed the crops of man from Biblical days to the present time. And they, in turn, have been used to some extent as food by man in certain parts of the world.

About 8,000 species of grasshoppers are known. Of this number more than 600 occur in North America. All of these species cannot be considered as destructive forms. Only a small percentage of this number ever increases in numbers large enough to seriously damage crops and other vegetation; however, every section of the country has its predominant forms which, on occasion, may prove to be pests of importance.

Grasshoppers usually have only one generation annually; however, some species, such as the American grasshopper (*Schistocerca americana*), may be two-brooded. As a rule the winter is passed in the egg stage; but certain species, such as *Schistocerca damnifica* and *S. americana*, may overwinter as adults, or in the nymphal stage (*Chortophaga viridifasciata*). With few exceptions, eggs of grasshoppers are deposited in the ground. In general the females lay 100 or more eggs, which hatch in the spring. Maturity is reached during the summer. There are usually five nymphal instars, but occasionally a sixth is observed. Grasshoppers are found in greatest abundance and are most destructive in prairie lands with an annual rainfall of less than 25 inches.

Every continent has its species of migratory locusts. The most important migratory locust found in North America is the Rocky Mountain locust (*Melanoplus spretus*). The most severe insect losses to agriculture ever suffered in this country were inflicted by this insect in the Great Plains regions a generation ago. The destruction of crops was so great that hardships unknown to the present-day farmers were experienced. These insects increased in indescribable numbers and migrated by flight for hundreds of miles leaving denuded and desolate areas behind them. Occasional outbreaks of this insect still occur. The best known of all migratory locusts is the desert locust (*Schistocerca gregaria*), of which accounts are found in the Bible. It occurs over large areas of the Middle East and plagues still occur as in Biblical days. *Locusta migratoria* is another species of much importance in these regions. Conditions producing the migratory phase of grasshoppers and others are not fully understood. The theory is advanced that this phase is produced when overcrowding occurs in the natural breeding grounds.

FIG. 67. The differential grasshopper (*Melanoplus differentialis*). (Courtesy of G. A. Bieberdorf, Oklahoma Agricultural and Mechanical College.)

Although the Rocky Mountain locust is found throughout most of the United States, it is considered a pest of importance only in the Great Plains region. The solitary phase of this species is known as the lesser migratory grasshopper (*Melanoplus sanguinipes*).

One of the most destructive grasshoppers throughout the Mississippi Valley region is the differential grasshopper (*Melanoplus differentialis*, Fig. 67). This brownish to olive green grasshopper is one of the largest economically important forms, measuring about

1½ inches long. Associated with the differential grasshopper in most of this region is the two-striped grasshopper (*Melanoplus bivittatus,* Fig. 68) which approaches it in size. The red-legged grasshopper

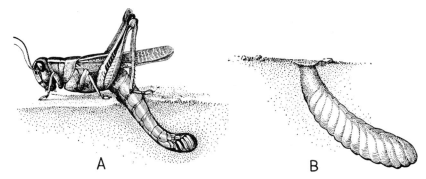

FIG. 68. The two-striped grasshopper (*Melanoplus bivittatus*). **A,** Laying eggs. **B,** An egg capsule deposited in the ground. (From Agricultural Research Service, U.S.D.A.)

(*Melanoplus femur-rubrum,* Fig. 69) is quite widely distributed and it is often of considerable economic importance.

The American grasshopper (*Schistocerca americana*) and the Carolina grasshopper (*Dissosteira carolina*) are two of the most widely distributed and best known species. Only on occasion do they become local pests. The American grasshopper is almost three inches long, reddish-brown with dark brown spots on the tegmina. When disturbed it often finds refuge in trees. The Carolina grasshopper is most often seen along dusty roadsides and margins of fields. It is readily recognized by the black hind wings which are bordered with yellow.

The lubber grasshopper (*Brachystola magna,* Fig. 70) is a native of the Southwest. This is a large brown clumsy grasshopper with wings reduced to mere pads. On account of its slightly humped appearance this species is often called the buffalo grasshopper. It cannot fly, but its hind legs are greatly enlarged and it is a strong hopper. Its counterpart, the eastern lubber (*Romalea microptera*), occurs in the Gulf States. This large species is yellow and black and the short hind wings are red and bordered with black. Locally, both species may become pests of importance. In addition to these grasshoppers, a number of other species may become pests of limited importance in various parts of the country.

Since the grasshoppers of most economic importance overwinter in the soil in the egg stage, fall and winter plowing will destroy

many of them. In localities where acreages of pasture and waste-
land are very extensive, this practice will not likely prove of much
value.

When a heavy emergence of grasshoppers is indicated by surveys, farmers must prepare to poison them. For most satisfactory

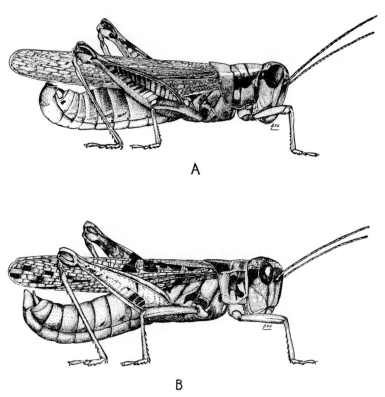

FIG. 69. **A,** The red-legged grasshopper (*Melanoplus femur-rubrum*). **B,** The clear-
winged grasshopper (*Camnula pellucida*). (From Agricultural Research Service,
U.S.D.A.)

results grasshoppers should be poisoned over large areas. Control
is most economically and efficiently done by poisoning the insects
soon after hatching and before they move into the crops.

Poison baits have long been the standard control for grasshoppers,
but under conditions of luxuriant succulent vegetation the use of
baits has often resulted in failure. The use of toxaphene, chlordane,
dieldrin, and aldrin, either as dusts or as sprays, has proved much
more satisfactory. These toxicants may be applied by means of either ground machines or airplanes.

Under conditions where vegetation is sparse or not very attrac-

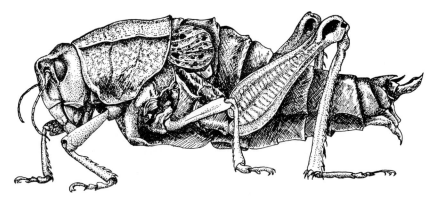

FIG. 70. The lubber grasshopper (*Brachystola magna*).

tive to the insects, especially in the more arid sections of the country, poison baits may be as effective as dusts and sprays and are much more economical to use. A number of bait formulas have been recommended and used through the years.

Family *Tettigoniidae* (Katydids and Meadow Grasshoppers)

Insects of this family are represented by the katydids, false katydids (Fig. 71), meadow grasshoppers, cone-headed grasshoppers, and others. They may be recognized as belonging to this family by the

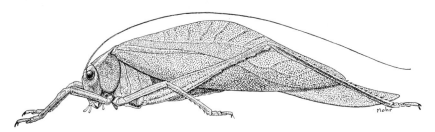

FIG. 71. A false or broad-winged katydid (*Microcentrum rhombifolium*). (From Illinois Natural History Survey. Drawn by C. O. Mohr.)

antennae as long or longer than the body, tarsi four-segmented, and the ovipositor of the female sword-shaped and exserted. The predominant color of these insects is green, but some brown forms occur. Some are wingless, such as the shield-backed grasshoppers and the camel crickets. Eggs of the tettigoniids are laid singly on leaves or twigs (Fig. 72) of trees and shrubs, in cracks of bark, within tissues of plants, or in the soil.

The katydids and false katydids are the chief music makers of this family. In this respect they rival the crickets. It is the true katydid (*Pterophylla*) that incessantly repeats, "katy did, katy didn't," during the late afternoon and night.

Very few members of this family have been recorded as pestiferous, although katydids have been known to injure orange trees and

FIG. 72.   Eggs of a false or broad-winged katydid deposited on a twig.

have been observed to denude completely rather large areas of post-oak forests. The most important exception is the Mormon cricket (*Anabrus simplex*, Fig. 73). This is a large wingless, dark brown insect found in the Great Basin region of the Rocky Mountains. It often occurs in epidemic proportions and causes considerable

FIG. 73.   The Mormon cricket (*Anabrus simplex*), fifth instar nymphs. **A,** Female. **B,** Male. (From Agricultural Research Service, U.S.D.A.)

damage to range and cultivated plants. In 1848 an outbreak of this insect of historical interest occurred in Utah. Hordes of the pest threatened the complete destruction of the crops of the Mormon settlement, but flocks of sea gulls made a timely appearance and devoured the insects. In appreciation the Mormons erected a monument to commemorate the event.

When the Mormon cricket is about half grown it starts migrating. If crops are in their pathway, they are destroyed. As the insects cannot fly, linear barriers of metal or boards have been used to check their march. Poison baits are extensively used with satisfactory results in their control.

Family *Gryllidae* (Crickets)

The friendly chirping of crickets is a familiar sound to nearly everyone. They are the principal music makers among the Orthoptera. The best known of all crickets are the field crickets and the house or hearth crickets.

Most crickets have a lance-shaped ovipositor, three-segmented tarsi, usually long antennae, and are usually winged. The front wings (tegmina) lie flat on the body and are bent abruptly downward to cover the sides of the body. Some forms are wingless. Most crickets have only one generation annually, and overwinter in the egg stage. The eggs are laid singly in the soil.

 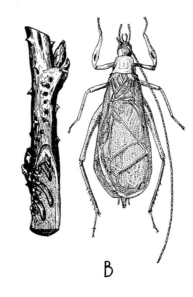

FIG. 74. **A,** A female field cricket (*Acheta assimilis*). (From Agricultural Research Service, U.S.D.A.) **B,** The snowy tree cricket (*Oecanthus niveus*) and egg puncture in a berry cane. (From the University of California Division of Agricultural Sciences.)

The field cricket (*Acheta assimilis*) is probably the most widely distributed species; it occurs in both North and South America (Fig. 74A). This black or brown jumping cricket with its prominent antennae and ovipositor is a most familiar insect. In cold climates it usually overwinters in the egg stage and produces one generation annually. In its southern range the insect may be more or less active throughout the year and may produce as many as three generations in a season. It feeds on both plant and animal materials rather indiscriminately, and cannibalism may occur. Field crops sometime suffer damaging attacks. The species is known to attack clothing and other household belongings. In the fall it frequently enters homes and becomes a pest. Attracted by the lights it may migrate into towns and cities and cause considerable annoyance. The dusts, sprays, and poison baits used in grasshopper control are recommended for control of the cricket. The European house cricket (*Gryllus domesticus*) is now established in the eastern part of the United States.

The tree crickets are frail, light green or yellow insects about ½ to ¾ inch long. *Oecanthus niveus* (Fig. 74**B**) is the best known species. These insects are found on the foliage of trees and shrubs. Their song is commonly heard throughout the night in the summer and fall. This high-pitched song or note is monotonously reverberated and the rapidity of the note is correlated with the prevailing temperature. All of the songsters in the neighborhood stay in tune. Should an individual stop to rest and then begin again, it is always in time with the others that have continued the music. Tree crickets are beneficial as they prey upon aphids. Conversely, the females may do material damage in laying their eggs. They make a series of deep punctures for the purpose of laying eggs in the twigs of trees, berry canes, and other plants, causing the twigs to die. The female has an unusual habit of packing a bit of her own excrement around each egg after it is laid.

The mole crickets differ markedly in appearance from the ordinary crickets. These differences are so great that some authors place them in a separate family. The most striking difference lies in the structure of the fore tibiae which are modified into digging organs and resemble the foot of a mole. These crickets are brown and the larger species are longer and stouter than the common field cricket. They burrow in the soil mole-like, disturb seed beds and young seedlings, and feed on the tender roots of growing plants. The European species (*Gryllotalpa gryllotalpa*) has the unusual habit (for an insect) of guarding its eggs and newly hatched young. This species has become established in the eastern United States. It is thought that the completion of a generation requires three or four years. The Puerto Rico mole cricket or "Changa" (*Scapteriscus vicinus*) and the southern species (*Scapteriscus acletus*) are found in the South and are pests of some importance. The northern mole cricket (*Gryllotalpa hexadactyla,* Fig. 75) is not so abundant. These indigenous species require only one year for the completion

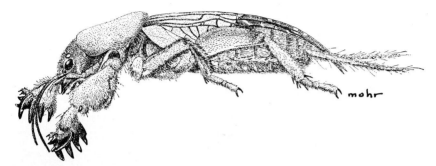

FIG. 75. The northern mole cricket (*Gryllotalpa hexadactyla*). (From Illinois Natural History Survey. Drawn by C. O. Mohr.)

of a generation. Treatment of the soil with chlordane, aldrin, or dieldrin in the form of a spray or a dust is recommended for the control of mole crickets should their damage become serious.

Order ISOPTERA[2]

Termites

The order Isoptera is characterized by:

1. **Winged members with two pairs of long narrow wings, similar in form, size and texture, which lie flat on the back when not in use.**
2. **Chewing type mouthparts.**
3. **Gradual metamorphosis.**
4. **Live in colonies under a caste system.**

Termites (Fig. 76) are also known as "white ants" because of the usual grayish-white color and their social habit of life. Their resemblance to ants is only that both live in colonies and have some habits in common. In termites the abdomen is broadly joined to the thorax instead of being constricted (wasp-waisted) at the base, as in ants. The wings of termites are similar, whereas the hind wings of ants are smaller and have fewer veins than the front pair. Termites spend their lives in the soil, wood, or earthen tunnels;

[2] *Isos,* equal; *pteron,* wing.

while ants may be commonly found running about on top of the ground.

Termites occur in greatest numbers in the tropical and subtropical parts of the world where their destructive capacity is best known, but they also are found throughout most of the temperate regions. About 2,000 species are known, of which more than 50 forms have been recorded from North America.

Termites vary much in color, size, shape, and mode of life. Wings are present only in the sexually mature males and females during the swarming season. The wings are long, narrow, semitranspar-

FIG. 76. Subterranean termites. **A,** Winged sexual adults. **B,** Adult worker. (From Agricultural Research Service, U.S.D.A.)

ent, and extend at least one-half their length beyond the end of the abdomen. Both pairs of wings are similar and are broken off along a suture at the base after swarming. Mouthparts are of a generalized chewing type, as found in grasshoppers and cockroaches. The termite workers, and probably the soldier caste as well, are blind. The winged sexual forms have pigmented compound eyes and also two ocelli. Metamorphosis is gradual and there is no pupal or quiescent stage, such as ants and numerous other insects have.

A number of castes of termites have been recognized but not all are ever found in the colony of any particular species. Male and female individuals of each caste are known. The castes present in colonies of the more common species include primary queens and kings, complemental queens and kings, workers, and soldiers.

Usually during the spring or fall, but at other times when conditions are favorable, the winged sexual members of a colony swarm from the colony. Normally only a few individuals of the dry-wood termite leave the parent colony at a time, but the flights from the colonies of subterranean termites consist of large numbers. Following a short flight the wings are broken off, the individuals separate in pairs and a cell is excavated in the soil or wood. Only then do the queens and kings mate. The relationship of the queens and kings is on a permanent basis and repeated matings occur. The king assists the queen in excavating the new home and rearing the first brood. After the first workers are produced, the sole duty of the queen is to lay eggs. Queens of native species become enlarged but the abdomens do not become so distended that the power of locomotion is lost as in some tropical forms. Also, queens of native species do not lay nearly so many eggs as tropical termites. The first offspring of a young colony consists of workers and a few soldiers. About a year is required for their development. The winged sexual forms are not produced in a colony until it is at least two years old. Workers do most of the work of the colony. The soldiers resemble the workers but they may be distinguished by their large heads and mandibles. Workers are not present in colonies of non-subterranean termites, and nymphs perform their duties.

Termites constitute one group of nature's scavengers. They convert logs, stumps, branches, and other plant material to humus. In this service they are beneficial to man. In his use of wood materials man too frequently provides both food and shelter for termites. There has been no sudden increase of termites in this country. They are widely distributed insects and will attack suitable wood products whenever conditions are favorable. The principal food of termites is the cellulose of wood. Feeding is primarily on dead wood, but living plants may be attacked. Most species of termites contain in their digestive tracts low forms of life, especially Protozoa. They secrete enzymes which digest the food for the termites.

The two groups of termites of most economic importance are the dry-wood termites and the subterranean termites. The dry-wood termites establish their nests in the tunnels and galleries they make in the wood upon which they feed. In the United States, damaging infestations occur only along the southern boundaries of the southernmost states and on the Pacific Coast. They are more destructive in the tropics. Solutions of DDT or pentachlorophenol are recommended for the treatment of wood infested by dry-wood termites.

Probably 95 percent of the termite damage in the United States is done by subterranean species belonging to the genus *Reticuli-termes*. *R. flavipes* is the most common species. Colonies of these insects may be found in the ground wherever food is available and moisture conditions are suitable. They require much moisture, which they obtain from the soil. Food consists of wood or wood products in the soil, in contact with the ground, or that which may be reached by means of tubes which they may construct (Fig. 77).

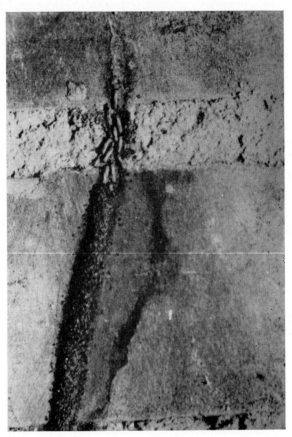

FIG. 77. Workers of subterranean termites exposed when section of tube was destroyed. (From Agricultural Research Service, U.S.D.A.)

These termites are most destructive in the South, but damage may occur throughout most of the United States.

For the protection of pilings, bridge timbers, power and telephone poles, cross ties, and other timbers that are used in contact with the soil against termite damage and rots (Fig. 78), chemical treatment is essential. These timbers should be treated under pressure with coal-tar creosote, pentachlorophenol, or other approved chemical compounds.

In the prevention and control of the common subterranean termites in buildings it is essential to remember that they maintain their colonies in the ground where requisite moisture conditions are found and food is available. Although the common termites may be feeding well above the surface of the ground, they are obliged to return to the colony in the soil. The most important steps in the prevention of termites in buildings are to create conditions unfavorable to termites and isolate the building as completely as possible from the ground. The soil of the building site may be treated with DDT, dieldrin, pentachlorophenol, or other chemical compounds. The lot should be graded so that water will not run or puddle underneath the structure. All stumps, pilings, stakes, wooden forms, and scraps of wood should be removed from the soil and building site. Adequate ventilation must be provided to maintain a dry condition underneath the house. Wooden floors should be at least 18 inches from the closest contact with the ground.

FIG. 78. Stair carriage in a basement almost completely destroyed by termites. (From Agricultural Research Service, U.S.D.A.)

Another essential requirement is that no wood should come in contact with the ground. The foundation should be constructed of concrete, stone or brick. If stone or brick are used, a good grade of cement mortar should be used to insure the closing of all cracks. Metal termite guards will materially aid in termite prevention if properly installed but constitute no guarantee of permanent protection. The sills and possibly the floor joists should be chemically treated to prevent termites as well as rots.

Concrete porches and chimneys often afford ready access for the entrance of termites into buildings. Concrete porches should preferably be of hollow construction but if the concrete is poured on an earthen fill, the soil next to the foundation should be removed after the concrete has set. The foundation of chimneys should be of open construction and a high grade of cement mortar used between the bricks to prevent cracks. Floors of concrete are no assured protection against termites, since they may enter such buildings through expansion joints and cracks in the concrete.

When a building becomes infested with termites control may involve the expenditure of considerable labor and money. Corrective measures may have to be taken. These may involve improvements in drainage and ventilation, and removal of wood which is in contact with the ground.

Soil poisoning is the most satisfactory treatment for the control of subterranean termites. Several chemical compounds have been found satisfactory for this purpose. Pentachlorophenol, DDT, dieldrin, and chlordane are among the more efficient and better known products used. No termite treatment can be considered permanent. Annual or semiannual inspections should be made and the treatment repeated in those places where termites may reappear.

12

ORDERS DERMAPTERA, EMBIIDINA, ZORAPTERA, CORRODENTIA, AND THYSANOPTERA

Order DERMAPTERA[1]

Earwigs

Characteristics of the order Dermaptera are:

1. Winged members with two pairs of wings; front pair short, leathery, without venation and meet in a straight line down the back when at rest. Hind wings membranous, broad, with veins radiating from a center, folded both lengthwise and crosswise when at rest.
2. Chewing mouthparts.
3. Gradual metamorphosis.
4. A pair of forceps-like cerci at the end of the abdomen.

The common name of earwig was given these insects in Europe because of the superstition that they would crawl in the ears of sleeping persons. The name could have come from "ear-wing" as the hind wings have a slight resemblance to an ear. This is a rather small order of insects, about 1,000 species, occurring mostly in warm countries. Less than 20 species are reported from North America. Earwigs are rather narrow and elongate insects. They may be confused with rove beetles by the novice, but may be readily distinguished from the latter by the forceps-like appendages on the end

[1] *Derma,* skin; *pteron,* wing.

of the abdomen (Fig. 79). Earwigs are nocturnal in habit, hiding during the day in the most convenient places. They feed chiefly on decaying materials and occasionally on living plants; some forms are carnivorous. Although flowers, foliage and fruits of plants may be attacked, the injury usually is not very important.

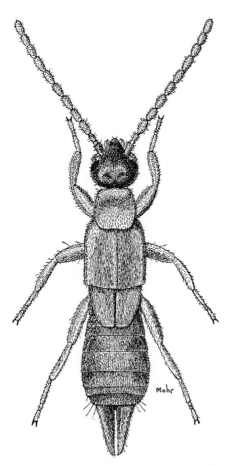

The eggs are laid within a cell in the soil in a protected place and the female watches over them until they are hatched. She continues her maternal care for a short time after hatching. The nymphs undergo four to six instars before attaining maturity. In temperate climates only one generation occurs annually.

Some earwigs have stink glands opening on the abdomen. These glands emit an ill-smelling liquid which probably has a repelling effect on natural enemies.

The European earwig (*Forficula auricularia*) has been introduced into the United States and is now established on the eastern and western seaboards. It feeds upon a variety of plant and animal materials, but it is of more concern as a nuisance in households.

FIG. 79. Adult of female of an earwig (*Labia minor*). (From Illinois Natural History Survey. Drawn by C. O. Mohr.)

Order EMBIIDINA[2] or EMBIOPTERA[3]

Embiids or Web-spinners

Embiids are characterized by:

1. Wings, when present, two pairs, similar in structure, elongate and membranous.

[2] *Embios*, lively.
[3] *Embios*, lively; *pteron*, wing.

2. Chewing mouthparts of primitive type.
3. Gradual metamorphosis but deviates somewhat from usual type.
4. Small insects with elongate and somewhat flattened bodies.

The order Embiidina comprises a small and rarely encountered group of insects (Fig. 80). About 70 species of the order are represented in the fauna of the warmer climates of the Americas.

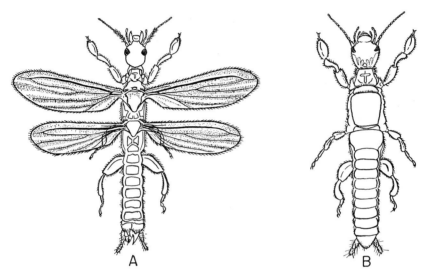

FIG. 80. Embiids or web-spinners (*Oligotoma saundersii*). **A,** Winged male. **B,** Wingless female. (Adapted from Essig by permission of The Macmillan Company.)

These small, feeble insects are found living gregariously in silken tunnels underneath stones, logs, bark of trees, and similar environments.

The silk with which their small tunnels are constructed is secreted from glands located in the enlarged basal segment of the tarsus of the forelegs.

All females are wingless; the males usually have two pairs of elongate, membranous wings with reduced venation. Some species develop parthenogenetically. The insects feed on plant materials of many kinds, preferably fungi.

Overwintered nymphal forms of embiids attain the adult stage in the summer months. Apparently the females lay only a small number of eggs. The latter are deposited in the silken tunnels; and after a comparatively short incubation period, hatch into nymphs which develop slowly. Only one generation annually has been observed.

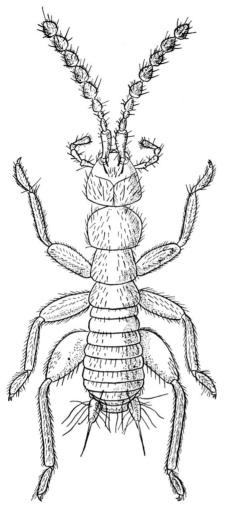

Order ZORAPTERA[4]

Zorapterons

The name Zoraptera is inappropriate for this small inconspicuous group of insects, as it was based upon wingless forms only. Subsequent discoveries have shown that winged members also occur in the order. These are among the rarest of insects; less than 20 species are known, of which only two are found in the United States. Both of these species occur in the South.

Zorapterons (Fig. 81) are quite small, measuring 1½ to three millimeters in length; both winged and wingless individuals may be found in the same colony. The winged forms have two pairs of wings which contain only a few veins. The wings are broken off as in the case of termites. The wingless forms are blind. Metamorphosis is gradual, and the mouthparts are of the generalized chewing type.

FIG. 81. A zorapteron, *Zorotypus guineensis*. (Adapted from Essig by permission of The Macmillan Company.)

The insects are found under bark, in rotten wood, and in piles of sawdust. They live in colonies which contain 25 to 100 individuals each. Zoraptera feed as scavengers or probably as predators on small arthropods.

Order CORRODENTIA[5]

Psocids, Book Lice

Psocids have the following characteristics:

1. Winged representatives of the order with two pairs of wings held

[4] *Zoros,* pure; *apterous,* without wings.   [5] *Corrodens,* gnawing.

    roof-like over the body when at rest, front pair larger; veins
prominent.

2. Mandibulate mouthparts.

3. Gradual metamorphosis.

4. Antennae slender, and as long or longer than the body.

Psocids (Fig. 82) are small and inconspicuous insects and are
rarely noticed by the layman. The best known are the light-colored
and wingless forms which are commonly called book lice. Book lice
are usually found feeding on paste and paper of unused books and
in birds' nests where their food consists of feathers and other waste
material.

Most species of psocids are found outdoors and normally possess
two pairs of wings. The front wings are larger than the hind pair

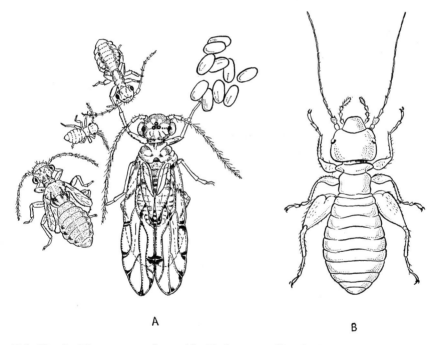

A   B

FIG. 82. **A,** The ten-spotted psocid *(Peripsocus californicus)*; eggs, nymphs and
adult. (From Essig by permission of The Macmillan Company.) **B,** A book louse
(Liposcelis divinatorius). (From the University of California Division of Agricultural
Sciences.)

and the wings at rest are usually held roof-like over the abdomen.
They are usually dusky or mottled in appearance. The insects resemble aphids in general appearance, and are often mistaken for
them by the novice.

Psocids are most often found on the bark of trees, or under lichens and fallen leaves. Here they feed on fungi, algae, dead plant tissues, and other waste materials. Eggs are laid singly or in small groups and may be covered with a silken web. Certain species are gregarious in habit and live under silken webs. One southern species (*Archipsocus nomas*) spins conspicuous webs on tree trunks and larger branches.

Certain book lice are capable of making a faint ticking sound somewhat like that of a watch. This sound can be heard only in the still of the night, and is called the deathwatch by superstitious people in the belief that it presages the death of some member of the household. It is believed that the insect produces the sound by tapping the abdomen against a resonant support such as a thin piece of paper. Small wood-boring beetles of the family Anobiidae also make a similar ticking sound by striking their heads or jaws against the sides of their tunnel.

Book lice sometimes become so abundant in dwellings that control measures are necessary. Sunning books, papers, and furniture will usually free such articles of the pest. Heating the rooms to a relatively high temperature will likewise prove effective in eliminating the insects. Ordinary household sprays are quite effective in control of book lice.

The biology of Corrodentia is imperfectly known. They usually overwinter outdoors in the egg stage, but in heated buildings breeding of book lice may continue throughout the year. More than 1,000 species are known of which number about 150 species occur in North America.

Order THYSANOPTERA[6]

Thrips

General characteristics of the Thysanoptera are:

1. **Two pairs of wings, often absent, long narrow, membranous and fringed with long hairs, particularly on posterior margin.**
2. **Mouthparts modified for rasping and sucking.**
3. **Gradual metamorphosis which differs from the usual type in that a quiescent (pupa) stage precedes the adult.**

---

[6] *Thysanos,* fringe; *pteron,* wing.

4. Tarsi are one- or two-segmented, each with a retractile bladder-like structure on the end.

5. Minute insects, usually less than ⅛ of an inch long.

Although quite numerous, thrips are seldom noticed because of their minute size. They are most readily found in flowers, e.g., those of primroses and legumes. When they get on the hands and arms of persons they may bite tender skin and cause some discomfort.

Thrips (Fig. 83) are slender in form and seldom measure more than two or three millimeters in length. Some have functional

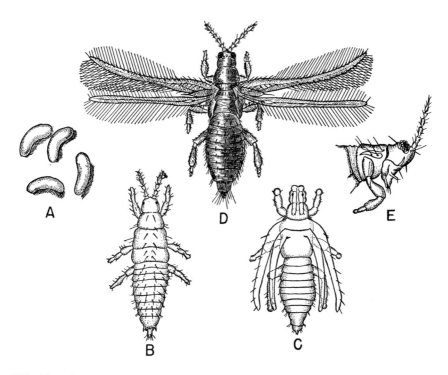

FIG. 83.   The pear thrips (*Taeniothrips inconsequens*). **A,** Eggs. **B,** Larva. **C,** Pupa. **D,** Adult. **E,** Side view of head to show mouthparts—all greatly enlarged. (Adapted from Agricultural Research Service, U.S.D.A.)

wings; others may be apterous or possess short nonfunctional wings. The normally developed wings are long and narrow, with few or no veins and are fringed with hairs particularly on the posterior margin. This fringe of hairs aids in flight and compensates, at least in part, for the small area of the membrane. The wings lie flat on the body when not in use. The antennae have six to nine segments; the compound eyes are relatively large, and the abdomen is ten-segmented.

The tarsi of thrips are quite distinctive in structure. They are one- or two-segmented, usually devoid of claws, and terminate in a cup-shaped depression. Within the latter is a bladder-like organ which is protruded when the tarsus is in contact with an object and retracted when it is not in use.

The mouthparts are of a rasping and sucking type, and are somewhat peculiar in structure. They are in the form of a blunt cone and are situated far back on the underside of the head. The rasping and piercing operation is performed by the needle-like maxillae, assisted by the left mandible. The right mandible is vestigial.

Metamorphosis of the Thysanoptera is gradual but deviates from the usual type in that a quiescent stage precedes the adult. The first two or three instars are similar in appearance and in feeding habits to the adults. These are known as larvae. Then follows a prepupal stage in which wing pads suddenly appear but the insect remains fairly active. In the fourth instar the wing pads and antennae are enlarged; the insect is completely inactive and does not feed. Some species even have a fifth instar. This type of development is not typically gradual metamorphosis, nor is it complete. It may be regarded as intermediate between the two types of development.

Although sexual reproduction is the rule, parthenogenesis is quite common. In some species males are quite rare; in others, parthenogenesis may occur even though males are commonly found.

Thrips commonly feed on plants, particularly the flower parts. They may occur in most species of flowers and attack a wide range of cultivated plants. A number are pests of flowers; greenhouse plants; and such crops as onions, pears, cotton, and citrus. Injury is produced by puncturing and rasping the surface of leaves, buds, stems, and flowers. All thrips are not phytophagous. Some are predators on mites, such as the red spider mite; small insects; and insect eggs. About 4,000 species of thrips are known, of which some 500 are recorded from North America.

The Onion Thrips (*Thrips tabaci*). This insect (Fig. 84**C**) is an important pest of onions. Often entire fields of the plant are destroyed by its attacks. It is a widely distributed pest, occurring throughout the United States, Canada, and Europe. Stems of infested onions assume a silvery appearance caused by the removal of juices from the cells. As the infestation continues, the stems turn brown and die. The heaviest concentrations of the insects are found between the sheaths and stems of the plants. A number of other plants also serve as hosts, e.g., numerous weeds, cotton, melons, turnips, cucumbers, and tomatoes.

The onion thrips is yellowish and about ½₅ inch in length. The females have fully developed wings, but the males are wingless and occur in much smaller numbers. Females regularly reproduce asexually. The larvae develop through four instars; the last two are passed without food in the ground. A life cycle varies in length from 15 to 30 days, and a number of generations may be developed in one season. Winter is passed as adults or larvae in protected places. Feeding may occur throughout this season in the South.

Weeds in the immediate vicinity of fields should be destroyed to prevent the build-up of infestations on these hosts. Applications of DDT, malathion, toxaphene, and related insecticides either as sprays or dusts are recommended in the control of the pest.

The Flower Thrips (*Frankliniella tritici*) **and the Tobacco Thrips** (*Frankliniella fusca*) . The yellowish to dark brown adults are about ½₅ inch in length. They attack a wide range of plants, as many weeds, flowers, wheat, the strawberry, alfalfa, clover, and cotton. In the South they are pests of importance of cotton in the early

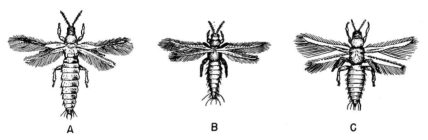

A   B   C

FIG. 84. Common species of thrips. **A,** Gladiolus thrips (*Taeniothrips simplex*) . **B,** Flower thrips (*Frankliniella tritici*) . **C,** Onion thrips (*Thrips tabaci*) . (From Agricultural Research Service, U.S.D.A.)

season. Both flower and vegetative buds are attacked, as are the leaves and flowers. Destruction of the terminal buds of the young cotton plants results in distorted and abnormal growth of the plants. At 87° F. the flower thrips (Fig. 84**B**) may complete a life cycle in ten days. When the temperature is lowered to 73° F. the life cycle is lengthened to 18 days, and at 61° F. the time is increased to 27 days. The length of a life cycle of the tobacco thrips is somewhat longer; about three more days are required for each temperature condition. Both species produce female offspring only after fertilization, and eggs from unmated females develop only into males. A number of generations are produced annually. Control measures recommended for the onion thrips are suggested for these species.

The Citrus Thrips (*Scirtothrips citri*).   This small yellowish insect is a pest of importance in the more arid regions of California and Arizona. Injury is produced through feeding on the buds, new growth, and fruit of citrus trees. Young trees may be retarded and the growth distorted as a result of the feeding injury. The value of the fruit is reduced because the skin is scarred and often ringed due to the feeding when the fruit is small. Many deciduous fruits and numerous other plants also serve as hosts of the insect. A new generation may be produced in two or three weeks. Winter is passed in the egg stage deposited in the leaves and stems of host plants. Applications of sulphur dust or sprays of DDT will control the pest.

The Gladiolus Thrips (*Taeniothrips simplex*).   The gladiolus thrips (Fig. 84A) is a pest of importance. Feeding of the insects causes a characteristic "silvering" of the leaves. Too, the flowers may be deformed and spotted, and the spikes and corms injured. Lilies and iris are other hosts.

The insect is brownish-black and about $\frac{1}{16}$ inch long. It overwinters on the corms except in warm climates when hibernation may occur outdoors. Some breeding may occur on corms in storage at temperatures above 60° F. A generation may be completed in two to four weeks during the warmer seasons.

Corms free from infestation should be used and in warm climates. Gladioli should not be grown in soil infested by the insect the previous year. Some varieties of gladioli are reported to be resistant to the pest. Thrips on corms may be eliminated by dusting them with DDT. The insect on growing plants may be controlled by applications of DDT, chlordane, or toxaphene dusts or sprays.

The Pear Thrips (*Taeniothrips inconsequens*).   This small, dark colored insect (Fig. 83) passes the winter in the ground and emerges in the spring as the fruit buds are swelling. It works its way between the bud scales and feeds on the delicate parts, thus causing the buds to shrivel and die. The leaves, flowers, and fruit are also injured. Eggs are deposited chiefly in the young leaves, fruit stems, and small fruit. The egg-laying period is about three weeks in duration. The eggs hatch in about a week, and the larvae feed on the leaves and young fruit for three or four weeks and then drop to the ground to enter the soil and complete the life cycle. A cell is formed in the soil where summer is passed and hibernation occurs during the winter. The life history of this insect is unlike that of other thrips as only one generation is developed each year and its activity is limited to a rather short period during the spring. Other hosts are fruits such as prunes, cherries, apples, apricots, and grapes. Timely sprays of DDT effectively control the pest. Thorough and deep cultivation of the soil in late summer or early fall will destroy many of the larvae in the soil; however, care must be taken to prevent injury to the trees in plowing.

13

ORDERS MALLOPHAGA
AND ANOPLURA

Order MALLOPHAGA[1]

Chewing Lice

The Mallophaga are characterized as:

1. Small wingless insects which live as ectoparasites of birds and mammals.
2. Metamorphosis gradual but approaching an ametabolous condition due to the parasitic habits.
3. Mouthparts formed for chewing, but modified.
4. Body considerably flattened and hard; the head generally large and the eyes degenerate.

The chewing or biting lice have been generally known as bird lice because they are found chiefly on these hosts (Fig. 85). Since quite a number of species also occur as parasites of mammals, the common name cannot be considered quite appropriate for the order as a whole.

The Mallophaga feed primarily on the feathers, hair, skin scales, possible blood clots, and other materials on the hosts. Recently certain species have been found obtaining blood by puncturing the base of young feathers. This method of feeding, however, does not appear to be of much importance. The principal injury produced is through constant irritation of the hosts. Birds dust themselves

---

[1] *Mallos,* wool; *phagein,* eat.

in the attempt to obtain relief from the parasites. Chewing lice are not known to be vectors of any diseases.

The tarsi of chewing lice infesting birds terminate in a pair of claws which are adapted for clinging to feathers. All lice on mammals, with the exception of rare species found on kangaroos, walla-

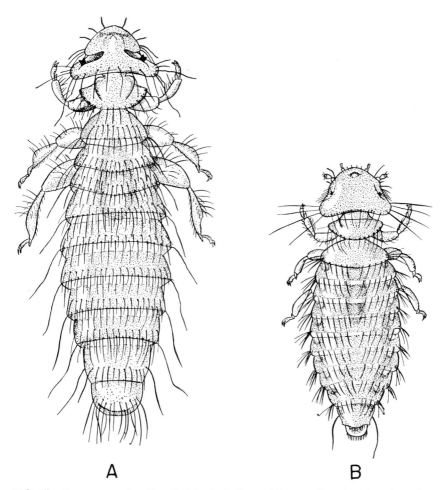

A   B

FIG. 85. Common poultry lice. **A,** The body louse (*Menacanthus stramineus*), male, dorsal view. **B,** The shaft louse (*Menopon gallinae*), female, dorsal view. (From Agricultural Research Service, U.S.D.A.)

bies and wombats, bear only one tarsal claw which folds against the tibia. The clasping organ thus formed is admirably adapted for clinging to hair. Chewing lice may also cling to the hair and feathers by means of the mandibles.

Mallophaga are quite specific in their host relationships. Most species parasitize only one host or closely related forms. The entire life cycle of these parasites is spent on the host animal and they are transferred from one individual to another mainly by contact. If a host dies, the lice also perish unless another host is readily available.

The life histories of relatively few species are known. The eggs, commonly called "nits," are glued near the base of the feathers or hair by a cement-like substance secreted by the female at the time of oviposition. The eggs hatch into nymphs which pass through several molts before the adult stage is attained. The duration of a life cycle depends upon the species concerned, and so far as is known may vary from three to seven weeks.

More than 2,500 species of Mallophaga are known, of which several hundred are found in North America. Over 40 species have been reported infesting poultry, seven of which are quite common. The more common species found on chickens are the body louse (*Menacanthus stramineus*), the head louse (*Cuclotogaster heterographus*), and the shaft louse (*Menopon gallinae*). Young chickens may be killed by heavy infestations of lice. As most young chickens are now grown in brooders there is small likelihood of louse infestations becoming established. Injury to older chickens is produced mainly through irritation caused by feeding and crawling activities of the parasites over their bodies. Many poultrymen are more concerned with the discomfort experienced when the lice crawl on them in caring for the birds than the injury produced. Pigeons often become heavily infested with the small pigeon louse (*Goniocotes bidentatus*) and the slender pigeon louse (*Columbicola columbae*).

In poultry louse control the birds may be dusted with 0.5 percent Co-Ral or by use of malathion. In use of the latter compound a 3 percent roost paint may be thoroughly applied on the perch poles, or the house carefully treated with a 1 percent spray. This treatment also aids in control of other pests. (The feed and water of poultry should not be contaminated with these sprays.)

Cats may suffer irritation from infestations of *Felicola subrostrata*. A powder containing rotenone is recommended for the control of the pest on cats. Dogs may harbor a small species (*Trichodectes canis*). Rotenone and malathion powders will readily eliminate this parasite on these animals.

Livestock are also subject to infestations of chewing lice. Horses become infested with *Bovicola equi,* and cattle with *B. bovis.* Sheep may become heavily infested with *Bovicola ovis. Bovicola caprae* and *B. hermsi* are harbored by goats. Control measures for chewing lice on domestic animals are the same as recommended for sucking lice under the order Anoplura.

Order ANOPLURA[2]

Sucking Lice

The order may be described as:

1. Small depressed wingless insects which live as ectoparasites only on mammals.
2. Mouthparts formed for piercing-sucking; head narrow and usually pointed in front.
3. Metamorphosis gradual but approaching an ametabolous condition due to the parasitic habits.
4. Eyes vestigial or wanting.

The order Anoplura is composed of blood-sucking lice. These are important parasites as they subsist on blood of mammals and are vectors of various diseases. Sucking lice attack only mammals and are never found on birds as are the chewing lice (Mallophaga). This is a small order of insects, consisting of less than 300 species.

The mouthparts are fitted for piercing and sucking, and are retracted within the head. The apex of the mouth is encircled with small hooks which are attached to the skin during feeding activities. The piercing and sucking organs consist of several stylets which are forced into the skin. The homologies of these parts are uncertain. The legs are fitted for grasping. Each tarsus ends in a single claw which folds back on a thumb-like projection of the tibia, thus forming an efficient organ for clinging to the hairs of the host.

The Anoplura, in common with the chewing lice (Mallophaga), are obligatory ectoparasites, and they are quite restricted to specific hosts. Under normal conditions the entire life cycle is spent on one animal. The parasites are transferred from one animal to another chiefly by bodily contact.

The Head and Body Louse (*Pediculus humanus*). The most important sucking louse is the head and body louse of man (Fig.

[2] *Anoplus,* unarmed; *oura,* tail.

86). The species was formerly considered as two, the head louse
and the body louse, but research has established that they are
varieties of the same. Head and body lice occur on man where
overcrowding and substandard living conditions exist. Infestations
of body lice become particularly prevalent during war conditions.
The use of DDT powder efficiently controlled the pest during

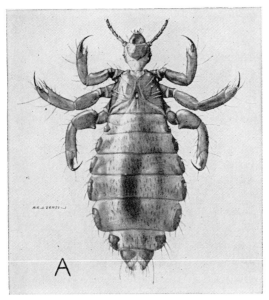

FIG. 86. **A,** The body louse (*Pediculus humanus* var. *humanus*). **B,** Egg of *P. humanus* attached to a human hair. (From Smart, courtesy of British Museum of Natural History.)

World War II and eliminated sporadic outbreaks of typhus fever.

The head louse inhabits the head, but it is said the louse may
also be found on other hairy parts of the body. It averages two or
three millimeters in length and is somewhat smaller than the body
louse. The eggs (nits) are cemented to the hairs and they hatch
in about a week. A complete life cycle from egg to egg is about
three weeks. Head lice may be eliminated by dusting lightly with
DDT powder.

The body louse occurs on most parts of the body, particularly
on the back and chest. Normally the eggs are laid in the seams of
the clothing, but also they may be attached to hairs. Body lice are
commonly found on soldiers, sailors, prisoners, and others who live
in overcrowded quarters and do not have the opportunity of changing clothing and bathing regularly. The life cycle of the body louse

is similar to that of the head louse, but the former is more prolific, since more eggs are laid by the female.

Head and body lice are to be feared as vectors of relapsing fever, trench fever, and the dreaded epidemic form of typhus fever. During and following World War I typhus fever swept over large areas of Europe and Asia, and caused the death of millions of people. The application of DDT powder under the clothing and on the head readily eliminates these lice. However, during the war in Korea, lice in that area were not effectively controlled with DDT, and other insecticides, such as lindane, had to be used.

The Crab Louse (*Phthirus pubis*). This species is distinctive in its crab-like appearance (Fig. 87A). It is nearly as broad as long and is about 1½ to two millimeters in length. A related

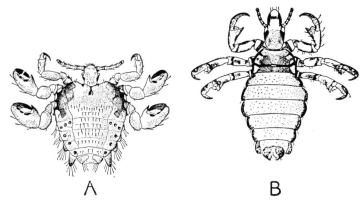

A   B

FIG. 87. **A,** The crab louse (*Phthirus pubis*). **B,** The hog louse (*Haematopinus suis*). (From Smart, courtesy of British Museum of Natural History.)

species, *Phthirus gorillae,* occurs on the gorilla. The crab louse inhabits particularly the pubic and perianal regions of the body. The eggs hatch in about seven days. Fewer eggs are laid and the life cycle is somewhat longer; therefore it is not so prolific as the head and body louse. The insect is not known to carry any disease. DDT dust readily controls the pest.

Sucking Lice of Domestic Animals

Sucking lice are important pests of domestic animals. The hog louse (*Haematopinus suis,* Fig. 87B) is a common pest of hogs. It is the largest of all Anoplura and measures ⅕ inch in length.

Four species of the order commonly infest cattle. Of these, the short-nosed cattle louse (*Haematopinus eurysternus,* Fig. 88**A**) is probably the most important in the United States. The cattle tail louse (*Haematopinus quadripertusus*) is a relatively recent introduction into the United States. This form appears to be spreading and it is assuming greater importance. Two other species which occur on cattle are the long-nosed cattle louse (*Linognathus vituli,* Fig. 88**B**) and the blue louse (*Solenopotes capillatus*). Horses and mules may become infested with *Haematopinus asini.* Two species, *Linognathus ovillus* and *Linognathus pedalis,* occur on sheep in

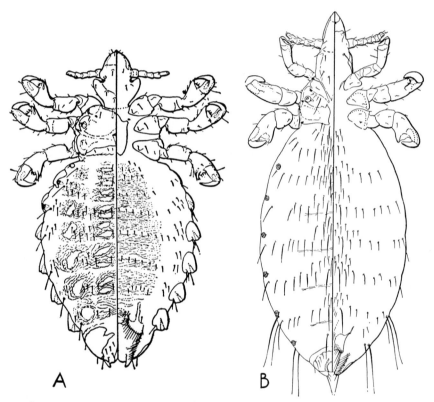

FIG. 88.   **A,** The short-nosed cattle louse (*Haematopinus eurysternus*) , female. **B,** The long-nosed cattle louse (*Linognathus vituli*) , female. (Courtesy of G. F. Ferris.)

the United States. Heavy infestations of *Linognathus stenopsis* occur at times on goats. Dogs may suffer from infestations of *Linognathus setosus.*

Lice on domestic animals may be controlled without difficulty. Sprays or dips containing DDT, malathion, or lindane will control hog lice. These parasites on beef cattle may be controlled by use of one of several insecticides, such as toxaphene, delnav, malathion, lindane or Co-Ral. The same compounds may be employed in control of sheep and goat lice. Pyrethrum and rotenone are designated for use on dairy animals.

14

ORDER HEMIPTERA[1]

BUGS

The Hemiptera are distinguished from insects of other orders by having:

1. **Two pairs of wings almost always present; the front wings, the hemelytra, with exceptions, thickened at the base with the apical portions membranous and overlapping when not in use.**
2. **Mouthparts typically piercing and sucking, without palpi, and arising from the front part of the underside of the head.**
3. **Gradual metamorphosis.**
4. **A plate usually triangular in outline, the scutellum, located between the base of the wings.**
5. **Body build usually broad and flattened dorsoventrally.**

Any insect or animal resembling an insect is known by the layman as a bug. But the name "bug" can be correctly applied only to a member of this large and important order of insects (Fig. 89). Bugs are among the more common insects. They are widely distributed throughout the world but they reach their greatest numbers and diversity of form in the tropical regions. They vary in size from extremely small insects to individuals measuring four or five inches in length. Hemipterous insects are chiefly terrestrial, but some are aquatic and others are semiaquatic in habitat.

Bugs are generally considered as plant feeders and a number of important plant pests belong to this order. Some, however, are predaceous, feeding on other insects, and others are parasites of man and animals.

In Hemiptera the body is normally broad and somewhat flattened

[1] *Hemi,* half; *pteron,* wing.

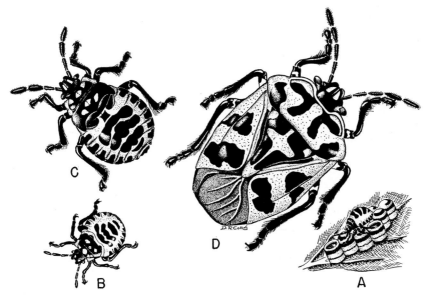

FIG. 89. The harlequin bug (*Murgantia histrionica*). **A,** Eggs with newly hatched nymph. **B** and **C,** Nymphs. **D,** Adult.

dorsoventrally. The thorax and abdomen are broadly joined. Between the base of the wings there is usually a large triangular plate known as the scutellum. In some groups this plate covers up most of the body behind the pronotum.

Wings are usually present, and four in number. They lie flat upon the body when not in use. The hind pair is membranous and covered by the front pair when the wings are folded. The front pair is thickened and corneous on the basal portion and membranous apically. The membranous parts of the front wings overlap when they are at rest. The corneous nature of the basal portion of the front wings is similar in texture to the elytra of beetles, hence they are known as hemelytra (half-wings). The divisions of the basal portion and the venation of the membranous apices of the hemelytra are of much value in the taxonomy of the order. (See Fig. 90.)

The mouthparts of Hemiptera are typically piercing and sucking. Insects with such mouthparts puncture the epidermis of plants and the skin of animals with the slender stylets and take up the sap or blood as food. The structure of the mouthparts and the manner in which they function are discussed on page 44. Obviously no type of stomach poison could ever function in the control of insects with such mouthparts. When chemical control of pests

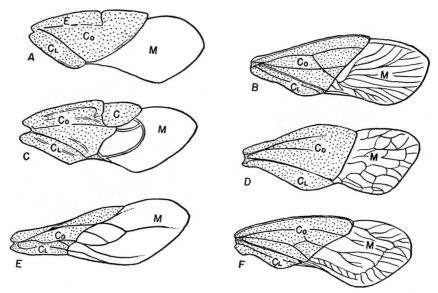

FIG. 90. Diagrammatic illustrations of front wings (*hemelytra*) of Hemiptera. **A,** *Anthocoridae.* **B,** *Coreidae.* **C,** *Miridae.* **D,** *Pyrrhocoridae.* **E,** *Reduviidae.* **F,** *Nabidae.* C, cuneus; Cl, clavus; Co, corium; E, embolium; M, membrane.

belonging to this order is needed, contact poisons and fumigants must be employed.

Most bugs secrete disagreeable odors for protection from their natural enemies. The scent glands of the bed bug are located on the dorsal surface of the first three abdominal segments. In stink bugs and squash bugs these glands open on the dorsum of the abdomen of the nymphs and on the ventral surface of the thorax of the adults.

KEY TO COMMON FAMILIES OF HEMIPTERA

1. Antenna as long as or longer than head, usually visible from dorsal view; rarely fitting in a pronotal groove (Phymatidae)   2
   Antenna shorter than head, usually concealed in cavity below compound eye; aquatic or semiaquatic in habitat   13
2. Claws attached to apex of tarsus; last segment of tarsus not split; habitat, terrestrial   3
   Claws attached before apex; last segment of tarsus more or less split; habitat, surface of water   16
3. Antenna 5-segmented (Stink bugs)   **Pentatomidae,** p. 176
   Antenna 4-segmented   4

4. Hemelytron reticulated and gauze-like (Lace Bugs) **Tingidae,** p. 184
   Hemelytron not as described, or vestigial   5
5. Beak 4-segmented   6
   Beak 3-segmented   10
6. Front tibia armed with double row of short spines on inner
   surface and capable of closing tightly on femur, forming
   a grasping organ (Damsel Bugs)   **Nabidae,** p. 190
   Spines on inner surface of front tibia absent; front leg not
   raptorial   7
7. Hemelytron with cuneus; membrane with one or two closed
   cells (Plant Bugs). Fig. 90.   **Miridae,** p. 185
   Hemelytron without cuneus   8
8. Ocelli wanting (Cotton Stainers)   **Pyrrhocoridae,** p. 183
   Ocelli present   9
9. Membrane of hemelytron with 4 or 5 simple veins arising
   from basal vein (Chinch Bugs)   **Lygaeidae,** p. 180
   Membrane of hemelytron with many veins arising from
   basal vein (Squash Bugs)   **Coreidae,** p. 178
10. Tarsus with 2 segments or none; femur of front leg one-
    half as wide as long (Ambush Bugs)   **Phymatidae,** p. 190
    Tarsus with three segments; femur of front leg not greatly
    thickened   11
11. Beak short and stout, not reaching middle coxae and rest-
    ing in cross-striated groove; ocelli, if present, either be-
    hind eyes or transverse depression (Assassin Bugs)
                                                       Reduviidae, p. 191
    Beak usually reaching middle coxae; if not, does not lie in
    cross-striated groove; ocelli, when present, usually in line
    with rear margin of eyes and not behind transverse de-
    pression   12
12. Ocelli wanting, hemelytra vestigial; parasitic on man and
    other animals (Bed Bugs)   **Cimicidae,** p. 193
    Ocelli present; hemelytra developed, embolium present
    (Flower Bugs)   **Anthocoridae,** p. 192
13. Hind tarsus with indistinct claws   14
    Hind tarsus with distinct claws   15
14. Front tarsus with one segment; body flattened dorsally
    (Water Boatmen)   **Corixidae,** p. 194
    Front tarsus with at least two segments, body convex dor-
    sally (Backswimmers)   **Notonectidae,** p. 195
15. Abdomen with long slender caudal appendages; tarsi 1-seg-
    mented; hind leg not modified for swimming (Water
    Scorpions)   **Nepidae,** p. 196
    Abdomen without long slender caudal appendages; tarsi
    with two segments; hind leg modified for swimming
    (Giant Water Bugs)   **Belostomatidae,** p. 197
16. Hind femur extending considerably beyond tip of abdo-
    men; beak 4-segmented (Water Striders)   **Gerridae,** p. 195

Hind femur not extending much beyond tip of abdomen;
beak 3-segmented (Broad-shouldered Water Striders)
Veliidae.

Family *Pentatomidae* (Stink Bugs)

Stink bugs are relatively large insects with five-segmented antennae and a large sized scutellum, triangular in shape, narrowing
posteriorly. Members of this family are generally plant feeders and
suck the sap of leaves, stems, and fruit. Some are predaceous, as
the two-spotted stink bug (*Perillus bioculatus*) which feeds almost
entirely on the Colorado potato beetle (adults, larvae, and eggs).
Others are both predaceous and phytophagous, e.g., the green stink
bug (*Acrosternum hilare*).

Stink bugs hibernate as adults, yet in the southernmost parts of
the United States certain species may remain more or less active
throughout the winter. Eggs are laid on end in clusters or in rows
on the host plants. The total number of eggs laid varies from 100
to several hundred. The generations produced in a season may
range from one to five; the number depending upon the species
and climatic conditions.

The Harlequin Bug (*Murgantia histrionica*). In the South
this insect (Fig. 89) is a well-known pest to every truck farmer and
gardener. It occurs as far north as Washington, Ohio, Wisconsin,
New Jersey, and New York, but rarely produces much damage
in the northern range of its distribution. This insect inflicts considerable damage and often destroys entire crops of cabbage,
mustard, turnips, and other cruciferous plants. Other plants
are occasionally attacked. Sap and chlorophyll are taken from the
leaves with the piercing-sucking mouthparts, and heavily infested
plants may appear as if they have been scorched by fire.

This conspicuous black and red or yellow-checkered bug is about
$\frac{1}{2}$ inch in length. Because of its markings it is also known as the
calico back, terrapin back, and fire bug. Another common name,
Lincoln bug, was applied by the farmers because, a native of Central America, it was first found in Texas during the Civil War.

Eggs are usually laid on the underside of the leaves and are arranged in two-row clusters of about 12 each. They are laid on end
and measure $\frac{1}{25}$ inch in height; are white and banded by two black
rings. In warm weather the eggs hatch in four or five days. The
nymphs pass through five instars before attaining the adult stage.

During the warmer parts of the season a life cycle may be completed in 40 to 60 days. Adults are long-lived and may live for a period of several months. During this time each female may lay more than 100 eggs. The insect hibernates as adults under crop residues, grass, brush, and other debris. In its southern limits some activity and breeding may occur during mild weather throughout the winter. As many as three complete generations and a partial fourth have been recorded.

In control of the harlequin bug it is important that crop residues and hibernation places be destroyed. Trap crops are of some aid in combating the insect. Rows of mustard, kale, or rape may be planted prior to the main crop and the bugs allowed to collect on them. These plants, together with the bugs, are then destroyed by spraying with oil or by burning.

Dusts of 10 percent DDT will control this pest. Sprays of this material are also recommended. If danger of insecticidal residue is feared, sabadilla dust may be applied as a substitute; however this compound is not so effective as DDT.

The Southern Green Stink Bug (*Nezara viridula*).   This insect (Fig. 91) is a wide-spread and well-known pest of peas, beans, cotton, tomato, pecan, citrus, and other field and garden plants. The

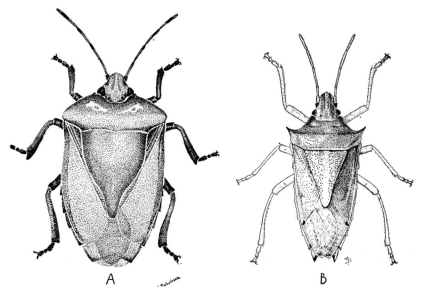

FIG. 91. Common stink bugs. **A,** The southern green stink bug (*Nezara viridula*). (From Department of Entomology, A & M College of Texas.) **B,** The rice stink bug (*Oebalus pugnax*). (From Agricultural Research Service, U.S.D.A.)

feeding punctures of this and related species may result in the destruction or partial destruction of cotton bolls, peas and beans in the pod, and deformation of the fruit of tomatoes and peaches. The kernels of pecans often have discolored spots and are bitter to the taste. This disorder, known as kernel spot, is caused by the feeding of this and other hemipterous insects before the nuts mature. DDT sprays and dusts are recommended as a control measure. The elimination of alternate host plants and hibernation quarters is also advisable.

The green stink bug (*Acrosternum hilare*) is a closely related species which causes similar injury. The conchuela (*Chlorochroa ligata*) and the Say stink bug (*Chlorochroa sayi*) are important species in the Southwest.

Family *Coreidae* (Squash Bugs)

Representatives of this family have four segments in both beak and antenna; ocelli are present, and the membrane of the hemelytron has many veins which arise from a transverse basal vein.

The Squash Bug (*Anasa tristis*). This species (Fig. 92) is the best-known member of this large family of bugs. The adult is a robust

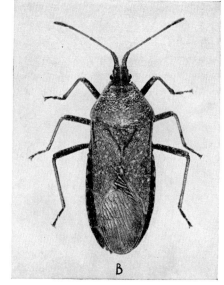

FIG. 92. Squash bug (*Anasa tristis*). **A,** Eggs. **B,** Adult. (**From** Agricultural Research Service, U.S.D.A.)

bug $\frac{1}{2}$ to $\frac{2}{3}$ inch in length and about $\frac{1}{4}$ inch wide. Its general color is dark brown, produced by a yellow background densely covered by black punctations. The nymphal stages are grayish, except the first instar which is green and black.

The insect attacks squashes, pumpkins, and other cucurbits. Infested leaves assume a grayish cast, wilt, and die. If the infestation is heavy, the entire plant may be killed. Following the death of the plant, clusters of the bugs may be found sucking the juices of the fruit. Most injury occurs in the latter part of the season when nymphs are numerous.

The squash bug overwinters in the adult stage under crop residues, piles of boards and trash, in buildings, and other available shelter. It emerges late in the spring. When the plants have emerged and are growing, the adults begin feeding and egg-laying. Eggs are usually laid in rows on the underside of the leaves between large veins. When plants are heavily infested, eggs may be laid on the upper surface of leaves and other places as well. The eggs are oval, brown, and about $\frac{1}{16}$ inch in length. About 24 eggs are laid in an average cluster. A female will lay a total of several hundred eggs before she dies. Eggs hatch in one to two weeks. Maturity is reached by passing through five nymphal instars and the egg to adult development ranges from 45 to 60 days. The number of generations annually varies from one to three.

The squash bug is difficult to control. The destruction of crop residues and elimination of hibernation quarters are essential practices in controlling the pest. Hand picking when the bugs first appear may be practical when only a few plants are involved. Chemical control has not proved very satisfactory. Heavy applications of sabadilla afford some measure of control. Parathion is recommended for use on commercial crops.

The Leaf-footed Bug (*Leptoglossus phyllopus*). This insect (Fig. 93) is commonly a pest of peas, beans, potatoes, tomatoes, pecans, and other plants. It feeds upon the fruit and tender growth. The fruit of the peach, tomato, and others may be disfigured and gnarled by the feeding of this species, and the attacks upon ripening fruit may result in rotting. Peas and beans are injured the most by puncturing the seed in the pod and sucking out the plant juices. Injury to the nuts of pecans is identical with that produced by stink bugs.

The leaf-footed plant bug is brown, oblong, and about $\frac{4}{5}$ inch in length. A white band extends across the front wings. The hind tibiae are dilated or leaf-like, which characteristic has suggested the common name of the insect.

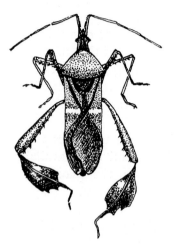

The insect overwinters as an adult in almost any sheltered place. The adults emerge in the spring and feed on a rather wide range of host plants. Fifteen to 35 eggs are laid in a cluster and in definite rows, and are usually placed on the smooth surface of twigs of host plants. Two generations annually have been observed in warm climates. Cleanup measures to eliminate hibernation quarters and alternate host plants, and dusting or spraying with DDT are recommended control measures.

FIG. 93. The leaf-footed plant bug (*Leptoglossus phyllopus*).

The Boxelder Bug (*Leptocoris trivittatus*). This bug often becomes a nuisance about homes in the fall and during warm winter days, when it may collect in large numbers upon tree trunks and porches or find its way into dwellings. It overwinters as an adult (Fig. 94) in homes or other dry protected places. These bugs are dark brown with three longitudinal red lines on the thorax and with the veins of the hemelytra red. They are somewhat narrow and about one-half inch long. This insect feeds principally on boxelder but it may also attack a number of other plants. The presence of the insects in dwellings is a nuisance only, as they do not injure man or any of his household belongings in any way.

Boxelder bugs may be controlled with chlordane sprays. Liberal applications of the spray should be made, particularly to tree trunks and other places where concentrations of the bugs occur.

Family *Lygaeidae* (The Chinch Bug Family)

Members of the chinch bug family have both beaks and antennae four-segmented; ocelli are usually present and the membrane of the hemelytra has four or five simple veins which arise from a transverse basal vein. This is a large family of small bugs including more than 1,500 species of which more than 200 occur in North America. All are phytophagous and several are important pests.

The Chinch Bug (*Blissus leucopterus*). This insect (Fig. 95) ranges in distribution from Central America northward to southern Canada, and is a pest of much importance in the Middle West. Host plants are corn, wheat, oats, barley, grain sorghums, and other members of the grass family.

This is a small insect not more than $\frac{1}{6}$ or $\frac{1}{5}$ inch in length, but its smallness belies its capacity for injury, as enormous numbers more than compensate for size (Fig. 96). The body is black. The front wings are white with a black spot near the middle of each outer margin.

The chinch bug hibernates as adults in any available cover. Clumps of grass are

FIG. 94. The boxelder bug (*Leptocoris trivittatus*). (From Agricultural Research Service, U.S.D.A.)

commonly selected as places of hibernation; however, it may be found in corn shocks, hedge rows, woodlands, stubble, and other places during the winter. In the spring the adults emerge from hibernation and fly to fields of small grain. Eggs are deposited behind the sheaths of the lower leaves and on the roots of the plants if the

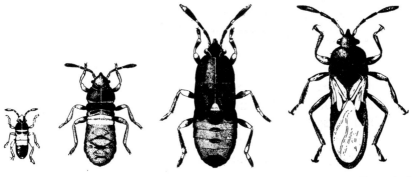

FIG. 95. Nymphs and adult of the chinch bug (*Blissus leucopterus*). (From Agricultural Research Service, U.S.D.A.)

soil is loose. Each female lays 200 or more eggs during a period of three or four weeks. The eggs are small, cylindrical, and yellow. They hatch in one to two weeks into reddish nymphs which are characterized by a light band across the back. The adult stage is reached in 30 to 40 days after passing through five nymphal instars. The chinch bug usually has two generations annually, but in the Southwest at least a partial third generation occurs.

FIG. 96. A heavy infestation of chinch bugs on a corn stalk. (From Agricultural Research Service, U.S.D.A.)

In the southernmost parts of the United States the chinch bug may fly directly from hibernation quarters to corn. Also, in parts of Oklahoma and Texas the first generation on small grain may be completed by the time these crops mature, and the migration to corn and grain sorghums is then accomplished by flight and not by crawling. In the Middle West small grains mature and are harvested before the first generation of the chinch bug is completed and the insect usually crawls to the corn fields.

Wet weather is the most important control factor of the chinch bug. Heavy beating rains destroy many of the insects at the time of hatching of the eggs. Wet cloudy weather also fosters outbreaks of the chinch bug fungus (*Beauveria globulifera*). The combination of these factors will usually eliminate serious infestations of the insect.

Chinch bugs avoid shade and prefer sunshine. The planting of cowpeas or soybeans in corn to shade the base of the plants creates conditions unfavorable for the bugs and will help reduce injury. Varieties of grain sorghums and corn are being developed which show some resistance to chinch bug attack. Rotation of crops so that fields of corn are not adjacent to wheat, oats, or barley is advisable. The burning of hibernation quarters is a worthwhile practice when the insects are found chiefly in bunch grass. The value of this practice is questionable in other areas.

When chinch bugs are migrating from small grain fields to corn by crawling, the construction of a barrier around the margin of the field which they are leaving is an effective method of control. A very satisfactory barrier may be made by spraying dieldrin in strips about four rods wide between the fields of small grain and corn or sorghum. To prevent the bugs from going around the barrier, short strips should be sprayed across each end. These need to be eight to ten rods long and two rods wide. The spray should be applied a few days prior to migration of the bugs. The time of application may be estimated by observing the stage of maturity or ripening of the small grain upon which the insects are feeding.

When the chinch bugs are concentrated on a few outer rows or on a few plants, control may be obtained by spraying with toxaphene or dieldrin.

Another species, the hairy chinch bug (*Blissus leucopterus hirtus*), is predominantly a short-winged form and lacks the migratory habit of the common chinch bug. Sometimes it is a pest of lawns and greens in the northeastern states. The use of fertilizers, watering, and frequent cutting aids the grass to withstand injury. Chlordane or DDT dusts will control the species.

The false chinch bug (*Nysius ericae*) feeds on grain sorghums, potatoes, grapes, cruciferous plants, cotton, and many other plants. Only occasionally is it an important pest of any crop. Superficially the insect resembles the chinch bug; its color is more uniform and ranges from grayish to fuscous. When control measures are advisable, applications of malathion are recommended.

Family *Pyrrhocoridae* (Stainers or Red Bugs)

Most members of this family are found in tropical and subtropical countries. About 25 species occur in the South and Southwest. These bugs are rather large, elongate-oval in outline, stout in form, and marked with contrasting colors. Both antennae and beak are four-segmented, no cuneus is present on the hemelytron, and ocelli are absent. The insects are plant feeders and gregarious in habit.

In tropical regions cotton stainers (*Dysdercus* spp.) are major

FIG. 97. A lace bug (*Corythucha*). (From Agricultural Research Service, U.S.D.A.)

cotton pests, but in the United States their injury to the crop is of little importance. Damage is caused by puncturing of the bolls, which may then be destroyed or the lint stained to a yellowish or brownish color. The staining is produced by exudations of punctured seeds.

Biology of the insects is not fully known. In addition to cotton, oranges, cockleburs, eggplants, and numbers of other plants serve as hosts. Eggs are laid in the soil or trash. The life cycle seems to be similar to that of stink bugs (*Pentatomidae*). The best known species in the United States are the cotton stainer (*Dysdercus suturellus*), the southwestern cotton stainer (*Dysdercus albidiventris*), and the bordered plant bug (*Euryophthalmus succinctus*). Sprays or dusts of endrin are recommended for use if control measures are needed.

Family *Tingidae* (Lace Bugs)

These small bugs are readily recognized by the reticulated and lace-like structure of the hemelytra, which characteristic is usually accompanied by lateral expansions of the pronotum of similar markings (Fig. 97). Members of this small family of bugs feed on the sap of plants and occur on the under surface of leaves. Infested leaves may be recognized by the light stippled effect of the dorsal surface. Trees, shrubs, cotton, and many other plants are attacked. Eggs are deposited in plant tissue and are usually covered by a secretion which hardens and forms conical projections on the surface. Nymphs are usually darker and have little resemblance to the adults.

About 100 species of lace bugs are known to occur in North America. The sycamore lace bug (*Corythucha ciliata*) is a common form. Eggs are laid in the ribs of the underside of leaves. Seven to

nine weeks are required for a life cycle. Two or more generations
are produced each season. The adult is the overwintering stage. The
oak lace bug (*Corythucha arcuata*) is another common species. Its
life history is similar to that of the sycamore lace bug, except the
winter is passed either in the egg or adult stage. The elm lace bug
(*Corythucha ulmi*), the cotton lace bug (*Corythucha gossypii*),
and the hawthorn lace bug (*Corythucha cydoniae*) are other common members of the family. Should control measures be necessary,
sprays of nicotine sulphate, DDT, and related contact poisons are
recommended for use.

Family *Miridae* (Plant Bugs or Leaf Bugs)

The Miridae are a large family of small to medium-sized bugs.
The most distinctive family characteristics are found on the hemelytra. The cuneus is present and one or two cells are found at the
base of the membrane. Other characteristics are the absence of ocelli
and the four-segmented beak. Most of the species feed on plant
juices; however, some are predaceous on other insects.

A wide variety of plants are fed upon by these insects, which cause
several types of injury. Fruit trees, vegetables, alfalfa, cotton, weeds
of various kinds, and grasses are typical host plants. Both fruit and
vegetative buds are injured or destroyed by the feeding activities of
plant bugs. Fruit may be attacked, and become malformed and of
reduced value. Flowers and seeds are subject to attack and may be
destroyed. Plant bugs may increase rapidly to large numbers, and
major damage to crops may be done.

The Tarnished Plant Bug (*Lygus lineolaris*). This insect (Fig.
98) is a well known pest throughout the United States. The adult
is brown and mottled with yellow, black, and red. It is about $1/4$
inch in length and less than half as broad. The nymphs are green.

Injury to leaves, stems, fruit and growth buds, flowers, seeds,
and developing fruit is caused by the feeding of the insect. The
adult overwinters in trash and other available shelter. In the spring
eggs are laid in the tissues of various herbaceous weeds, vegetables,
and other plants. Eggs hatch in one to two weeks and two to three
weeks later the adult emerges from the fifth developmental instar.
So a generation may be completed in three to five weeks. Five generations may occur during a season.

Elimination of favorable hibernation quarters and the destruction

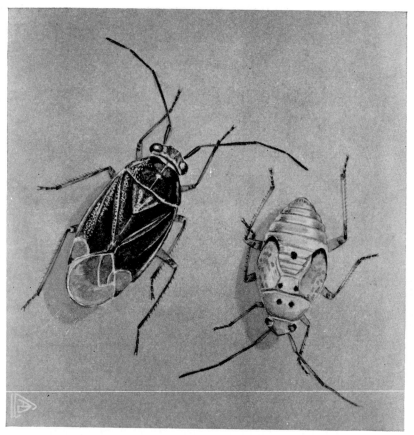

FIG. 98. Left, adult; right, nymph, of the tarnished plant bug (*Lygus lineolaris*). (Courtesy of Hercules Powder Co.)

of weeds will help to reduce the numbers of this insect. Dusts of DDT, BHC, or toxaphene will control the pest. Spraying fruit trees with DDT is recommended.

Two species related to the tarnished plant bug and commonly known as lygus bugs, *Lygus elisus* and *L. hesperus,* are important pests of alfalfa and cotton in the West and Southwest. These bugs are slightly smaller and somewhat lighter in color. The biology of the two species is similar to that of the tarnished plant bug. The rapid plant bug (*Adelphocoris rapidus,* Fig. 99A) is often associated with the lygus bugs, to which it is similar in both biology and type of injury.

These plant bugs are serious pests of alfalfa, particularly when it is grown for a seed crop. Buds are destroyed, flowers drop, and seeds shrivel and turn brown when they are fed upon by the in-

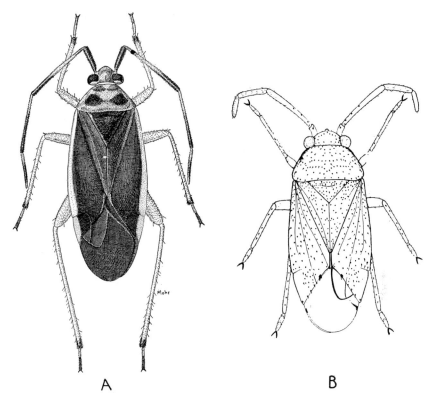

A   B

FIG. 99. **A,** The rapid plant bug (*Adelphocoris rapidus*). (From Illinois Natural History Survey.) **B,** The cotton fleahopper (*Psallus seriatus*). (From Texas Agricultural Experiment Station.)

sects. The effect of these attacks also is evident in the vegetative growth. Stems branch excessively, and frequently the leaves become distorted, smaller, and more numerous. DDT dusts or sprays are recommended for use in the late bud stage of alfalfa. If control measures are needed during the blooming period, toxaphene is recommended; because this insecticide is less toxic to honey bees, which are needed for pollination.

When alfalfa and weeds are cut or have become unsuitable as hosts, the plant bugs migrate to cotton fields. Feeding on this crop causes squares, blooms, and young bolls to drop. Malformations of the plants also result. Dusts or sprays of DDT, toxaphene, and related insecticides are recommended as control measures on this crop.

The Cotton Fleahopper (*Psallus seriatus*). The cotton fleahopper (Fig. 99B) is an important pest of cotton, particularly in the southern part of the cotton belt. The adult is obovate in outline, pale green, and about ⅐ inch in length. The insect may be recognized by four black marks near the tips of the front wings and small dark spots on the body surface, legs, and antennae. The nymphs are green.

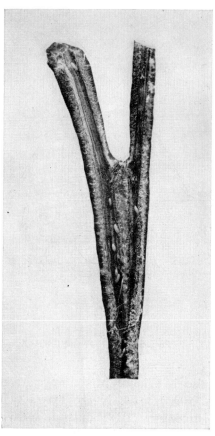

The fleahopper injures cotton by puncturing and feeding on the terminal buds and newly formed squares with its piercing-sucking mouthparts. The young squares are shed, which often results in tall, whip-like plant growth without the formation of fruiting branches. Injury to the terminal buds often produces abnormal plant growth.

The cotton fleahopper hibernates in the egg stage in the stems of its host plants, particularly goat weeds (*Croton* spp.). (See Fig. 100.) The eggs hatch in the spring, and the nymphs feed on available weeds such as evening primrose (*Oenothera* spp.) and horsemint (*Monarda* spp.). When a scarcity of suitable host plants occurs, the winged forms may migrate to cotton fields. Later in the season

FIG. 100. Eggs of the cotton fleahopper in the bark of a goat weed (*Croton capitata*). (From Texas Agricultural Experiment Station.)

when the weeds, particularly goat weeds, become more attractive than the cotton plant, a reverse migration to the weeds occurs.

The length of the egg stage averages eight days. Upon hatching the nymphs progress through five instars and attain the adult stage in about 11 days. Three days after maturity the females begin egg-laying. An entire life cycle may be completed in 22 days. Theoretically at least, seven or eight generations may be completed in one season.

The cotton fleahopper is not a difficult insect to control. When cotton has reached the fruiting stage it should be examined at weekly intervals for fleahoppers. When 15 to 35 fleahoppers per 100 plant terminals are found, control measures should be employed. A number of insecticides may be used either as sprays or as dusts in control of this pest. Some of the commonly used compounds are toxaphene-DDT, dieldrin, endrin, and heptachlor.

The Garden Fleahopper (*Halticus bracteatus*). These small blackish insects resemble plant lice (Fig. 101), and their type of injury is quite similar. They attack peas, beans, cabbage, tomatoes, and numbers of other plants; and suck sap from the leaves and stems. Winter is passed as adults. Eggs are laid in punctures made by the mouthparts in the stems and leaves of the hosts. The nymphs are green and develop rapidly to the adult stage. Two types of females develop: a long-winged and a short-winged form. The jumping habits and the hosts of the species have probably suggested the common name. As many as five generations in one season have been

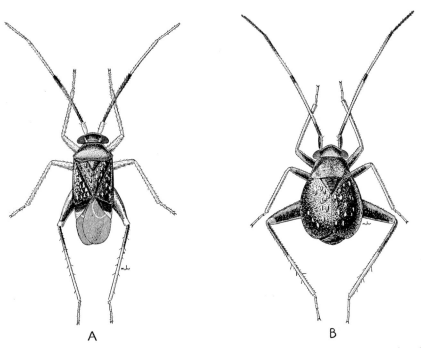

A   B

FIG. 101. The garden fleahopper (*Halticus bracteatus*). **A,** Male. **B,** Short-winged female. (From Illinois Natural History Survey. Drawn by C. O. Mohr.)

recorded. DDT and malathion have been recommended as control measures. Destruction of weeds which serve as hosts is recommended, because this practice will aid in prevention of the buildup of populations of the pest.

Family *Phymatidae* (Ambush Bugs)

The front legs of members of this family provide the most striking marks of identification (Fig. 102). The femur is short, thickened, and at least one-half as broad as long. The tibia is small

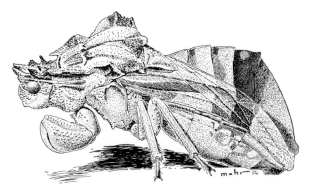

FIG. 102.   An ambush bug (*Phymata pennsylvanica*). (Courtesy of C. O. Mohr.)

and curved. The two form an efficient organ for grasping the prey, for they fit closely together and both are armed with teeth. Antennae are knobbed and in *Phymata* each fits in a groove under the lateral margin of the pronotum.

Phymata erosa is the most common representative of this group of predaceous insects in the United States. It is yellowish-green and one-third to ½ inch in length. The bug hides in flowers and feeds on the insect visitors. Among its victims may be such relatively large insects as bees, wasps, and butterflies.

Family *Nabidae* (Damsel Bugs)

Bugs of this family are rather small with the body somewhat narrowed anteriorly. The front tibia is armed on the inner face with a double row of short spines and is capable of closing tightly on the femur to form a grasping organ. Damsel bugs are predaceous and feed on such insects as aphids and caterpillars. Some species have both long- and short-winged forms. Most common species of this small group of insects belong to the genus *Nabis* of which *N. ferus* is the best known. The bug is yellowish-brown and about ⅓ inch long. It hides among foliage or in flowers and captures the insects upon which it subsists.

Family *Reduviidae* (Assassin Bugs)

The assassin bugs are medium to large in size, diverse in form, and some are of contrasting colors. The beak is three-segmented,

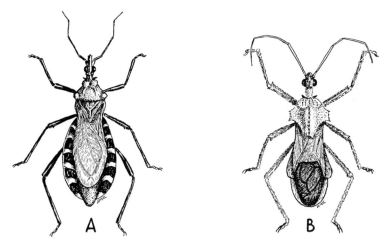

FIG. 103. Assassin bugs. **A,** The bloodsucking cone-nose (*Triatoma sanguisuga*). **B,** The wheel bug (*Arilus cristatus*).

arises from the tip of the head, and when at rest it lies in a cross-striated groove between the front coxae. These bugs are predaceous. They feed upon diverse groups of insects and in a few cases on man and large animals. Chagas disease, an important disease of man, is transmitted by assassin bugs. This disease is found from Mexico southward through South America.

The genus *Triatoma* includes a number of species of which *T. sanguisuga* (Fig. 103A) is probably the best known. It passes under the common names of cone-nose, big bed bug, and Mexican bed bug. The insect may enter homes, and its bite is quite severe. It is occasionally found in poultry houses and feeds on the blood of poultry as the fowl tick (*Argus persicus*).

The "kissing bug" (*Reduvius personatus*) is one of the more common species of the family. It is found in dwellings and commonly feeds on bed bugs, flies, and other insects. The insect occasionally bites man. The nymphs cover themselves with particles of lint to camouflage their presence.

Melanolestes picipes is often attracted to lights in the home. The insect is to be avoided as it may inflict painful bites if handled carelessly. This species is black and occurs outdoors where it feeds on insects of various kinds.

Probably the most striking representative of the family is the wheel bug (*Arilus cristatus,* Fig. 103**B**). It was given the name because of the presence of a crested pronotum, notched along the median line. The insect is quite large and the general color is gray. It is predaceous on other insects. When molested this insect defends itself by inflicting a painful bite.

Family *Anthocoridae* (Flower Bugs or Minute Pirate Bugs)

The members of this family of small predaceous bugs, unlike most Hemiptera, have hemelytra provided with a well-developed embolium. The species are small and are usually black with white markings. They feed on insect eggs, newly hatched larvae, nymphs, spider mites, thrips, and other small forms.

Orius insidiosus (Fig. 104) is the best known species. It is an important predator in the fields and gardens where it feeds on a rather wide variety of small insect life. The adults are about $\frac{1}{12}$ inch long and black. The corium of the hemelytra is yellowish-white and is marked by a large triangular black spot at the tip; the

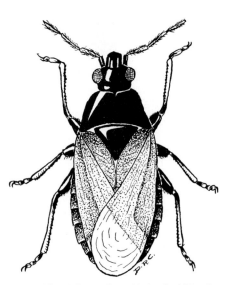

FIG. 104.   A flower bug (*Orius insidiosus*).

membrane is white. The insect bears a superficial resemblance to the chinch bug. The tiny nymphs are yellowish. Adults overwinter in trash. Eggs are deposited in plant tissues. Several generations are completed each season.

Family *Cimicidae* (Bed Bugs)

Bed bugs are wingless parasites that feed on the blood of mammals and birds. Wings are absent, but vestigial front wings are usually present. The body is decidedly flattened dorsoventrally so that the bugs may readily hide in cracks and crevices. The beak is three-segmented, and ocelli are absent. About 30 species have been described and of these, eight are found in North America.

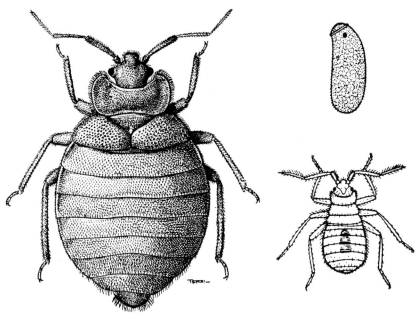

FIG. 105. The bed bug (*Cimex lectularius*); adult male, nymph and egg (not all of the same magnification). (From McKinney-Hughes and Johnson, Courtesy of British Museum of Natural History.)

The common bed bug (*Cimex lectularius*, Fig. 105) is an old and unwelcome guest of man. It is reddish-brown, ovate, about ⅕ inch long, and possesses a distinctive odor. The insect is nocturnal and is known to feed only at night. Besides man, other common hosts are rats, mice, and poultry. Chicken houses and coops may become infested as with the fowl tick.

The bed bug is capable of living for a year without food. It may crawl from one apartment to another or to another house in close proximity. Incipient infestations are usually established by bringing the insect into the home in clothing, hand bags, and other articles.

The bed bug reproduces rapidly. A female lays 200 to 500 eggs during a period of two to three months. When conditions are favorable a life cycle can be completed in six to eight weeks. Three or four generations in a year are possible.

Since the bed bug is a common parasite of man it has been carefully studied as a possible vector of human diseases, but it has been found to be an important vector of no disease.

A number of remedies have been employed in bed bug control, but their use has now been superseded by the newer chlorinated hydrocarbon insecticides. The bed, together with the springs and mattress, should be thoroughly sprayed with DDT household spray. The cracks and crevices of the woodwork of the room should also be treated. Chlordane is also efficient in bed bug control, but its toxicity to man is greater than DDT.

A counterpart of the common bed bug is the tropical bed bug (*Cimex hemipterous*). Whereas the common bed bug is a cosmopolitan form, the tropical bed bug is confined more or less to tropical regions. It is common in India and Africa, and is also found in Jamaica and Brazil.

The poultry bug (*Haematosiphon inodorus*) infests poultry houses in Mexico and the southwestern part of the United States. *Oeciacus vicarius* infests the nests of swallows, and *Cimexopsis nyctalis* feeds on chimney swifts.

Several families of Hemiptera are aquatic or semiaquatic in habit. With the exception of most water boatmen (Corixidae), all are predaceous forms. These aquatic families are of little economic importance and only a few of the more common and more interesting families will be mentioned here.

Family *Corixidae* (Water Boatmen)

Water boatmen (Fig. 106B) are found particularly in fresh water where an abundance of vegetation grows. They are oval and flattened dorsally. The hind legs are long, flattened, and fringed with bristles, and are adapted for swimming. These insects can remain submerged even in impure water for awhile by enveloping most of the body surface with a bubble of air. Air is also collected in a depression underneath the wings.

Water boatmen feed in ooze at the bottom of streams and ponds, on algae and diatoms—a few forms feed on small animal life. Eggs

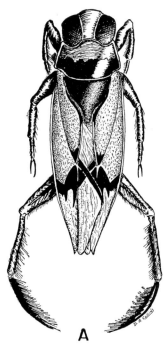
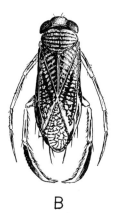

A   B

FIG. 106. **A,** A backswimmer *(Notonecta undulata)* . **B,** A water boatman *(Arctocorixa alternata)* .

are laid on stems of submerged plants. One species, at least, deposits its eggs on the body and appendages of crayfishes. Dispersion is by flight, and members of the family are often attracted to lights in large numbers.

Family *Notonectidae* (Backswimmers)

The backswimmers are easily recognized by the peculiar habit of swimming on the back and by the long oar-like legs (Fig. 106A). The back of the insect is keel-shaped like the bottom of a boat, which results in the body being relatively thickened. These insects may leave the water by flight, as do the water boatmen.

Backswimmers are predaceous and feed on small animal life such as insects, Crustacea, and newly hatched fish. Members of the family are relatively small insects but have a powerful beak and may inflict painful bites when carelessly handled.

Family *Gerridae* (Water Striders)

Water striders (Fig. 107**B**), known as Jesus bugs in some communities, are small, elongate, and long-legged insects. They are

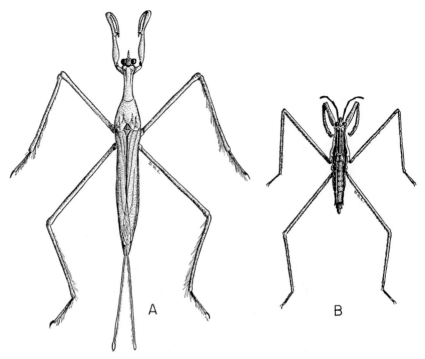

FIG. 107. **A,** A water scorpion *(Ranatra fusca)*, **B,** A water strider *(Gerris nyctalis)*.

commonly seen running around or resting on the surface of ponds and other bodies of still water. They feed on dead insects and others they may catch. Both winged and wingless insects of the same species exist.

The genus *Halobates* consists of species that live on the surface of seas. These are the only truly salt-water inhabiting insects. They are most common in the calms of tropical regions.

Family *Nepidae* (Water Scorpions)

Water scorpions (Fig. 107**A**) can be recognized by the long respiratory tube on the end of the abdomen. The tube is formed by the two cerci which are grooved on the inner face and applied closely together. This respiratory apparatus permits the bugs to feed on the bottom of shallow pools and obtain air from the surface. The insects are predaceous and the front legs are modified for grasping the prey. Although aquatic in habitat, the second and third pairs of legs are modified for walking and not for swimming. The body of members of the family may be almost linear, as in the genus

Ranatra, and oval in other genera. The species of Ranatra resemble walking sticks somewhat in appearance. Eggs are embedded in aquatic plants. Wings are fully developed but the insects seldom fly. The ability to inflict painful bites when handled probably suggested the common name.

Family *Belostomatidae* (Giant Water Bugs)

This family includes some of the largest insects of the order (Fig. 108). A South American species is about four inches in length. They are most commonly found in bodies of shallow water which contain an abundance of plant life. Members of this group are brown, broad, and flat, with the front legs fitted for grasping of prey.

Giant water bugs feed on insects, tadpoles, snails, and small fish. They will bite when handled and their bites

FIG. 108. A giant water bug (*Lethocerus americanus*). (From Department of Entomology, A & M College of Texas.)

are quite painful. These insects fly at night; they are often seen around lights and are known as electric light bugs in some sections. Females of certain species deposit their eggs on the back of the males where they remain until hatched.

15

ORDER HOMOPTERA[1]

APHIDS, SCALE INSECTS, LEAFHOPPERS, AND OTHERS

Chief characteristics of the order are:

1. **When present, two pairs of wings (male scale insects excepted) of the same texture throughout and when at rest usually held roof-like over the body. Many wingless forms occur.**
2. **Mouthparts (not always present) of piercing-sucking type, arising from the underside of the head near the prothorax.**
3. **Gradual metamorphosis excepting male scale insects and white-flies.**
4. **Excretion of honeydew common to many members of the order.**

The order Homoptera is comprised of a heterogeneous group of insects. They range in size from minute forms to individuals two or more inches long. Many members are wingless. When wings are present, they are of uniform thickness throughout, though in some species the front pair may be subcoriaceous in texture. The wings are held sloping over the body, like the roof of a house, when not in use. The male scale insect has only one pair of wings in contrast to the two pairs of other winged members of the order.

Mouthparts are for piercing and sucking, as are those found in the Hemiptera. In contrast with the mouthparts of the Hemiptera, which arise near the front of the underside of the head, they arise far to the rear near the prothorax. In those members that do not partake of food in the adult stage, e.g., the male of scale insects, mouthparts may be absent.

Metamorphosis is gradual as with the true bugs. However, the white-flies (*Aleyrodidae*) and males of scales (*Coccidae*) have a

[1] *Homos,* same; *pteron,* wing.

quiescent stage prior to the emergence of the adults, comparable to the pupa in complete metamorphosis. So metamorphosis of these members is not gradual nor may their development be considered wholly holometabolous, but probably intermediate between the two types.

Many members of the Homoptera excrete a sweet substance known as honeydew. This material drops on the leaves, stems, bark, and fruit of the plants where it dries. When the insects are in abundance, honeydew may be excreted so copiously that the foliage may drip with it. A sooty mold grows in this medium producing a blackened appearance. Ants and honey bees feed on honeydew avidly. Some most interesting biological relationships have developed between ants and aphids where the ants protect and care for the aphids to secure the honeydew they excrete.

KEY TO FAMILIES OF HOMOPTERA

1. Wings present although occasionally reduced to scales   2
   Wings absent   10
2. Only 1 pair of wings present (Males of Scale Insects)   **Coccidae,** p. 218
   Two pairs of wings present   3
3. Three ocelli present; large insects (Cicadas)   **Cicadidae,** p. 200
   Two ocelli present or absent   4
4. Pronotum extending posteriorly over abdomen (Treehoppers)   **Membracidae,** p. 202
   Pronotum not extending posteriorly over abdomen   5
5. Antennae located on cheeks below eye (Lantern Flies)
        Fulgoridae.
   Antennae located between eyes on front of head   6
6. Tarsus 3-segmented   7
   Tarsus 1- or 2-segmented   8
7. Hind tibia with scattered stout spines except apex which
   bears crown of spines (Spittlebugs)   **Cercopidae,** p. 201
   Hind tibia with double row of spines (Leafhoppers)
        Cicadellidae, p. 203
8. Wings white, covered with fine powdery wax (White Flies)
        Aleyrodidae, p. 215
   Wings transparent or patterned; not covered with powdery
   wax   9
9. Jumping insects; abdomen never with cornicles; antenna
   with 7 to 10 segments (Jumping Plant Lice)   **Chermidae,** p. 205
   Walking insects; abdomen usually with cornicles; antenna
   with 3 to 7 segments (Plant Lice or Aphids)   **Aphidae,** p. 206
10. Body covered with hard shell, scale, or waxy secretions;
    tarsus, when present, 1-segmented (Scale Insects)   **Coccidae,** p. 218

Body never covered with shell or scale, and seldom with
waxy secretions; abdomen usually with cornicles; tarsus
2-segmented (Plant Lice or Aphids)   **Aphidae, p.** 206

Family *Cicadidae* (Cicadas or Harvest Flies)

These insects (Fig. 109) are probably better known in the United
States as locusts than by any other name. This is a misnomer. The
term locusts, correctly used, refers to migratory species of grasshoppers. The name was given them by early settlers in the eastern

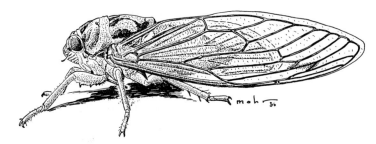

FIG. 109. A common cicada (*Tibicen pruinosa*). (Courtesy of C. O. Mohr.)

states when they observed swarms of the periodical cicada (*Magicicada septendecim*). These swarms of cicadas or harvest flies reminded
them of locusts (grasshoppers) of the Old World.

The harvest flies and the shrill notes of their males are a part of
summer and its long sultry days. One with a trained ear and acute
hearing may differentiate the various species by their songs. Sound
is produced by complicated vibratory organs located at the base of
the abdomen on the ventral side of the body.

Harvest flies are generally large with a large blunt head and a
subconical body; however some species are rather small. Eyes are
prominent and are located on the outer angles of the head. The
three ocelli are prominent and are triangularly arranged between
the eyes.

The only discernible injury produced by cicadas is the oviposition
punctures of the females in twigs of shade, forest, and fruit trees.
Serious damage to fruit trees may be done by the periodical cicada.
Twigs and sometimes small trees are killed. Eggs deposited in these
punctures hatch and the nymphs drop to the ground. They enter
the soil and feed on the sap of roots of trees. The length of a life
cycle is one, two, or more years, depending upon the species and the

climate. The periodical cicada (*Magicicada septendecim*) has a life cycle requiring 17 years for development in the northeastern states. A race of this species develops in 13 years in the South. Its range extends westward to Kansas and Nebraska. Specimens have been taken on rare occasions in east and northeast Texas. The species is black with reddish legs, wing veins, and eyes; and about one inch in length. A blackish W is discernible near the apex of the forewings. The appearance of a brood of these insects with the W on the front wings was thought to presage war by superstitious people of the Southeast.

Family *Cercopidae* (Spittlebugs)

A white frothy mass of material is often observed on weeds, grass, and shrubs during the summer months. Within this mass may be found the nymph of a spittlebug. It lives here until the adult stage is reached. This froth is formed by a fluid voided from the anus of the nymph in which is mixed a mucilaginous substance excreted by hypodermal glands and into which air bubbles are incorporated. The purpose of the frothy covering is to provide a moist environment and to protect the insect from its enemies. The adults are dark and small. These insects usually hibernate in the egg stage and produce only one generation annually.

The meadow spittlebug (*Philaenus leucophthalmus*, Fig. 110) is the common representative in the eastern part of the country. Its common

FIG. 110. The meadow spittlebug (*Philaenus leucophthalmus*). (From Ohio Agricultural Experiment Station.)

hosts are a wide variety of meadow and garden plants, and weeds. Heavy infestations seriously affect the yield of hay crops. Satisfactory control of the insect is obtained by spraying with BHC.

Family *Membracidae* (Treehoppers)

The pronotum of treehoppers extends posteriorly over the abdomen and in some species completely covers the wings. The presence of lateral and vertical prolongations of the pronotum often results in giving many species an odd appearance. These insects are sometimes referred to as the clowns of the insect world.

Treehoppers are found on trees, shrubs, grasses, and other plants. Their food is the juices of plants; however, most species never become sufficiently abundant to become pests of economic importance. The buffalo treehopper (*Stictocephala bubalus*) is the best known and most widely distributed member of the family (Fig. 111). It becomes a pest of nursery stock and young fruit trees

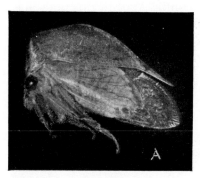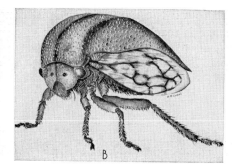

FIG. 111. **A,** The buffalo treehopper (*Stictocephala bubalus*). (From Agricultural Research Service, U.S.D.A.) **B,** The three-cornered alfalfa hopper (*Spissistilus festinus*). (From Texas Agricultural Experiment Station.)

through injury produced by numerous egg punctures in the stems of young plants. Injury through feeding of the nymphs and adults is negligible. The insect is about ⅓ inch long, green or yellow with short stout horns on the pronotum.

The three-cornered alfalfa hopper (*Spissistilus festinus*) is often an important pest of alfalfa. Injury is produced by the insect girdling the stems with its feeding punctures. The insect also attacks other legumes, weeds, and fruit trees. It is about ⅕ inch in length, bright green in general color and without pronotal horns. Winter is passed in the adult stage. Four or five generations may develop annually in warm climates. Malathion and sevin are recommended in the control of this pest.

Family *Cicadellidae* (Leafhoppers and Sharpshooters)

This is a large family of small elongate insects. The most characteristic feature of the family is the double row of spines on the hind tibiae. As the name leafhopper implies, these insects are alacritous hoppers. Both nymphs and adults have the habit of running sidewise. Leafhoppers are usually about ¼ inch in length and of variable colors with some species very beautifully marked. They may become extremely abundant and do considerable damage to a wide variety of field crops, fruits, shrubs, and other plants. Injury results not only in feeding but also in the transmission of plant diseases. Leafhoppers produce from one to four generations annually. Some of the more common species overwinter as adults; others hibernate in the egg or nymphal stages; while in the Gulf Coast states reproduction of some forms may continue throughout the winter with a migration of the winged forms northward in the spring.

Probably more than 1,000 species of leafhoppers occur in North America. Although a number are of economic importance, only a few can be mentioned here. The potato leafhopper (*Empoasca fabae*, Fig. 112A) is one of the most common and best known pests

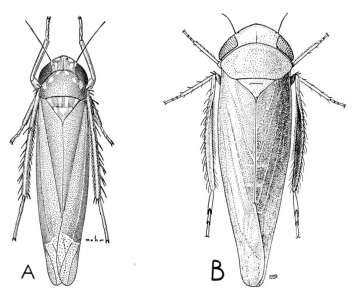

FIG. 112. **A,** The potato leafhopper (*Empoasca fabae*). (From Illinois Natural History Survey. Drawn by C. O. Mohr.) **B,** The beet leafhopper (*Circulifer tenellus*). (From Utah Agricultural Experiment Station.)

of this family. It is a small green leafhopper, wedge-shaped, and about ⅛ inch long. A row of six rounded light spots is found along the anterior margin of the pronotum. The insect attacks potatoes, beans, alfalfa, apple trees, peanuts, and other plants. A disorder known as tipburn or hopperburn is produced on potatoes. The cause of this trouble has not been fully explained. Stunting, crinkling, and curling of the leaves are characteristic injuries on beans and apples. Alfalfa leaves turn yellow when the plants are attacked. A diseased condition known as "peanut pouts" is caused by infestations of the insect on peanuts. The potato leafhoppers apparently do not winter in the North in any stage and migrate from the Gulf States, where it breeds throughout the year. DDT dusts or sprays will control the insects. The use of toxaphene, malathion and methoxychlor are also satisfactory for control.

The Grape Leafhopper (*Erythroneura comes*).   This insect is a widespread and consistent pest of grapes. Besides grapes, it attacks Virginia creeper, apple, and other plants. The foliage of infested plants assumes a grayish cast and later the leaves become shriveled and brown. Both quantity and quality of the fruit are affected. When infested plants are examined, countless numbers of the pale yellow insects with red or black markings are found. The pest hibernates as an adult in fallen leaves and other trash. Only one generation of the insect annually may be developed in its northern range while there may be three in the southern states.

Destruction of leaves, grass, and other trash around vineyards will eliminate many of the overwintering adults of the grape leafhopper. DDT sprays or dusts applied prior to setting of fruit will effectively control the insect.

The Beet Leafhopper (*Circulifer tenellus*).   This leafhopper (Fig. 112B) is the vector of a virus disease of sugar beets known as "curly top." It is a serious disease of the crop and it has caused the abandonment of the growing of sugar beets in some localities. The insect is also a vector of tomato yellows. The small yellowish-green insect overwinters on Russian thistle, wild mustard, and other plants from which the first generation may migrate to beet fields hundreds of miles away. There may be several generations annually. DDT sprays and dusts will readily control the insect but it is difficult to prevent transmission of the disease. Varieties of sugar beets with a measure of resistance to the leafhopper have been developed. Destruction of winter host plants has met with success in some sections.

Several species of leafhoppers, called sharpshooters (Fig. 113), are commonly found on the cotton plant. The most important is a large dark form (*Homalodisca triquetra*) which is also found on okra, various weeds, and trees. Damage caused by the feeding of these insects on cotton has been shown to be minor.

Family *Chermidae* (Jumping Plant Lice)

The jumping plant lice are quite small; they are less than 1/5 inch in length. They have some resemblance to winged aphids, but they appear more like extremely small harvest flies. They are very active insects, readily jumping or taking flight when disturbed. These insects subsist on plant juices and some species cause the formation of galls.

One of the best known gall-forming species is the hackberry nipple gall (*Pachypsylla celtidis-mamma*). Unsightly galls are formed on the leaves and heavy infestations cause the leaves to drop early. Spraying with nicotine sulphate or DDT early in the season as the galls are beginning to form is suggested as a control measure.

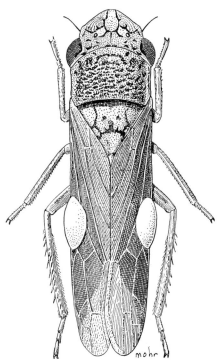

FIG. 113. A sharpshooter (leafhopper) (*Oncometopia undata*). (From Illinois Natural History Survey. Drawn by C. O. Mohr.)

The pear psylla (*Psylla pyricola*) is the most important economic form of this group. It is widespread in the East and it is also an important pest of the pear in the Northwest. Leaves turn brown and are often shed; and, when the trees are heavily infested, the fruit drops prematurely or is of inferior quality. The pear psylla winters as an adult in sheltered places, such as under the bark of trees. There are three to five generations annually. The insect is difficult to control. Several treatments are recommended as control measures. The use of dormant spray oil and summer sprays of toxaphene, malathion and parathion are recommended.

Family *Aphidae* (Plant Lice or Aphids)

Plant lice or aphids are among the more important groups of insects from an economic viewpoint. Growers of nearly all plants will have aphid problems at times. The life histories with the involved life cycles and relationships of many species are intriguing and of much interest.

Aphids are small, delicate, and more or less pear-shaped insects, the largest species are not more than $\frac{1}{4}$ inch in length. Both winged and wingless individuals are found, with the latter the

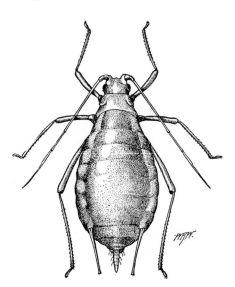

predominant form. Antennae and legs are generally long. Most aphids have a pair of tubes, known as cornicles, projecting upward and backward from the dorsal surface of the abdomen. (See Fig. 114.) They secrete a wax-like substance. It was formerly thought honeydew was excreted by them, but it is now known that this substance is from the anus. Aphids as a group excrete honeydew copiously. This falls on the leaves, twigs, and fruit. A number of insects, particularly ants, feed upon this sweet substance, and a sooty mold grows in it.

FIG. 114. Adult stem mother of the pea aphid (*Macrosiphum pisi*). Note the paired tubes, cornicles, on the abdomen. (From Agricultural Research Service, U.S.D.A.)

In most instances no biological relationship exists between ants and aphids, but in others definite relationships have developed. The best known of these relationships is between the corn-field ant (*Lasius alienus americanus*) and the corn-root aphid (*Anuraphis maidiradicis*). These aphids are dependent on the ants for care and protection, and in turn the ants are repaid for their services in honeydew as food.

Much variation is found in the biology of aphids. However, there are certain general biological facts that may be applied to the group as a whole. Aphids usually reproduce parthenogenetically (asexual reproduction) and by giving birth to living young (ovoviviparous reproduction). With some exceptions, males and eggs of aphids are unknown in the southern states. In the North, aphids reproduce in the spring and summer as they do in the warmer climates; but with most species a generation of true sexual forms, males and females, appears in the fall. These forms mate and the females lay black, shining, overwintering eggs which hatch the next spring. Conversely, certain species of aphids in the tropics lay eggs to carry the species over the hot dry season.

Most aphids are wingless; winged forms are relatively scarce. In general, only wingless individuals are found when the food supply is adequate and no overcrowding occurs. With deterioration of the host plants or overcrowding the tendency is for the development of winged forms which migrate to other plants. It is true, certain species have a series of wingless generations followed by a winged generation which migrates to another host, but such species are in the minority. Species of aphids are usually rather restricted in their host plants, feeding on a group of more or less related plants. Some species have alternate hosts on which they are found at different seasons.

Aphids have the highest reproductive potential of any insect. For example, under greenhouse conditions the cotton aphid (*Aphis gossypii*) may complete a maximum of 51 generations in a year, with each adult producing about 85 young. In the Gulf coast region, the turnip aphid (*Rhopalosiphum pseudobrassicae*) may produce a maximum of 35 to 46 generations annually with each adult reproducing 50 to 100 young. Under the above conditions all of these aphids are females. These examples probably represent those known forms with the highest reproductive rate—aphids as a group normally may not increase so rapidly. But, under conditions favorable for the insects, any species may be considered as a potential pest.

Aphids are normally held in check by natural factors. The more important of these are adverse weather conditions such as low temperatures and beating rains, fungus diseases, and insect predators and parasites. The most beneficial insect enemies are lady beetles, syrphus fly larvae, aphis lions, and small wasp-like braconid parasites of the subfamily *Aphidiinae*.

Those crops most susceptible to aphid injury should be carefully checked during those periods when infestations most commonly occur; or else, because of the rapid rate of reproduction, major damage may result before control measures can be used. Nicotine sulphate sprays and dusts have been generally used in the past in aphid control. Rotenone is also an efficient aphicide on vegetable crops. Some of the more recently developed insecticides that are efficient are lindane, parathion, tetraethyl pyrophosphate, and malathion. Some of the systemic poisons, such as demeton, are efficient. Precautions in the use of these insecticides must be observed.

The Cotton Aphid (*Aphis gossypii*).   The cotton aphid (Fig. 115) is of world-wide distribution. It attacks cotton and melons wherever

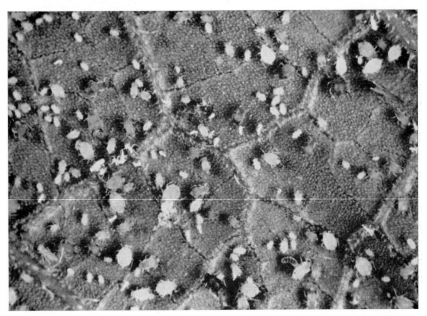

Fig. 115. A colony of cotton aphids (*Aphis gossypii*) on cantaloupe leaf. (From Department of Entomology, A & M College of Texas.)

they are grown. In addition, it seriously injures other cucurbits, okra, and citrus. Cowpeas, beans, beets, eggplants, strawberries, and many weeds also serve as hosts.

The cotton aphid injures plants by sucking sap from the stems and foliage, and by the excretion of honeydew. Another type of injury to cotton is caused by honeydew falling on open bolls which lowers the grade of the lint.

Light and dark phases of the cotton aphid are found with the latter the predominant form. The light phase is yellowish-green; the dark phase is black, brown or dark green. There are no distinct broods of the cotton aphid. The length of a life cycle depends upon weather conditions. Sexual maturity is reached in four to ten days. The reproductive period is about three weeks and the average length of life of an adult is approximately a month. A maximum of 51 generations may be completed in one year with each female producing about 85 young under greenhouse conditions.

Several insecticides will effectively control the cotton aphid when they are properly applied. Dust or spray applications of nicotine sulphate, rotenone, malathion and parathion are recommended for use on truck crops. Demeton, methyl parathion, and parathion are in common use to keep the pest in check on cotton.

The Turnip Aphid (*Rhopalosiphum pseudobrassicae*). The turnip aphid (Fig. 116) is probably the most destructive insect attack-

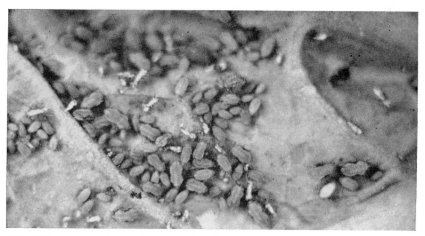

FIG. 116. The turnip aphid (*Rhopalosiphum pseudobrassicae*). (From Department of Entomology, A & M College of Texas.)

ing turnips, mustard, and radishes in the warmer climates. This widely distributed insect is rarely observed during the summer months in the southern states. It appears in the fall on cruciferous plants with the advent of cool weather. Reproduction is rapid and damaging numbers of the insect are reached soon if the pest is not checked by cold weather or other factors. In late spring the insect tends to disappear with the multiplication of its natural enemies or the deterioration of the host plants.

The turnip aphid is about $\frac{1}{16}$ of an inch in length and colored light to dark green. Wingless and winged forms may be present on plants, with the former predominant. Sexual maturity is reached in ten to twelve days and the reproductive period extends over a period of 20 to 30 days. Reproduction is rapid with a maximum of 35 to 46 generations and 50 to 100 offspring produced by each female.

A number of parasitic and predaceous insects prey upon the turnip aphid. In warm moist weather fungus diseases may almost eradicate it. Although these factors are very helpful, insecticidal control is necessary for the successful production of crops. Rotenone and nicotine dusts applied at intervals of ten days will prevent infestations. Malathion, parathion, and other synthetic organic compounds are also efficient in the control of the pest, but precautionary measures must be carefully observed to prevent harmful residues.

The Cabbage Aphid (*Brevicoryne brassicae*).   The cabbage aphid and the turnip aphid are quite similar in general appearance and were not recognized as different species for many years. The two species may be most readily separated by the appearance of the colonies. Colonies of the cabbage aphid are covered by a conspicuous waxy bloom which is absent in the turnip aphid. The cabbage aphid attacks the same group of plants as the latter species, but it is more frequently found on cabbage, collards, and rape.

The number of generations and the rate of reproduction appear to be similar to that of the turnip aphid; however the cabbage aphid is somewhat more difficult to control. Thorough and timely applications of dusts or sprays containing malathion, parathion, or diazinon are recommended in control of the insect. Young infested cabbage and collard plants may be dipped in nicotine sulphate and soapy water before transplanting. Crop residues should be destroyed as an aid in the prevention of subsequent infestations.

The Greenbug (*Toxoptera graminum*).   This aphid is one of the most destructive pests of wheat and other small grains in the Southwest. This old-world insect was introduced into the United States many years ago. It is now found in most parts of the United States and Canada. Most damage is done in the grain-growing states west of the Mississippi River, particularly in Kansas, Oklahoma, Texas, and Nebraska.

The favorite host plants of the greenbug are wheat, oats, and barley, but the insect will also attack corn, rice, sorghum and other cultivated plants of the grass family, and many native grasses.

Outbreaks do not occur every year due to a complex of weather and other natural control factors. When widespread outbreaks of the insect occur, enormous losses may result.

First indications of the presence of the greenbug in late fall, winter, or early spring are spots of bare ground bordered by yellow dying plants in the grain field. If conditions are favorable for the insect, these spots enlarge and entire fields may be destroyed in the spring.

The most critical period in the seasonal history of the insect is during the summer months. If the weather is hot and dry, there will be few volunteer oat and wheat plants or other hosts to tide the insect over this critical period. Cool, wet summer months provide adequate host plants. When small grain is growing in the fall, winged forms migrate to the grain fields. Reproduction continues at temperatures as low as 40° F. Warm, dry winter weather is favorable for the insect's multiplication. The most important natural enemy of the greenbug is the small hymenopteron parasite, *Lysiphlebus testaceipes*. This parasite is not active at temperatures below 65° F. Late cool spring months may hold it in check but permit the greenbug to reproduce in great numbers and destroy large areas of wheat and oats. Thus, cool, wet summers; mild, dry winter months; and cool springs favor outbreaks. While hot, dry summer months; cold, winter weather; and early springs tend to prevent infestations.

The pale green wingless females are about $\frac{1}{16}$ inch in length. They have a dark green stripe down the back and have black tarsi (feet). The winged females may be recognized by the discoidal vein of the forewing with but one branch.

North of the thirty-fifth parallel the pest overwinters in the egg stage. In warmer climates the insects breed continuously throughout the year and eggs are never laid. Each female gives birth to 50 or 60 young on an average. There may be 20 or more generations annually.

Greenbug infestations do not occur sufficiently often to warrant regular control programs. The destruction of volunteer grain, especially oats, during the summer months is recommended, as this practice tends to minimize chances of infestations of fall-planted grain. The grazing of infested fields to obtain some benefit out of the crop and later plowing it under and planting other crops is sometimes advisable. Crops growing in dry soil are more severely injured than when grown under moist conditions.

Both parathion and methyl parathion are recommended for

control of the greenbug. These sprays should be applied when the temperature is not lower than 50° F. Parathion should not be applied within 15 days of harvest or feeding. The recommended precautions must be taken in the applications of these compounds.

The English grain aphid (*Macrosiphum granarium*) may be associated with the greenbug in the grain fields. Infestations of this insect tend to be more widespread over the fields and usually are not confined to spots. The English grain aphid may be distinguished from the greenbug in the winged forms by the presence of two branches in the discoidal vein instead of only one as is found in the front wings of the latter species. The biology of this insect is similar to that of the greenbug. Should the natural enemies fail to control the pest, insecticidal control as recommended for the greenbug may be employed.

The Pea Aphid (*Macrosiphum pisi*).   The pea aphid (Fig. 114) is a green, long-legged insect infesting field and garden peas, vetch, clover, alfalfa, and other leguminous plants. When plants are heavily infested their white cast skins may litter the ground. These insects cause the plants to wilt, and bronze-colored patches appear throughout the field. Flower heads of vetch and other crops are attacked and the seed crops may be destroyed or greatly reduced.

The pea aphid overwinters in the northern states either in the egg stage or as ovoviviparous females, and further south reproduction continues throughout the year. Each ovoviviparous female gives birth to 50 to 100 young. Seven to 20 or more generations may occur within the course of a year.

The pea aphid is held in check by adverse weather conditions, parasites, predators and fungus diseases. When conditions are favorable, it increases in large numbers.

In control of this pest several insecticides may be employed. Rotenone, nicotine sulphate, and malathion may be used, particularly in home gardens. In commercial plantings demeton sprays, and parathion sprays and dusts are recommended for use. Parathion is frequently used also in protection of seed crops of vetch. The two latter compounds should be applied only by trained operators.

The Black Pecan Aphid (*Melanocallis caryaefoliae*).   This aphid may produce serious defoliation of pecan trees with the subsequent reduction of the crop of nuts. Infestations most generally occur following sprays for the control of the pecan nut casebearer and the use of Bordeaux mixture. The insect feeds on the foliage and produces bright yellow spots somewhat rectangular in shape. These areas turn brown and if a number of feeding spots are present, the leaflets may drop prematurely.

The mature insect is about $\frac{1}{16}$ inch in length, and dark green with a series of prominent black humps on the back and sides of the body. The insect is quite agile and jumps when disturbed. Winter is passed as small black eggs deposited in the crevices of the bark. Normally about 15 generations occur during the year, with each ovoviviparous female producing 50 to 100 living young.

Satisfactory control is rather difficult; however, sprays of malathion and parathion provide adequate control if properly applied.

The Woolly Apple Aphid (*Eriosoma lanigerum*).   The woolly apple aphid is of world-wide distribution and it is a pest of the apple wherever the fruit is grown. The presence of the aphid is indicated by white cottony masses which conceal clusters of the purplish insects. The trunks, branches, foliage, and roots of the apple, mountain ash, pear quince, and elm are attacked. In the northern states winter is passed in the egg stage, chiefly on the elm. Clusters or rosettes of leaves of the elms in the spring are caused by the feeding of the insects. A winged generation later migrates from the elm to the apple and other trees; however the insect lives entirely on the apple trees in most of the western states. Chief injury to the apple trees results from the feeding of the aphids on the roots.

Those insects living on the trunks and branches may be killed by spraying the trees with thorough applications of parathion. Applications of paradichlorobenzene around the base of the trees have been found to be successful in the control of the soil-infesting forms. Those practices which tend to keep the trees in vigorous condition, such as fertilization and cultivation, will be of aid in lessening the damage produced by these insects.

The Grape Phylloxera (*Phylloxera vitifoliae*). Species of Phylloxera differ from common plant lice in that both parthenogenetic females and sexually perfect females lay eggs.

The best known and most destructive of all the species of Phylloxera is the grape phylloxera (Fig. 117). This insect is a native of middle and eastern United States, feeding on the native varieties of grapes of these regions. Grapes here have developed partial immunity to their attacks.

The grape phylloxera was introduced into France about 1860 and it destroyed nearly one-third of the vineyards of this country before control measures were found. The insect was discovered in California about the same time it was found in France. It is a serious pest here of the European or vinifera varieties of grapes.

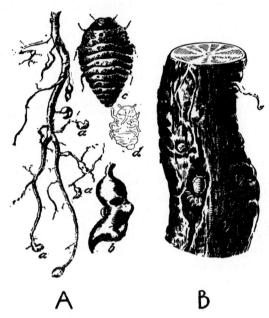

FIG. 117. The grape phylloxera (*Phylloxera vitifoliae*). **A,** a, galls on grape roots; b, enlarged gall with louse feeding; c, adult louse; d, cast skin of nymph. **B,** Root of grape vine showing louse with eggs. (From Agricultural Research Service, U.S.D.A.)

The biology of this insect is rather involved as there are several distinct forms, and both roots and leaves are involved in the injury produced. Hibernation is either as nymphs on the roots or as eggs on the canes. Overwintered eggs hatch in the spring into nymphs which produce small galls in which a number of young are produced. After several generations on the leaves some of the insects drop to the ground, burrow into the soil, reach the roots and produce galls upon them, causing serious injury to the vinifera varieties. Toward the end of the season winged migrants leave the soil and find their way to the vines. The migrants produce a generation of true sexual forms which mate, and each female deposits an egg on the bark of the two-year-old wood. The root-infesting form of the Phylloxera is rare in the East, but this is the only form found on the Pacific Coast.

The most effective control is grafting susceptible European varie-

ties of grapes on resistant rootstock of the middle and eastern sections of the United
States. Most of the grapes sold
by nurseries are grafted on
resistant rootstock. In those
parts of Europe and California where European rootstock
is used, the insect is controlled
by fumigating the soil with
carbon disulphide and by
flooding the vineyards at certain periods of the year.

Several species of the Phylloxera attack the pecan, hickory, and walnut (Fig. 118).
One of the most destructive is
the pecan phylloxera (*Phylloxera devastatrix*). The insect attacks the current
year's growth and produces
galls on leaves. Severe infestations result in heavy defoliation of the trees. The small insects appear in the early
spring and begin to feed on
the unfolding buds. The effects of the feeding cause the
growth of the gall which soon
envelops the insect. Within
this gall large numbers of
young are produced. Later
the gall splits and releases the
insects.

FIG. 118. Galls of *phylloxera* on pecan
twig. (From Texas Agricultural Experiment Station.)

Sprays containing BHC, lindane, or malathion are suggested
for control of the pecan phylloxera. They should be thoroughly
applied as delayed dormant sprays, or until buds show 1 to 2 inches
of growth in the springtime.

Family *Aleyrodidae* (Whiteflies)

The adults are small, four-winged insects about three millimeters
in length. Superficially they bear a resemblance to tiny moths. They

are covered with a waxy powder which is usually white. In contrast with the appearance of the adults, the larvae are small, flattened, oval bodies which resemble early stages of soft scales. Metamorphosis of whiteflies approach the holometabolous type. Eggs hatch into larvae or crawlers which attach themselves to the underside of leaves (Fig. 119). With the first molt the larvae lose their legs and antennae. Following two additional molts, the insects enter a pupal or transformation stage from which the winged adults soon emerge. Whiteflies are tropical or subtropical insects. The injury they produce is similar to that of scale insects and aphids. They suck quantities of sap from the plants and also excrete honeydew copiously. The sooty mold which grows in the honeydew produces a black unsightly appearance on the leaves of infested plants.

FIG. 119. Whitefly larvae and eggs on the underside of a gardenia leaf.

The Citrus Whitefly (*Dialeurodes citri*). The citrus whitefly attacks citrus, gardenia, crepe myrtle, chinaberry, privet, and many other plants. It is an important pest of citrus in Florida and other Gulf States. In its range of distribution all stages of whiteflies may be found throughout the year; however, there is little development during cold weather.

The small, pale yellow and oval eggs of the citrus whitefly are laid on the underside of the leaves to which they are attached by tiny stalks. Under Florida conditions three main generations occur annually.

White summer-oil emulsion sprays thoroughly applied to the underside of the leaves of hardy plants will control this pest. In case of heavy infestations, applications of at least two sprays annually are recommended. Spraying with parathion is a satisfactory control measure, but this insecticide cannot be used around homes because of its toxicity. When numbers of adults are present on gardenias the application of malathion dust will destroy many, reducing subsequent infestations.

The Citrus Blackfly (*Aleurocanthus woglumi*). This is an important pest of citrus. It also attacks mango, coffee, and a large number of other plants which serve as secondary hosts. Injury is through feeding on the sap of the plants and the excretion of honeydew.

The citrus blackfly is a native of the Orient. It is now found in Cuba, West Indies, Central America, Mexico, and in other parts of the world. The minute yellowish eggs have a spine arising from the truncate end which anchors the egg to the underside of the leaf. The larvae are black, oval, convex, and armed with spines. The small four-winged adults are grayish-black. Four generations of the insect are thought to occur annually in Mexico. Each female lays about 100 eggs. In heavy infestations large numbers of eggs may be deposited on a single leaf.

A parasite, *Eretmocerus serius,* and a predator, *Catana clauseni,* together with several other natural enemies, control the pest in most countries where it is found. Oil sprays are recommended for the control of the blackfly. Rotenone in a light-medium oil spray appears quite promising in the control of the pest. DDT sprays have also been recommended.

The Greenhouse Whitefly (*Trialeurodes vaporariorum*). This common pest of greenhouses is found throughout the country. When conditions are favorable outdoor plants are also attacked. It feeds on hibiscus, coleus, begonia, tomato, cucumber, and many other plants. The white adults are less than two millimeters in length. Each female lays about 100 yellowish eggs on the leaves. The eggs are often deposited in a ring. The larvae are small, oval, flattened, and light green. They resemble small soft scale insects. The length of the larval stage is about one month. Several overlapping generations are produced in the course of a year.

Several sprays are recommended in the control of the greenhouse whitefly. Regardless of the spray employed, the application must be thoroughly applied, especially to the underside of the leaves. Applications of nicotine sulphate and soap solutions at weekly intervals for two or three weeks are recommended. White oil emulsion sprays may be used on hardy shrubs. However, applications of this spray at short intervals are not advisable as injury to the plant may result. The use of parathion aerosols are the most successful means of control of whiteflies in a greenhouse.

Family *Coccidae* (Scale Insects and Mealybugs)

These insects are unusual inasmuch as they are so modified in appearance that they do not resemble ordinary insects, with the exception of the adult males, which are winged. They are usually quite small and inconspicuous, and most of them are found on the leaves, stems and fruit, but some species infest the roots of plants. A majority of the species remain immotile at least for a part of their life cycle and they may be transported alive long distances on nursery stock.

More than 2,000 species of scale insects are known. Some of the most important pests of fruit trees, shade trees, shrubs, and plants in greenhouses are found in this group of insects.

The products of certain species have a commercial value. Shellac is a product of the secretions of the lac scale (*Laccifer lacca*). This scale insect is found in India and some neighboring countries. It feeds chiefly on trees belonging to the *Malvaceae* and *Leguminosae* families. Chinese wax is a product of *Ericerus pela*. It is used in the manufacture of candles. Dyes made from the bodies of a cactus scale (*Coccus cacti*) and *Kermes ilicis,* found on oaks, were once rather important.

In scale insects the male has complete metamorphosis while the metamorphosis of the female is gradual. The males begin their development much as the females, but pupate at the end of the developmental period. From the pupae emerge small two-winged flies without mouthparts—the males do not feed in the adult stage. The females remain wingless throughout life and most of them are immotile on the host plants. All species have their bodies covered with a waxy or resinous secretion, a thickened integument, or a waxy scale. Mealybugs and soft scales excrete honeydew.

The biology of scale insects has not been studied adequately except in the more important species, and taxonomy of the family is difficult. Scale insects may be placed for general study into three groups: (1) the mealybugs, (2) the soft scales, and (3) the armored scales. Only a few species can be considered for study here.

The Mealybugs. The mealybugs (Fig. 120) are the least degenerate of all the Coccidae. Legs and the power of locomotion are retained throughout life. The bodies have remained distinctly segmented and the eyes and antennae have not been lost during their

FIG. 120. Mealybugs showing winged males. (From Department of Entomology, A & M College of Texas.)

development. The bodies are covered with a waxy powder which may extend from the sides of the body in cottony threads or plates. Injury is caused in feeding on the sap, and the excretion of honeydew in which a sooty mold grows. Mealybugs generally lay eggs, but in some cases, as with the long-tailed mealybug (*Pseudococcus adonidum*), living young are produced. Eggs are laid in conspicuous sac-like masses of a cottony material secreted by the females.

The Citrus Mealybug (*Pseudococcus citri*). This is the most common species; it attacks greenhouse plants and in warmer climates it is a pest of importance on a large number of hosts—citrus, ornamental, and flowering plants.

Cottony masses of the insects may be found on twigs, foliage, fruit, and under loose bark of the host plants. A female may lay 300 to 600 eggs. The length of the egg stage is a week or longer.

The nymphs develop through three instars, each instar being somewhat more than two weeks in duration during warm weather. At the end of the third instar, the males pupate; from the pupa a two-winged adult later emerges. There are two or three generations annually of this insect; winter may be passed in all stages, but chiefly as eggs.

The Long-Tailed Mealybug (*Pseudococcus adonidum*). The long tailed mealybug is another widely distributed species. The insect has very long anal filaments as its common name implies. This pest is common in greenhouses and also outdoors in warm climates. It attacks a wide range of plants as does the citrus mealybug. This species gives birth to living young, the average number of offspring being about 200.

FIG. 121. The cottony-cushion scale (*Icerya purchasi*) on *Pittosporum*. (From Department of Entomology, A & M College of Texas.)

Mealybugs are very difficult insects to control. Fortunately in the citrus groves of California, biological control with introduced hymenopterous parasites and lady beetles has been very effective; and at the present time other control measures are not usually necessary.

A measure of control of mealybugs on ornamentals and other plants may be obtained by syringing with water, employing as much pressure as the plants will stand without causing injury to them. A spray containing white oil emulsion and nicotine sulphate, repeated in two weeks, will provide fair control. The most effective control in greenhouses is the use of parathion aerosols. All precautionary measures must be taken when parathion is used as this insecticide is highly toxic to human beings. Applications of malathion are also recommended.

The Cottony-Cushion Scale (*Icerya purchasi*). This insect (Fig. 121) is not a true mealybug, but it is more closely related to this group than to the soft scales. It is an important pest of citrus and a wide variety of other plants. At one time it was considered a serious threat to the citrus industry of California. The pest was brought into California in 1868 or 1869 on *Acacia* from Australia. The insect is not a pest in its native home, and investigation showed it was held in check there by a lady beetle, *Rodolia* (*Vedalia*) *cardinalis*. The importation of this lady beetle to California led to its control in this country. This was the first successful introduction of a beneficial insect into a country to control an insect pest. Similar successes have since been attained in the control of other insect pests. Both larvae and adults of the vedalia lady beetle feed upon the pest. The extensive use of insecticides recently has reduced the populations of the predator in some localities. With the resulting increase in infestations of the pest, control with parathion or malathion may become necessary.

The cottony-cushion scale is one of the larger coccids. The insect is brown, red, or yellow-orange and is about six to eight millimeters in length, the egg sac not included. The egg sac is large, elongate, white, and fluted. The most characteristic feature of the insect is the fluted egg sac. Within the egg sac may be

FIG. 122.   A common soft scale, the cottony maple scale (*Pulvinaria innumerabilis*). (From Texas Agricultural Experiment Station.)

found 600 to 800 eggs. Several generations occur during the year.

The Soft Scales.   Soft scales (Fig. 122) are rather large. Their bodies are soft in the nymphal instars; but in the adult females the exoskeleton on the back becomes thickened, tough, and often quite convex. Antennae and legs are not lost during development, and the insects are capable of limited locomotion, but the adult females appear to remain quite sessile. When wax is secreted, it is usually for the formation of an egg sac at the rear end of the body. The soft scales, as the mealybugs, excrete honeydew.

The European Fruit Lecanium (*Lecanium corni*). Several species of soft scales of economic importance belong to the genus *Lecanium*. One of the most common is the European fruit lecanium. It commonly attacks plum, pecan, peach, apple, apricot, pear, grape, and a host of other plants. The scale varies considerably in shape, size, and color. Typical specimens are brown, nearly hemi-spherical in shape, and three to five millimeters in length. Winter is passed in the nymphal stage. The insect grows rapidly when the weather becomes warm. After maturity in the spring the females lay a great number of eggs which fill the cavity beneath the scale. More than 2,000 eggs may be deposited. Only one generation is produced annually.

The terrapin scale (*Lecanium nigrofasciatum*) is another well-known and widely distributed member of this genus. The scale is usually dark brown, semi-hemispherical with somewhat crinkled margins of the body, and three to four millimeters in

FIG. 123. The terrapin scale (*Lecanium nigrofasciatum*). (From Agricultural Research Service, U.S.D.A.)

length (Fig. 123). It attacks peach; plum; apple; and many other common fruits, shrubs, and shade trees. Winter is spent as fertilized females. They reproduce ovoviviparously and begin giving birth to young in the spring. Only one generation annually is produced. Lecanium scales may be controlled with malathion or parathion sprays.

The **Hemispherical Scale** (*Saissetia hemisphaerica*).   This soft scale may become a serious pest in greenhouses and it also attacks avocado, citrus, and other plants. It is hemispherical, shiny brown, and about three millimeters in length. The insect usually reproduces parthenogenetically. Males are rare. Five hundred to 1,000 eggs are produced. There are usually two generations annually. Spraying with either parathion or malathion, or a combination of the two, is recommended for control of this scale.

The **Black Scale** (*Saissetia oleae*).   The black scale is widely distributed and it is an important pest, especially of citrus. The insect attacks a wide variety of other plants as apple, plum, pear, fig, grape, and greenhouse plants. More damage is produced by the excretion of honeydew on the fruit and leaves than by the feeding of the insect.

The black scale is dark brown to black, about five millimeters in length, and has a letter H on its back formed by ridges. The females deposit about 2,000 eggs each. These hatch and the young nymphs usually settle on the leaves and other new growth. While they are partly grown, most of the scales migrate to the branches and twigs. Males are rare, and reproduction is usually by parthenogenesis. One or two generations are produced annually.

In citrus groves the black scale is controlled with oil emulsion sprays or with hydrocyanic acid fumigation. Promising results have been shown with parathion sprays. The black scale may be controlled in greenhouses in the same manner. Also, spraying with nicotine sulphate in soapy water, especially during the hatching period of the scales, is effective. The applications on greenhouse plants should be repeated at 10- to 14-day intervals until the scales are controlled.

The **Armored Scales.**   The armored scales (Fig. 124) constitute the most important group of scale insects. Some of the most injurious pests of fruit trees, shade trees, and ornamentals are armored scales. The bodies have undergone greater modifications than other scales. In general, the scales are smaller; they may be circular, elongate, or thread-like. Females are active only after hatching. When the crawlers once settle on the host plant no further movement occurs. With the first molt legs are lost and antennae reduced.

In armored scales, the small insect is hidden by a protective cover-

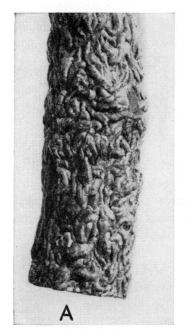
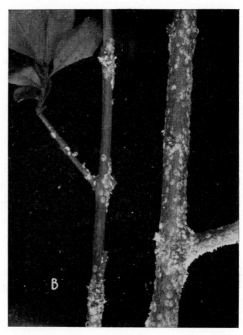

FIG. 124. Common armored scales. **A,** The oystershell scale (*Lepidosaphes ulmi*). (From Agricultural Research Service, U.S.D.A.) **B,** The euonymus scale (*Unaspis euonymi*). (From Texas Agricultural Experiment Station.)

ing. This scaly covering is separate from the body of the insect and it consists of secreted wax within which is incorporated the exuviae (cast skins) of the molts. Another striking characteristic of armored scales is the fusion of the last four abdominal segments into a structure known as the *pygidium*. Identification of armored scales is largely by structures located on the pygidium. Armored scales do not excrete honeydew as do the mealybugs and soft scales.

The San Jose Scale (*Aspidiotus perniciosus*). The San Jose scale (Fig. 125) is the most widely known and one of the most destructive of all armored scales. The native home of the insect is believed to be China and it was introduced into California about 1870, whence it soon spread throughout the country. The insect is also quite widespread throughout other parts of the world.

Peaches, plums, apples, pears, apricots, and many other plants are attacked by the San Jose scale. All parts of the trees except the roots may become infested. Great numbers of deciduous fruit trees die annually from attacks of the pest. The fully grown scales are circular, about $\frac{1}{16}$ inch in diameter, and gray. They have a dark,

FIG. 125. The San Jose scale (*Aspidiotus perniciosus*) on a peach limb. (From Department of Entomology, A & M College of Texas.)

central elevation, the exuviae, surrounded by a yellowish ring. The immature scales are black with a gray spot in the center. This spot is ringed by a black depression which is bordered by gray. Heavily infested limbs assume a gray appearance produced by the overlapping scales.

Winter is usually passed in the nymphal stage; however, in the southern states some reproduction may occur throughout the season unless the weather is unusually cold.

The San Jose scale reproduces ovoviviparously. Each female produces about 400 young. The crawling young disperse over the trees. When a suitable place is found, an insect inserts its mouthparts into the tissues of the bark and does not move again. Five to six weeks later a new generation is begun. The number of generations annually may be from two in the North to six or more in the southern states.

During the crawler stage the insects may be blown over the orchard by the wind, or carried on the feet of birds or bodies of beetles and other insects. Most infestations have arisen from infested nursery stock.

A number of natural enemies prey upon the San Jose scale but its rate of reproduction is so great that it still may increase to damaging numbers. A number of small hymenopterous parasites and lady beetles are the most important natural enemies. The twice-stabbed lady beetle (*Chilocorus stigma*) is the most common lady beetle predator. Either lubricating oil sprays or lime-sulphur will control the San Jose scale, provided the spray is thoroughly applied. The sprays should be applied during the dormant season. Malathion, sevin and parathion are also recommended in the control of the San Jose scale.

The White Peach Scale (*Pseudaulacaspis pentagona*). This insect is often referred to as the West Indian peach scale. It is sometimes injurious to peaches, cherries, privet, and other plants. The mature females are circular, about $\frac{1}{10}$ inch in diameter, and dirty white with brown or yellow exuviae located slightly away from the center of the scale. The males occur in clusters and are usually found at the base of the branches. These are white and elongate in outline. This insect winters as mature females. Four or five generations may occur annually in warm climates.

Lime-sulphur applied as a dormant spray on deciduous trees controls the white peach scale. Lubricating oil emulsion sprays will also control the pest. Parathion sprays have shown promising results in controlling the insect.

The Obscure Scale (*Chrysomphalus obscurus*). This species is an important pest of pecans. The scale also attacks hickory, oak, and other trees. Chief injury resulting from attacks of the insect is the killing of smaller branches and weakening the trees which results in lower yields of nuts. This dark gray scale resembles closely the bark of its host plants. The female scale is $\frac{1}{10}$ to $\frac{1}{8}$ inch in diameter with a black concentric exuviae. The insect winters in the nymphal stage and eggs are produced in the spring. Only one generation occurs annually. Spraying the trees in the dormant season with lubricating oil emulsion sprays will control the scale but the spray must be thoroughly applied.

The California Red Scale (*Aonidiella aurantii*). The California red scale ranks as possibly the most important pest of citrus. In addition to citrus, the insect attacks acacia, fig, willow, rose, grape, and other plants. Injury results from the sucking of sap and also the probable injection of a toxic substance through the mouthparts into the tree. It attacks fruit, stems, leaves, branches, and the trunk of the tree. The female scale is reddish-brown, circular, flat, and about $\frac{1}{12}$ inch in diameter. The exuviae are located in the center and are darker colored.

Each female gives birth to about 150 young. The young emerge and crawl around on the host plant until a suitable place is found.

Mouthparts then are inserted and feeding is begun. The developmental period is usually 10 to 12 weeks. The females produce young over a period of about two months. Males are present; there is no parthenogenesis. A maximum of four generations has been recorded in one year but the average is less.

Spraying with suitable oils has been a standard control measure for this pest for many years. A combination of either parathion or malathion with oil provides effective control. Also parathion and malathion, either alone or in combination, may be employed.

The Florida Red Scale (*Chrysomphalus aonidum*). This important pest of citrus also attacks palm, oleander, holly, ivy, poinsettia, and a number of other plants. In comparison with the California red scale, this scale is slightly larger, convex, and dark reddish-brown. The centrally located exuviae are lighter than the remainder of the body. The scale appears to be adapted to conditions of higher humidity than the California red scale. Therefore, it is not a pest of any consequence in California, but it is important in Florida and other Gulf States.

The life history of the Florida red scale is approximately the same as that of the California red scale except eggs are laid. The Florida red scale is controlled with white summer oil sprays. Parathion sprays are also quite effective. They are recommended for use particularly during the latter part of the summer.

The Purple Scale (*Lepidosaphes beckii*). This is the most important scale insect pest of citrus trees in Florida and the Gulf Coast. It is also a pest of importance in California. Although feeding primarily on citrus, this insect also attacks such plants as avocado, eucalyptus, and fig.

The female scale is oyster-shell shaped, about ⅛ inch long, and brown. The female deposits 40 to 50 eggs underneath the scale covering and it then dies. Upon hatching, the crawlers or nymphs emerge and seek the shady part of the trees where they settle in a suitable place. Two to four generations may occur during the year. The same recommendations are given for the control of the purple scale as for the California red scale.

CHAPTER

16

ORDERS COLEOPTERA
AND STREPSIPTERA

Order COLEOPTERA[1]

Beetles

Characteristics of the Coleoptera are:

1. Wings (rarely absent) two pairs; front pair (*elytra*) greatly thickened and horn-like, and when at rest meet in a straight line down
   the back; hind wings membranous and protected by the front
   pair.
2. Chewing mouthparts.
3. Complete metamorphosis.
4. Bodies usually quite stout.

The Coleoptera, beetles, comprise the largest order of insects.
(See Fig. 126.) More than a quarter of a million species have been
described. Of this huge number, nearly $\frac{1}{10}$ are known to occur in
North America north of Mexico. Most species of beetles are plant
feeders, and there are many important pests of a wide variety of
plants in this order. However, some beetles are predaceous and
others live as scavengers. Most beetles are terrestrial, but some are
aquatic or semiaquatic.

The most distinctive morphological characteristic of beetles is the
structure of the first pair of wings, which are horny veinless sheaths
(*elytra*) and, when the insect is not in flight, are folded to form a

[1] *Coleos,* sheath; *pteron,* wing.

228

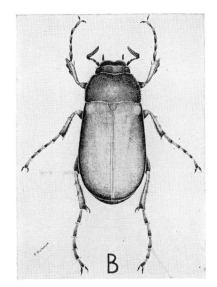

FIG. 126. A May beetle (*Phyllophaga*). **A,** larva. **B,** Adult. (From Department of Entomology, A & M College of Texas.)

straight line down the back. Only the earwigs (*Dermaptera*) have similar front wings, but they may be distinguished from the beetles by a pair of forceps-like appendages on the end of the body. Only the membranous hind wings of beetles are used in flight. When not in use they are folded underneath the front pair.

Beetles are generally stout-bodied. Their exoskeletons are usually thick and strong. Both larvae and adults possess chewing mouthparts which are strongly developed. Some families of beetles have the head prolonged into a snout which may be longer than the entire body. On the end of the snout functional chewing mouthparts are found. This long snout enables the insects to feed on the inner tissues of plants and make deep holes for the deposition of eggs.

Larvae of beetles are commonly known as grubs. They usually have three pairs of thoracic legs; snout beetle grubs are legless. The head is distinct and ordinarily dark in color. The thorax and abdomen usually bear conspicuous spiracles. Pupae are of the exarate type, which means that the appendages are free. Generally both larvae and adults have the same hosts and feeding habits; however, exceptions may be found. In many species of blister beetles the adults feed on the foliage of plants, while the larvae are beneficial since they feed on grasshopper eggs in the soil.

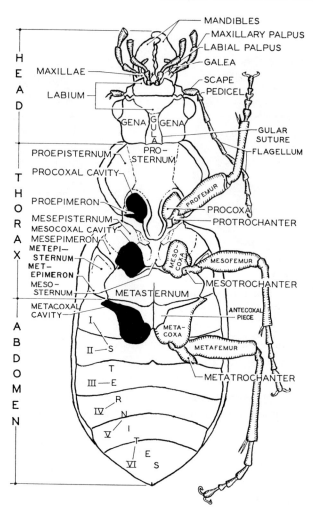

FIG. 127. Ventral view of a ground beetle with principal body parts named. (Courtesy of L. S. Dillon.)

KEY TO COMMON FAMILIES OF COLEOPTERA

1. First abdominal segment divided on the ventral side by the hind coxal cavities (Fig. 127)   2

   First abdominal segment on the ventral side not divided by the hind coxal cavities   5

2. Metasternum with a triangular antecoxal piece, separated anteriorly by a distinct transverse suture and extending posteriorly between hind coxae (Terrestrial Beetles)   3

   Antecoxal piece absent on the metasternum (Aquatic Beetles)   4

3. Antenna inserted between the eye and base of the mandible (Ground Beetles)   **Carabidae**, p. 232

   Antenna inserted above base of the mandible on the front (Tiger Beetles)   **Cicindelidae**, p. 234

4. Compound eye horizontally divided into 2 distinct parts (Whirligig Beetles)   **Gyrinidae**, p. 236

   Compound eye not divided (Predaceous Diving Beetles)   **Dytiscidae**, p. 235

5. Head not prolonged into a snout; 2 gular sutures present; palpi flexible   6

   Head with or without a distinct snout; 1 gular suture present; palpi rigid   23

6. All tarsi with same number of segments   7

   Tarsi variable in number of segments   22

7. Hind tarsus with 3 or 4 segments but apparently only 3-segmented. Small oval predaceous beetles (Lady Beetles)   **Coccinellidae**, p. 247

   Hind tarsus with 5 segments with the small fourth segment concealed by the lobed third   8

   Hind tarsus with 5 clearly defined segments   10

8. Antenna usually longer than elongate body; larvae are wood borers (Longhorned or Roundheaded Wood Borers)   **Cerambycidae**, p. 260

   Antenna short; body usually short and somewhat ovate   9

9. Head not prolonged into beak; elytra usually cover tip of abdomen; larvae and adults feed on foliage of plants (Leaf Beetles)   **Chrysomelidae**, p. 264

   Head prolonged into broad beak; tip of abdomen exposed; larvae normally live in seed of leguminous plants (Pea and Bean Weevils)   **Bruchidae**, p. 272

10. Antenna terminating in lamellate club; the lamellae capable of close apposition (Scarabs or Lamellicorn Beetles)   **Scarabaeidae**, p. 255

   Antenna variable in form but not lamellate   11

11. Elytra short leaving most of abdomen uncovered dorsally; abdomen quite flexible (Rove Beetles)   **Staphylinidae**, p. 236

   Elytra covering most of abdomen dorsally   12

12. Maxillary palpus longer than or nearly equal in length to antenna which is clavate (Water Scavenger Beetles)   **Hydrophilidae**, p. 235

   Maxillary palpus shorter than antenna   13

13. Abdomen with 6 or more segments visible ventrally   14

   Abdomen with less than 6 segments visible ventrally   16

14. Tip of abdomen exposed; not covered by elytra (Carrion Beetles)   **Silphidae** (in part), p. 238

   Tip of abdomen covered by elytra   15

15. Antenna usually serrate and 11-segmented; abdomen with 7 or 8 segments visible ventrally (Fireflies)   **Lampyridae**, p. 237

Segments of antenna usually enlarged apically in compact
club; abdomen with 6 or 7 segments visible ventrally
(Carrion Beetles)   **Silphidae** (in part) , p. 238
16. Femur joined to or near apex of trochanter   17
    Femur attached to side of trochanter   20
17. Antenna inserted on the front; head and pronotum nar-
    rower than wing covers; antenna conspicuous; hairy
    brown beetles; small (Spider Beetles)   **Ptinidae**, p. 254
    Antenna inserted on side of head in front of eye   18
18. Tibia devoid of spurs; small, yellowish-brown to black bee-
    tles; oval and compact in form (Death-watch Bee-
    tles)   **Anobiidae**, p. 254
    Tibia armed with spurs; body elongate   19
19. Body depressed or flattened; small, black or brown beetles
    (*Lyctus* Powder Post Beetles)   **Lyctidae**, p. 254
    Body cylindrical in cross section; head usually deflexed;
    larger, reddish-brown to black (Larger Powder Post
    Beetles)   **Bostrichidae**, p. 254
20. Front coxa conical, prominent; generally small, plump,
    and oval beetles (Dermestids)   **Dermestidae**, p. 241
    Front coxa globular, usually not prominent   21
21. First 2 abdominal segments fused ventrally; prothorax and
    metathorax firmly joined (Metallic Wood Borers or Flat-
    headed Borers)   **Buprestidae**, p. 243
    First 2 ventral abdominal segments not fused; prothorax
    loosely joined to mesothorax (Click Beetles)   **Elateridae**, p. 245
22. Front coxal cavity closed behind; tarsal claws simple
    (Darkling Beetles)   **Tenebrionidae**, p. 250
    Front coxal cavity open behind; tarsal claws cleft (Blister
    Beetles)   **Meloidae**, p. 238
23. Head   prolonged   into   a   distinct   snout   (Wee-
    vils)   **Curculionidae**, p. 275
    Head without distinct snout (Bark Beetles)   **Scolytidae**, p. 283

Family *Carabidae* (Ground Beetles)

This is a large family comprising more than 2,500 species in this
country alone (Fig. 128). Most members of this family are beneficial, preying on other insects in both the larval and adult stages. A
few are harmful, but only rarely does their feeding produce economic damage.

Ground beetles are commonly found running on the ground in
search of prey or hiding under stones, logs, and rubbish. Most of
them feed at night. Their bodies are somewhat flattened; they have
long legs, and are usually dark in color. Some, however, are colored
blue, brown, or green. The elytra of most species are marked with

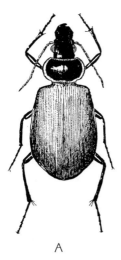
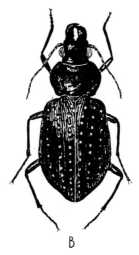

A   B

FIG. 128. Ground beetles. **A,** *Calosoma scrutator*. **B,** *C. calidum*. (Courtesy of L. S. Dillon.)

rows of longitudinal ridges and punctations. The larvae (Fig. 129), which are seldom seen, are elongate, have sharp mandibles, and usually bear a pair of bristle-like appendages on the end of the abdomen.

The most common ground beetles belong to the genus *Harpalus*. A number of species, the adults of which are dark colored, are found in this genus. *Calosoma scruta-tor* is perhaps the most strik-ing native species. It is a large beetle measuring more than one inch in length. Its elytra are violet or green and are bordered with reddish-brown. The body is green, gold, blue, and copper.

The bombardier beetles (*Brachinus*) are interesting in their unusual means of self-

FIG. 129. Larva of a ground beetle feed-ing on a cutworm. (From Agricultural Re-search Service, U.S.D.A.)

defense. At the posterior end of the abdomen are glands that secrete a fluid which, when discharged, changes into a smoke-like gas. This substance has an irritating effect on tender skin. The fluid is ejected with such force that an audible sound is produced, like that made by a tiny popgun. When pursued, the bombardier beetle shoots its astonished attacker in the face and then escapes behind the smoke screen. These beetles are commonly found under rotten logs and in similar environments. They have black or bluish-black wing covers and their bodies are reddish-brown.

Family *Cicindelidae* (Tiger Beetles)

Tiger beetles (Fig. 130) are commonly found along country roads, dusty pathways, and sandy shores of ponds and streams. When approached, they readily take flight and then alight several yards ahead of and usually facing the observer. Most tiger beetles are strikingly

FIG. 130.   Tiger beetles. **A,** *Cicindela purpurea.* **B,** *C. sexguttata.* (Courtesy of L. S. Dillon.)

colored. They are usually blue, bronze, or green and are spotted or marked with yellow or white. Some are dark gray or grayish-white. Their beautiful colors and remarkable color patterns have made these insects collectors' favorites.

Tiger beetles are smaller, more cylindrical, and more brightly colored than ground beetles. Like the latter, both larvae and adults are predaceous on other insects. Most of them are diurnal; however species of certain genera, such as *Tetracha,* feed at night.

The ugly, hump-backed larvae of tiger beetles live in cylindrical vertical tunnels in the soil. They place themselves at the opening of their tunnels to await the passing of their prey, which they seize with their powerful mandibles and readily devour. Children often thrust straws in their burrows, which the larvae grasp. The children attempt to jerk them out, and sometimes succeed. The larvae are sometimes called doddlebugs, but doodlebugs or ant lions are the larvae of a neuropteroid insect which, as adults, superficially resemble damselflies.

Family *Dytiscidae* (Predaceous Diving Beetles)

Predaceous diving beetles (Fig. 131) abound in pools, lakes, and streams. They are shining dark in color, and oval and flattened in outline. They may be distinguished from the water scavenger beetles by their thread-like antennae. The hind legs are long and fitted for swimming. Some of the largest species may approach 1½ inches in length. Both larvae and adults are predaceous, feeding on insects as well as other small animal life in the water, including small fish.

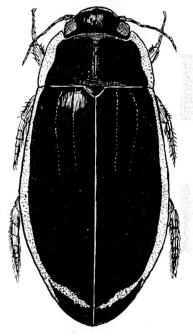

The larvae are rapacious creatures, which characteristic has won them the name of water-tigers. They are elongate and spindle-shaped with a pair of needle-sharp, sickle-like mandibles. They seize their prey, secrete enzymes into the body cavity of the victim and then suck out the body contents through channels in the mandibles.

Family *Hydrophilidae* (Water Scavenger Beetles)

FIG. 131. Predaceous diving beetle (*Dytiscus verticalis*). (Courtesy of L. S. Dillon.)

Members of this family resemble the carnivorous diving beetles but they may be distinguished from them by their club-shaped antennae. They are elongate, oval in shape, and some are as much as two inches in length. These insects are commonly found in quiet bodies of water. Their food consists mainly of decaying plant and animal material, but they feed also on living animals and plants.

FIG. 132. A whirligig beetle (*Dineutes horni*). (Courtesy of L. S. Dillon.)

Family *Gyrinidae* (Whirligig Beetles)

Whirligig beetles (Fig. 132), "apple bugs" or "mellow bugs," are as familiar to a country boy in the South as the sun-flecked swimming pool. These insects are usually seen in groups gyrating, or resting on the surface of still pools. They are agile and difficult to capture. When captured, they may secrete a milky fluid which has the odor of over-ripe apples. Whirligig beetles are bluish-black, oval, and some-what flattened. The compound eyes are divided by the front margin of the head so that the insects appear to have four eyes instead of two. The pair on the underside of the head looks into the water and the upper pair into the air. Both the larvae, which develop in the water, and the adults are predaceous on small insects. The adults have well developed wings and readily fly from one body of water to another. The North American fauna includes three genera of this family, *Dineutes, Gyretes,* and *Gyrinus.*

Family *Staphylinidae* (Rove Beetles)

Rove beetles (Fig. 133) are small elon-gate insects with short wing covers. The largest species are hardly more than ½ inch in length. They run rapidly, and when disturbed lift up the end of the ab-domen in a menacing way as if they were preparing to sting their adversary. Thou-sands of species of this group are known. They are chiefly associated with decaying plant and animal material and are com-monly found around manure piles and similar places. The larvae, which are found in the same environment as the adults, resemble those of the ground

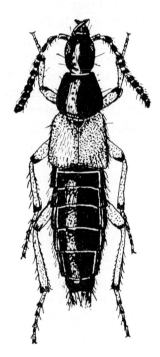

FIG. 133. Rove beetle (*Phi-
lonthus fusciformis*). (Courtesy of L. S. Dillon.)

beetles. A number of species are predaceous; others live with ants and termites in their colonies. As a whole, the family is considered beneficial.

Family *Lampyridae* (Fireflies)

The twinkling light of fireflies (Fig. 134) is first seen in the warm spring evenings. As dusk deepens into darkness, the number of flashes increases. This continues well into the night. These are

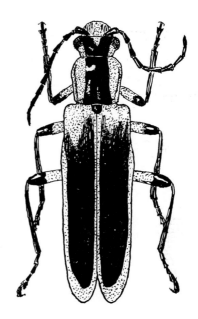

FIG. 134. A firefly (*Photinus pyralis*). (Courtesy of L. S. Dillon.)

FIG. 135. A soldier beetle (*Chauliognathus marginatus*). (Courtesy of L. S. Dillon.)

signals of courtship, and it seems each species has its own code.

The light-producing organs are located on the underside of the abdomen. The light, which is yellow, blue or green, is not continuous but is produced in flashes. This luminescence is produced by the oxidation of a substance known as luciferin in the presence of an enzyme, luciferase. Light production appears to be controlled by the nervous system. Larvae and pupae also produce light but it is continuous. The larvae and the wingless females of certain species are known as glowworms.

Larvae and adults are nocturnal and prey on small, soft-bodied animals. Many adults, however, probably do not feed. The larvae do not devour their food but inject predigestive enzymes into the body of the victim and suck out the partly digested body contents through grooves in the curved mandibles.

The soldier beetles (Fig. 135) belong to a closely related family, *Cantharidae*. These insects are active during the day and feed on pollen of flowers. They do not emit light. *Chauliognathus pennsylvanicus* is a common species often seen on flowers. This is a yellow beetle with a dark area on the thorax and on the apical half of each elytron.

Family *Silphidae* (Carrion Beetles)

Often a dead rat or bird is found in the process of being buried by an insect which burrows underneath and pushes the soil up around it. This is the work of certain species of carrion beetles of the

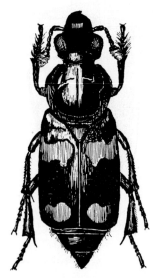

FIG. 136. A carrion beetle (*Necrophorus orbicollis*). (Courtesy of L. S. Dillon.)

genus *Necrophorus* (Fig. 136). Eggs are laid and the larvae develop in the decaying flesh. Carrion beetles are elongate, ranging from ½ to 1½ inches in length. Most of them feed on dead animal matter. However, some live in colonies of ants; others subsist on fungi; and certain species are plant feeders. The family is considered beneficial.

Family *Meloidae* (Blister Beetles)

The blister beetle family is a comparatively small group, represented in the North American fauna by about 300 species. Blister beetles are of medium size and their bodies are cylindrical and relatively soft. Their wing covers are soft and flexible. The prothorax is narrower than the wing covers. The head is narrowed into a neck where it joins the prothorax. Adults of blister beetles feed on plants, and several species are pests of potatoes, tomatoes, eggplants, beans, peas, melons, spinach, carrots, chard, and other cultivated crops. Larvae of many species of blister beetles are beneficial since they feed on grasshopper eggs.

Blister beetles have been given this name because their bodies contain a substance, cantharidin, which has been used as a vesicant. The compound also has properties as a diuretic and a stimulant to the reproductive organs. Cantharidin is obtained chiefly from the dried bodies of a European species (*Lytta vesicatoria*), which is commonly known as the Spanish fly.

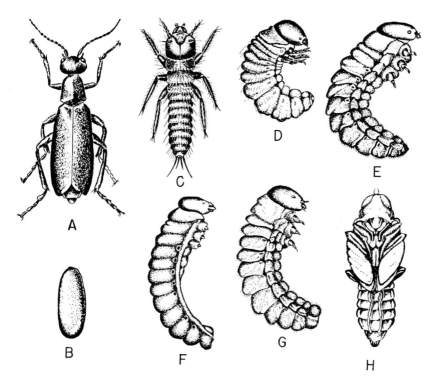

FIG. 137. Stages in the development of the immaculate blister beetle (*Macrobosis immaculata*). **A,** Adult. **B,** Egg. **C,** First larval stage, triungulin. **D,** Second larval stage, caraboid. **E,** Third larval stage, scarabaeoid. **F,** Pseudopupa or coarctate stage. **G,** Last larval stage. **H,** Pupa. (After Gilbertson, from South Dakota State College Agricultural Experiment Station.)

Blister beetles have a rather unusual life cycle in that the larvae appear in a different form after each molt (Fig. 137). This type of development is known as hypermetamorphosis. Females lay 50 to 300 eggs in cavities prepared in the ground. The eggs hatch into active and very agile larvae known as triungulins. The triungulins search for pods of grasshopper eggs. When an egg pod is found, the larva immediately begins feeding. Shortly afterward, it molts into a second stage, the caraboid. The caraboid molts and emerges as a scarabaeoid larva. These are summer stages. The scarabaeoid stage changes in molting to a pseudopupa or coarctate stage. This is the overwintering stage. In the spring the coarctate larva molts into an active stage which prepares a cell in which it soon pupates. The adult emerges about two weeks later. Some species may remain in the soil for one to two years in the coarctate stage. Normally, there is one generation annually, but in the South some species are known to have a partial second generation.

The larvae of some species develop in the nests of solitary bees. In these species, the triungulin climbs a plant and waits on the flowers for a visiting bee. It clings to the bee and is carried to the bee's nest. There it remains in the cell and eats the eggs and the stores provided for the bee larva.

Blister beetles are often called "old-fashioned potato bugs" as they were pests of the potato before the Colorado potato beetle invaded the East. Blister beetles often appear suddenly in fields of tomatoes, potatoes, and other crops in swarms traveling like armyworms.

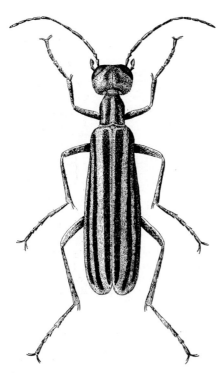

Some of the more important species are the three-striped blister beetle (*Epicauta lemniscata*), the striped blister beetle (*Epicauta vittata*, Fig. 138), the black blister beetle (*Epicauta pennsylvanica*), the spotted blister beetle (*Epicauta maculata*), and the margined blister beetle (*Epicauta pestifera*).

As blister beetles are usually found first in a small part of the field, it may not be necessary to apply insecticides to the entire crop. Cryolite, DDT, or toxaphene dust is recommended for their control. The insecticides should be applied directly upon the beetles as much as possible.

FIG. 138. The striped blister beetle (*Epicauta vittata*). (From Agricultural Research Service, U.S.D.A.)

Family *Dermestidae* (Dermestids)

Dermestids are small, oval, plump beetles. They can be differentiated from beetles with related habits by the wing covers which completely cover the abdomen. The adults are dull colored and are usually marked with brown, reddish, or white scales. The adults of common species feed on the pollen of plants. The larvae are hairy or bristly grubs about 1/4 inch long. They feed on woolens, furs, feathers, bristles, silk, meat, waxes, insect specimens, and many other animal and plant products.

The Larder Beetle (*Dermestes lardarius*). The larder beetle is a common pest of pantries, kitchens, and other places where meat, cheese, and similar products are stored. The adult is about 1/4 inch long and black with a broad yellowish band across the wing covers near the base. The larva is brown and is clothed with long black hairs. It attacks meats, cheese, waxes, and similar oily materials. Eggs are laid directly on the food. The life cycle is completed in about seven weeks.

Cleanliness and close checking of those food materials that are fed upon by this pest should be practiced. Infestations should be eliminated in their incipiency. Meats in cold storage will not become infested. Infestations in cured meat may be eliminated by dipping in hot water and trimming away the infested parts. Hides and skins may be protected by dusting or spraying with DDT.

Carpet Beetles. The larvae of four species of carpet beetles are pests of importance on rugs, upholstery, furniture, padding, clothing, curtains, and other articles. The two most common and most destructive species are the common carpet beetle (*Anthrenus scrophulariae*, Fig. 139) and the black carpet beetle (*Attagenus piceus*, Fig. 140).

The common carpet beetle is about 1/8 inch long, and its color consists of mottled black and white with markings of red along the middle of the back. Adults are often found on window screens. Eggs are laid on the food material of the larvae. Fully grown larvae are brownish plump grubs clothed with black hairs. Injury consists of irregular holes eaten into fabrics, or slits in the carpets along cracks in the floors. The length of a life cycle is from three months to a year, depending upon temperatures and food supply.

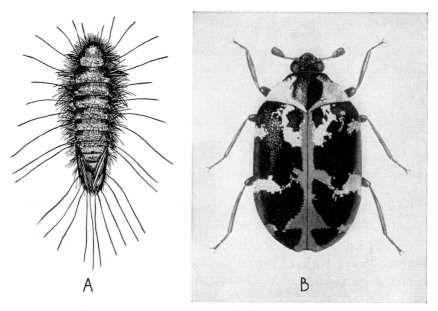

A

B

FIG. 139. The common carpet beetle (*Anthrenus scrophulariae*). **A,** Larva. (From Connecticut Agricultural Experiment Station, New Haven.) **B,** Adult. (From Agricultural Research Service, U.S.D.A.)

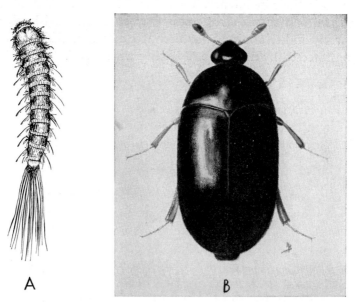

A

B

FIG. 140. The black carpet beetle (*Attagenus piceus*). **A,** Larva. (From Connecticut Agricultural Experiment Station, New Haven.) **B,** Adult. (From Agricultural Research Service, U.S.D.A.)

The black carpet beetle is small, black, and about ⅛ inch in length. Its larva is reddish-brown, slender, and bears a tuft of long reddish hairs on the tip of the abdomen. The life cycle of the black carpet beetle may extend from eight months to more than a year. Adults feed particularly on the pollen of *Spiraea*.

Good housekeeping helps to prevent carpet beetles from becoming established in homes. Old clothing, blankets, and draperies should be discarded, fumigated in tight boxes or chests, or sprayed with DDT or chlordane. Lint and dust should not be allowed to accumulate. Such materials as rugs (Fig. 141) and blankets should

FIG. 141. Carpet beetle larvae feeding on a carpet. (From Agricultural Research Service, U.S.D.A.)

be periodically cleaned and sunned. Should infestations develop, thorough spraying with DDT or chlordane is recommended. Upholstered furniture may be sent to companies to be mothproofed if it is badly infested. Cedar chests may prevent infestations through the repellent action of the cedar oil in the wood, but will not kill the insects. Cedar-lined closets are helpful in preventing infestations, but should not be depended upon entirely.

Family *Buprestidae* (The Flatheaded Borers)

The adults are stout, broad, and hard-bodied. They are generally dark with a metallic luster but some are brightly colored. The larvae are legless grubs, with the thorax broadly flattened. They lie with the abdomen inclined to one side in shallow flat burrows mostly underneath the bark in the cambium and the sapwood of trees. The adults are quite active and fly readily. They prefer sunlight and are usually found on the sunny side of the trunks of trees and the larger limbs. A life cycle is generally completed in a year. Devitalized, dying, and dead trees are usually attacked. Healthy trees are not generally subject to injury by these borers, because the sap repels them.

The Flatheaded Apple Tree Borer (*Chrysobothris femorata*). This widely distributed insect (Fig. 142) is an important pest of fruit, shade, and forest trees. It kills many trees and shrubs each

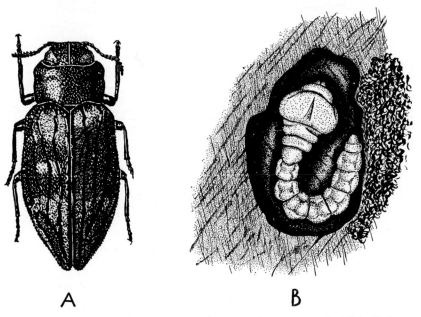

A   **B**

FIG. 142.   Flatheaded apple tree borer (*Chrysobothris femorata*). **A,** Adult. **B,** Larva. (From Agricultural Research Service, U.S.D.A.)

year. Indications of the presence of this insect are brown sawdust pushed out of cracks in the bark, dead areas of bark, exudation of sap, and the broad shallow burrows in the cambium. The fully grown larva or borer is about one inch long with the characteristic yellowish-white color and flattened thorax. The adult beetle is about $\frac{1}{2}$ inch long, dark grayish-brown with a metallic sheen, and with slight depressions on the wing covers.

The insect overwinters as a larva. Pupation occurs in the spring, and the adult emerges a few weeks later. Eggs are laid during late spring and summer usually on unhealthy trees in crevices of the bark or in injured spots. One generation develops each year.

Maintaining trees in a vigorous growing condition is important in preventing infestations of the flatheaded apple tree borer. Trees grown in the proper soil tend to be more thrifty and less subject to attack by this insect. Approved horticultural practices entailing proper cultivation, fertilization, and maintenance of soil moisture should be followed. Low heading of trees to provide more adequate shading of the trunks reduces egg laying as the females prefer to oviposit in the sun. All prunings should be burned. The trunks of recently transplanted trees should be wrapped with heavy paper or burlap. These wrappings should remain through the second season. The borers may be removed with a knife and the wounds painted with a tree paint. Spraying the trunks and larger branches with wettable DDT powder helps to prevent attacks.

Other important species of flatheaded borers are the bronze birch borer (*Agrilus anxius*), Pacific flatheaded borer (*Chrysobothris mali*), and the flatheaded cherry tree borer (*Dicerca divericata*). Their biologies and habits are similar to those of the flatheaded apple tree borer.

Family *Elateridae* (Click Beetles)

Click beetles are elongate, robust insects, somewhat tapered at each end, and usually brownish in color. They are so named because they can suddenly snap their bodies when they are on their backs, and throw themselves in the air with an audible clicking sound in an effort to land on their feet. Because of this habit they are also called skip-jacks or snapping bugs. More than 500 species of click beetles are known in North America. The larvae are known as wireworms because of their body characteristics. They are long, cylindrical, distinctly segmented, and usually yellow or brown. The terminal segment of the abdomen usually bears structural characteristics which are of value in identification of the insects. In most species the larvae are found in the soil, but some live in rotten wood, moss, under bark of trees, and in other environments. The life cycles of click beetles are extremely variable. Some species complete a life cycle in one year; others require five or six years. Winter is passed either in the larval or the adult stage.

The eyed elater (*Alaus oculatus*, Fig. 143) probably has attracted more interest than any other click beetle. It is a large insect about

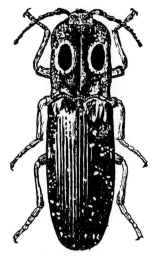

FIG. 143. The eyed elater (*Alaus oculatus*). (Courtesy of L. S. Dillon.)

1½ inches in length, black and dotted with white. Its most striking characteristic is the presence of two large velvety black eye-like spots on the pronotum. The larvae live in decaying wood and are predaceous on other insects.

In the southernmost part of the United States and in the tropics are found species of *Pyrophorus* which bear yellowish "eye spots" near each rear corner of the pronotum. These spots intermittently emit a greenish-yellow light at night. The larvae are also said to be luminous; they are predaceous on white grubs.

A number of species of wireworms (Fig. 144) are injurious to cultivated crops. Seeds of such crops as peas, beans, and corn are destroyed by the larvae. Tubers of potatoes and the roots of tomatoes, watermelons, cotton, corn, turnips, and onions may suffer injury. Cultural practices designed to control wireworms should be suitable for the crops affected. If a field is known to be infested with wireworms and is to be planted to a susceptible crop, it should be plowed during summer and thoroughly cultivated until cold weather to eliminate as many of the insects in the soil as possible. Then for a period of two years, crops that are not seriously attacked, such as clover, should be grown before the planting of the susceptible crop. If the infested land is poorly drained, drainage will be of great aid in eliminating the infestation. Flooding the land in irrigated districts during warm weather is also beneficial. In some cases early planting, fertilizing, and intensive cultivation will pro-

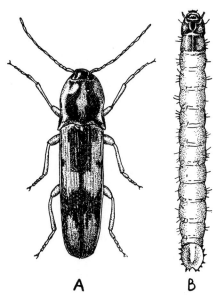

A   B

FIG. 144. The southern corn wireworm (*Monocrepidius vespertinus*). **A,** Adult. **B,** Larva. (From Agricultural Research Service, U.S.D.A.)

duce early and vigorous crops which will not be seriously injured by the pests.

Soil applications of DDT have been found to control certain species of wireworms. The insecticide should be disced into the soil to a depth of six to nine inches. Chlordane, dieldrin, aldrin, and other insecticides have been recommended for use also. Seed treatments with dieldrin, lindane, or heptachlor will afford protection to stands of young grain.

When valuable crops are grown on infested land, the soil may be fumigated. D-D mixture (dichloropropane and dichloropropylene) and ethylene dibromide are efficient fumigants. Equipment is available for the application of these compounds into the soil. Small garden plots may be treated by pouring the desired amount of the product in holes six inches deep made at intervals of 12 inches. Crops should not be planted for two or three weeks following treatment of the soil.

Family *Coccinellidae* (Ladybird Beetles or Ladybeetles)

Ladybird beetles are semi-hemispherical insects and have much the appearance of split peas. They are tan, black, or red, and spotted or marked with contrasting colors of red, yellow, or white. They are rather small, varying in length from $\frac{1}{16}$ to $\frac{1}{4}$ inch. Ladybird beetles often are confused with leaf beetles from which they may be distinguished by the presence of three distinct segments in the hind tarsi, while the latter have four apparent segments. The larvae are elongate, tapering posteriorly. Their general color is dark with bright markings and their bodies are covered with spines. The larvae are sometimes mistaken for aphis lions (lacewing fly larvae) but they lack the large sickle-like jaws of the latter.

With few exceptions, both adults and larvae are beneficial. They are predaceous on aphids; scale insects; spider mites; eggs of a number of insects; and small larvae of many pests, such as the corn earworm and the cotton leafworm. Some conception of the beneficial results obtained from the predatory activities of ladybird beetles may be derived from the fact that larvae have been observed to devour 11 to 25 aphids, and adults 16 to 56 aphids daily.

Ladybird beetles hibernate as adults, often in numbers, in places affording protection and reasonably dry conditions. Their eggs are yellow and are laid on end in clusters. When a larva has completed its development, it attaches itself to some part of the plant upon which it has been feeding or to some nearby object and pupates. It pupates within the slit larval skin or works this skin downward to the end of the abdomen. In a common representative species a female lays 200 to 500 eggs. The length of a life cycle varies with the species and temperature, but it usually is three to four weeks in duration. Since ladybird beetles reproduce rapidly and have voracious habits, they are among the most beneficial of all insects.

The convergent ladybird beetle (*Hippodamia convergens*, Fig. 145) is the most common North American species. It is so named

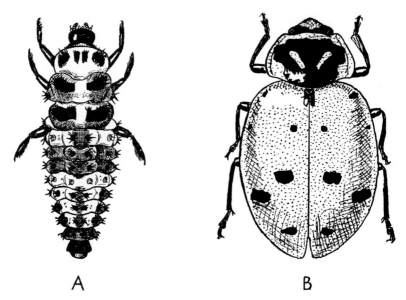

A   B

FIG. 145. *Hippodamia convergens,* the convergent ladybird beetle and larva. **A,** Larva. (From Agricultural Research Service, U.S.D.A.) **B,** Adult. (Courtesy of L. S. Dillon.)

because of two converging light marks on the pronotum. The body color is tan with the elytra spotted with black. This is a large species, measuring about ¼ inch in length. In mountainous regions of the far West the adults often collect in huge numbers for hibernation in protected places.

The genus *Scymnus* includes a number of small black or brown species, measuring about $\frac{1}{12}$ inch in length. The larvae are usually clothed with a waxy secretion and they are often mistaken for mealybugs by the novice. Other common native species (Fig. 146) are the twice-stabbed ladybird beetle (*Chilocorus stigma*), the spotted ladybird beetle (*Coleomegilla fuscilabris*), and the nine-spotted ladybird beetle (*Coccinella novemnotata*).

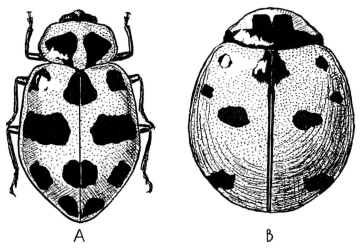

FIG. 146. Two common ladybird beetles. **A,** *Coleomegilla fuscilabris.* **B,** *Coccinella novemnotata.* (Courtesy of L. S. Dillon.)

A number of species have been imported to prey on introduced pests. The best known of these introductions is the vedalia ladybird beetle (*Rodolia cardinalis*), which was brought from Australia to control the cottony-cushion scale (*Icerya purchasi*).

Another introduced ladybird beetle, the mealybug destroyer (*Cryptolaemus montrouzieri*), has been quite successful in controlling mealybugs in California, where it is well established. It has also been reared in insectaries in large numbers and liberated in the citrus groves.

All ladybird beetles are beneficial with the exception of a small number of species in the genus *Epilachna* which are phytophagous in habit. The best known and most destructive pest in this genus is the Mexican bean beetle (*Epilachna varivestis*, Fig. 147). It is an important pest of snap and Lima beans. It will on occasion attack cowpeas, soybeans, and other legumes. The larvae and adults feed on the underside of the leaves, skeletonizing them and giving them a lace-like appearance.

Adults of the Mexican bean beetle are 1/4 to 1/3 inch in length, oval, brown or yellow, with 16 black spots on the wing covers. The full-grown larvae are oval, 1/3 inch in length, and are covered with branching spines tipped in black. Winters are spent as adults in trash or rubbish. After feeding on the young beans in the spring, the adults begin egg deposition. Each female deposits about 500 yellow eggs in batches of 40 or 50 on the underside of the leaves.

FIG. 147.   Eggs, larvae, and adults of the Mexican bean beetle (*Epilachna varivestis*) on bean leaf. (From Agricultural Research Service, U.S.D.A.)

A generation may be completed in about one month. Malathion, methoxychlor, or rotenone thoroughly applied as a dust or spray will control the pest if the applications are made at ten-day intervals. Crop residues should be destroyed following harvest.

The Mexican bean beetle is an old pest in Mexico, New Mexico, Arizona, Utah, Wyoming, Colorado, and western Texas. Only in comparatively recent times has it been found east of the Mississippi River. It is now present throughout this area with the possible exception of Wisconsin.

The squash beetle (*Epilachna borealis*) is another ladybird beetle which is a pest of plants. It attacks squashes, pumpkins, melons, and other cucurbits. The adults are yellow and are spotted with black. The larvae are covered with branching spines. They feed on the leaves of the host plants. The biology of this insect is similar to that of the Mexican bean beetle as are the control measures.

Family *Tenebrionidae* (Darkling Beetles)

Darkling beetles (Fig. 148) comprise a large family of Coleoptera, with more than a thousand species in North America. They vary much in size but most of them are uniformly dark in color, superficially resembling ground beetles. They may be distinguished from the latter by the presence of four segments instead of five in the hind tarsi. They are found chiefly in the West and Southwest. Food consists mostly of vegetable matter but a few species are predaceous.

The confused flour beetle (*Tribolium confusum*, Fig. 149) is a common pest of such food products as flour, grains, beans, dried fruit, nuts, chocolate, and pepper. The adults are reddish-brown and are

FIG. 148. A common darkling beetle. (From Texas Agricultural Experiment Station.)

about $\frac{1}{7}$ of an inch in length. They are often found in large numbers in grain elevators, mills, groceries, and other places where food products are stored.

The confused flour beetle is long-lived, adults often living for a year or more. During this period, the female may lay 400 to 500 eggs. The brownish-white larvae feed on the same food products as the adults. In warm weather the developmental period may be as short as a month, but the time is usually longer. Several generations occur during a twelve-month period. A closely related but less common species is the red flour beetle (*Tribolium castaneum*).

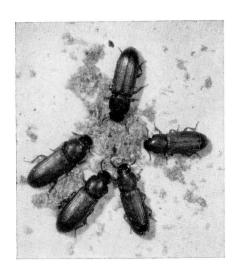

FIG. 149. Confused flour beetles (*Tribolium confusum*) feeding on flour. (From Agricultural Research Service, U.S.D.A.)

Infested places should be cleaned and badly infested residues destroyed. Painting or spraying the woodwork and walls with methoxychlor will aid in preventing infestations. Infested material may be fumigated with an ethylene dichloride-carbon tetrachloride mixture, methyl bromide, or other fumigant.

Mealworms (*Tenebrio* spp.) often become pests around grain bins and other places, particularly in dark and damp environments. They prefer to feed on farinaceous products that are in a poor or decaying condition. The two common mealworms are the yellow mealworm (*Tenebrio molitor*) and the dark mealworm (*T. obscurus*). The adults are black beetles about one inch in length. The larvae resemble wireworms since they are brown or yellowish, smooth, and distinctly segmented. There is usually one generation annually.

Another related pest of grain is the cadelle (*Tenebroides mauritanicus*, Fig. 150). It is not a darkling beetle but belongs to

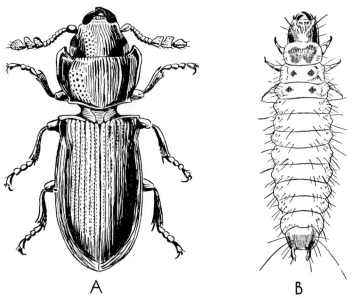

A   B

FIG. 150. The cadelle (*Tenebroides mauritanicus*). **A,** Adult. **B,** Larva. (From the University of California Division of Agricultural Sciences.)

a related family, *Ostomidae*. The cadelle is black, elongate, flattened, and about 1/3 inch long. The adults have the habit of cutting bolting cloth and making holes in sacks and cartons, even though these materials are not used as food.

The full-grown cadelle larvae are about 3/4 inch in length with dark heads, dark spots on the thorax, and a pair of hooks on the end of the abdomen. Both adults and larvae make burrows in the woodwork of grain bins. Here they may remain for long periods until new grain is available. Although primarily grain feeders, larvae and adults may prey on other grain-infesting insects. The cadelle is long-lived, having been known to live for nearly two years. Females lay about 1,000 eggs each. Development from egg to adult may occupy as little as two and one-half months, but the time is often greatly prolonged. Control measures recommended for flour beetles are suggested for mealworms and the cadelle.

The plains false wireworm (*Eleodes opaca*) and related species are occasionally pests of importance in the dry regions of the West and Southwest. Wheat primarily, but also oats, maize, cotton, corn, native grasses, and other plants are attacked. The chief injury consists of larval feeding on germinating seed and roots. The adults are general feeders and are usually considered harmless, although they may seriously injure young cotton plants.

The larvae are brown or yellowish and have the general appearance of wireworms, but differ in the possession of longer antennae and legs. Adults are dark colored with ridged, granulate or smooth wing covers, which characteristic depends upon the species. They are less than one inch in length.

Hibernation is either in the adult or partly grown larval stage. In the spring, eggs are laid in the soil. When conditions are favorable, larvae hatched from these eggs mature in about four months. Two to three weeks after pupation in the soil the adults emerge. Later in the season there is another period of egg laying. Larvae developing from these eggs hibernate in a partly grown stage.

The growing of corn or other less susceptible crops for two years or longer between crops of wheat is the most effective cultural control. Seed treatment with aldrin, lindane or other approved toxicants provides satisfactory control of the larvae.

Powder Post Beetles. Powder post beetles often seriously damage lumber, floors, furniture, frames of houses, and books. They make long cylindrical tunnels through these materials, and heavy infestations often reduce them to mere shells. The pests are infrequently seen and their presence is usually first indicated by the small exit holes (Fig. 151) made by the adults and tiny piles of sawdust on the floor.

Powder post beetles constitute a heterogeneous group of beetles belonging to several families, *Lyctidae, Bostrichidae, Anobiidae,* and *Ptinidae.* The most destructive forms are members of the genus

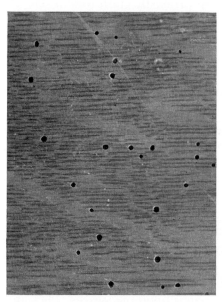

Lyctus and the furniture beetle (*Anobium puncta-tum*). These are small dark colored stout insects, usually about ⅕ inch in length. Exit holes made by the adults may not be more than 1/16 inch in diameter. Usually there is one generation annually of these insects. Under natural conditions the winter is spent in the larval stage.

As *Lyctus* beetles attack only sapwood of hardwoods, the use of only heartwood will eliminate them. Painting or varnishing all surfaces will fill the pores of the wood and prevent egg-laying. Kiln-drying the lumber is effective in destroying the borers but

FIG. 151. Exit holes of adults of the southern lyctus beetle (*Lyctus planicollis*) in an oak file case. (From Agricultural Research Service, U.S.D.A.)

this treatment does not prevent reinfestation. Treatment of floors, furniture, and other woodwork with pentachlorophenol in a petroleum solvent is highly recommended. Painting furniture and woodwork with a solution of DDT in kerosene is also recommended. Fumigation of lumber and furniture with methyl bromide is suggested.

Some adults of the *Bostrichidae* have the mischievous habit of boring through solid objects. In the West, one species, *Scobicia declivis,* bores through the lead sheathings of aerial telephone cables which results in short circuits. Some of the beetles of this family have been known to tunnel through wine barrels and wooden water tanks.

The most interesting of the *Anobiidae* is the death-watch beetle (*Zestobium rufovillosum*). This beetle is the chief source of the superstition that a ticking sound presages the death of some member of the family. The ticking noise so often heard in the walls of old houses during the silent hours of night is probably produced in the most part by this insect and a closely related species. The sound, which is believed to be a sex call, is produced by the insect striking its head or mandibles against the walls of its tunnel in the wood.

The well-known cigarette beetle (Fig. 152) is another representa-

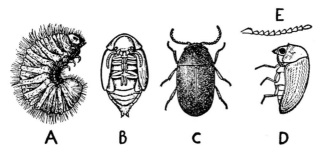

FIG. 152. The cigarette beetle (*Lasioderma serricorne*). **A,** Larva. **B,** Pupa. **C,** Adult. **D,** Lateral view of adult. **E,** antenna. (From Agricultural Research Service, U.S.D.A.)

tive of the family *Anobiidae*. Some of its food materials are stored food products, tobacco, drugs, pepper, raisins, ginger, and uphol-stered furniture. This insect is an ancient pest of man and it has shown no respect for royalty or dignity, as indicated by evidences of its presence in the tomb of King Tut. As many as three generations may occur annually in the United States. Control of the cigarette beetle should begin with thoroughly cleaning warehouses and other places before new products are stored. Infested materials may be fumigated with commercial fumigants. The use of approved space and residual sprays in enclosures is recommended. Infested up-holstered furniture may be thoroughly sprayed with DDT.

Family *Scarabaeidae* (Scarabs or Lamellicorn Beetles)

These are short, robust beetles of variable size. They are most readily recognized by the lamellate club of the antennae which is formed by three or more flattened terminal segments capable of close apposition. The family is large, with more than 1,000 North American species. It may be divided into two groups based on habits, the scavengers or tumble-bugs and the leaf chafers.

The scavengers (Fig. 153) are of slight importance; however, their habits attract attention. Common species of these beetles, often in pairs, form a ball of dung which is rolled over the ground for some distance and then buried. An egg is laid on the organic matter, and the grub feeds on this decomposing food material. The best known of the scavenger beetles is the sacred scarab of Egypt (*Scarabaeus sacer*).

Most species of scarabaeids belong to the group known as the leaf chafers. These beetles are so named because the adults commonly feed on the foliage of trees; however, some feed on pollen, flowers, and fruits of various plants. Larvae, commonly known as white grubs, are chiefly found in grasslands feeding on the roots of many plants; others develop in decaying organic material. They have fleshy, curved bodies with brown heads and well developed legs.

FIG. 153. A tumblebug (*Canthon viridia*). (Courtesy of L. S. Dillon.)

May Beetles or June Bugs. The May beetles or June bugs (Fig. 126) are the most common leaf chafers and their larvae are among the most destructive of soil pests. Most species belong to the genus *Phyllophaga*. The adults are brownish, stout in form, and are rather large, measuring about ¾ inch in length. About 150 species are recorded from the United States. They are nocturnal and are strongly attracted to lights, around which they fly clumsily with a loud buzzing sound. Emergence of the adults of some species may occur as early as March and April in the South, although their appearance is later for the country as a whole. The adults feed on the foliage of a number of trees, such as hickory, birch, elm, ash, and persimmon, which occasionally may be defoliated. With the approach of dawn, the insects return to the soil or debris in which they conceal themselves during the daylight hours.

Each female lays 150 to 200 eggs in the soil. Permanent pastures and lawns are the favorite places for oviposition. Cleanly cultivated row crops and clean stands of legume, such as clover and alfalfa, are the least preferred places for egg deposition. Eggs hatch into white grubs which feed upon the roots of grain crops, other grasses, strawberries, onions, potatoes, and numerous other plants. The larvae are much more injurious than the adults.

The length of the life cycle of May beetles depends upon the climate and species. Some species complete a life cycle in one year, and four years may be required for other species in colder climates. The two-year life cycle is the most common in the southern states and the three-year life cycle is the rule in the North. Both larvae and adults are found in the soil during the winter months. In the South common species such as *Phyllophaga crassissima* and P. *calceata* oviposit in April. The larvae feed on grass and other plant roots during this season and overwinter as larvae. It is during the second year that most damage is done to plant roots by the larvae. In the fall of the second season, pupation occurs. The adult emerges from the pupal stage but remains in the pupal cell in the ground until the next spring before emergence, thus completing a two-year life cycle.

Crops susceptible to white grub attacks, such as corn, small grains, and potatoes, should not be planted on land likely to be infested, but should follow such crops as legumes and cotton. Thorough discing of fields in late summer or fall will not eliminate the pests, but many larvae and pupae will be destroyed.

Aldrin, dieldrin, and heptachlor are effective insecticides in the control of white grubs in the soil. Should adult beetles threaten serious injury to the foliage of trees, they may be protected by sprays of lead arsenate.

The Green June Beetle (*Cotinis nitida*).   The adults of this insect are often pests of foliage and fruits of various plants. The larvae may do serious injury to the roots of grasses, vegetables, and ornamental plants. They also feed on decaying organic matter.

The adults are rather large, about one inch in length, flattened, green, and with the body margined with yellow or bronze. They fly during the daylight hours. The larvae are robust dirty-white grubs. They have the peculiar habit of crawling on their backs.

Winter is passed in the larval stage, which completes its development in the spring and then pupates. The adults emerge, feed, and the females lay eggs in soil rich in vegetable matter during the summer. There is one generation annually.

Soil applications of lindane have given fair control of the grubs. The insecticides recommended in the control of the common white grubs are also suggested for use. Bait pails containing malt extract, benzoate of soda, and water have been suggested for use to reduce infestations when ripe fruits are attacked.

The Rose Chafer (*Macrodactylus subspinosus*).   This insect (Fig. 154) is distributed over eastern United States as far south as Virginia and westward to Texas and Colorado. It is particularly abundant in localities with sandy soils. The adults feed on foliage, flowers, or fruit of many plants such as grapes, peaches, and roses. They are tan colored beetles with long legs and about ⅓ inch in length. The larvae, which resemble small May beetle grubs, live in the soil and feed on grass roots. There is one generation annually, the winter being passed in the larval stage. The insects are poisonous to poultry when eaten. The adults are controlled by sprays of wettable DDT powder. A second application of the spray ten to 14 days later may be needed.

FIG. 154. The rose chafer (*Macrodactylus subspinosus*). (From Agricultural Research Service, U.S.D.A.)

The Japanese Beetle (*Popillia japonica*). The Japanese beetle (Fig. 155), a serious pest of many plants, was imported into New Jersey in about 1916 on the roots of nursery stock from Japan. The adults feed on the fruit and skeletonize the foliage of many plants. Roots of grasses and other plants are destroyed by the feeding larvae. This pest is found in most states east of the Mississippi River with the exception of those

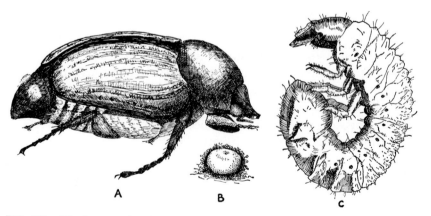

A   **B**   **C**

FIG. 155. The Japanese beetle (*Popillia japonica*). **A,** Adult. **B,** Egg. **C,** Larva. (From Connecticut Agricultural Experiment Station, New Haven.)

along the Gulf of Mexico. It is well established in New Jersey and neighboring states.

The adults are about ⅜ inch long, and broadly oval with brownish elytra. The head and thorax are greenish-bronze. There are two prominent white spots and also several smaller ones near

FIG. 156. A rhinoceros beetle from the tropics.

the end of the abdomen. The larvae are similar in appearance to common white grubs, but they are much smaller.

Larvae complete their development in early summer and the adults appear in large numbers in July and August. The adults live for 30 to 40 days, depositing eggs in small clusters in the soil. Winter is passed as larvae in the soil. Normally, there is one generation annually, but larvae in cold wet soil may develop more slowly and the adults may not appear until the second season.

DDT or methoxychlor sprays will control the adults feeding on foliage and fruits. Several applications of the spray may be necessary. Treating the soil with DDT or dieldrin is recommended for the control of the larvae. These compounds will remain in the soil and provide adequate protection against the grubs for several years. Inoculation of the soil with spores of the milky disease (*Bacillus popillae*) is also being employed for control of the larvae.

Rhinoceros beetles (Fig. 156) are the largest known Coleoptera. These beetles are so named because males of the best known species bear a horn on the head. One or more horns may be present on the thorax also. One of the largest species is a greenish-gray form, *Dynastes tityrus*. Adults of the genus *Strategus* are black and somewhat smaller than *Dynastes*. The larvae of both genera which are found in the southern states develop in rotten wood and other decaying vegetative material.

FIG. 157. A stag beetle or pinching bug (*Lucanus elaphus*); family *Lucanidae*, closely related to the lamellicorn beetles. (Courtesy of L. S. Dillon.)

Family *Cerambycidae* (Roundheaded or Longhorned Borers)

The roundheaded or longhorned borers constitute a large family of beetles with more than 1,000 species represented in North America. As a whole, the adults are rather large, some of them being several inches in length. They are usually elongate and rather cylindrical in shape, and are often strikingly marked. Antennae are at least as long as the combined length of the head and thorax, and, in many cases are much longer than the entire body.

The larvae are wood borers. They are white or yellow, thin-skinned, and more or less cylindrical in outline. Small thoracic legs are present on some species. The straight, cylindrical body is in sharp contrast with the curved body outline and flattened thorax of the flatheaded borers.

Roundheaded borers attack primarily dead or dying and devitalized timbers. However, some forms, such as the locust borer and the roundheaded apple tree borer, feed on healthy trees. Most damage to shade and forest trees occurs when droughts, defoliation, or diseases have devitalized and made them susceptible to attack. Based on these facts, the best control of roundheaded wood borers on shade and other valuable trees is to keep trees as healthy and vigorous as possible through fertilization, watering, pruning out dead and dying limbs, and other cultural practices.

The Banded Hickory Borer (*Chion cinctus*). This wood borer (Fig. 158) is one of the common borers in the southern, eastern, and central states. The larvae feed upon dead and dying hickory, pecan, oak, and other hardwoods. The adult is brown with a grayish pubescence; the elytra are crossed by a yellowish band near the base. In warm climates, a generation is completed in one year. Two years are required for a life cycle in colder climates. Long tunnels are made under the bark and through the wood. Rustic furniture and log cabins also may become infested by this borer.

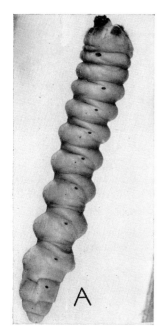
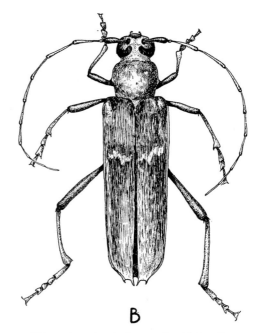

FIG. 158. The banded hickory borer (*Chion cinctus*). **A,** Larva. **B,** Adult. (Larva from Agricultural Research Service, U.S.D.A.)

As this borer attacks only dying or dead wood, it cannot be considered an important pest of shade and forest trees. The larvae appear to be completing a job of destruction started by other agencies. Should rustic woodwork become infested with the borers, spraying or painting it with a solution of pentachlorophenol is recommended.

The Roundheaded Apple Tree Borer (*Saperda candida*). The roundheaded apple tree borer (Fig. 159) is probably the best known of the cerambycids. It is commonly found in most parts of the country. The insect attacks healthy trees and is a particularly important pest of apple trees. In addition to the apple, it feeds on pear, serviceberry, haw, mountain ash, and others. The grubs burrow through the inner bark, sapwood, and also into the hardwood.

The adult is somewhat less than an inch in length, and velvety brown with two white stripes extending dorsally along the entire length of the body. The full-grown grubs are more than an inch in length. Two or more years are required for a life cycle.

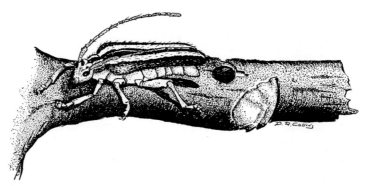

FIG. 159.   The roundheaded apple tree borer (*Saperda candida*).

The roundheaded apple tree borer is difficult to control. The grubs may be removed with a knife in a few trees. This should be done in late summer or early fall and repeated in the spring. DDT sprays, prepared with wettable powders and applied when the adults are active, will kill many of them.

The Locust Borer (*Megacyllene robiniae*).   This destructive pest is a dark, robust beetle of medium size, strikingly marked with transverse yellow bands (Fig. 160). Adults emerge and are found feeding on the pollen of goldenrod in the fall when this plant is in full bloom. Eggs are laid in the fall underneath bark scales of locust trees. These soon hatch and the young larvae tunnel into the corky bark where they overwinter. The next spring the grubs resume activity and tunnel through both the sapwood and heartwood. Pupation occurs in the burrows during middle or late summer and the adults emerge when goldenrod begins to bloom. There is one generation annually.

The locust borer is difficult to control. Dense stands are attacked less severely than sparse plantings. Rapidly growing trees are less susceptible to injury than trees in poor condition. Interplantings are damaged less than pure stands of locust trees. Severe pruning of heavily infested trees produces a dense growth and a shaded condition which discourages attacks by this insect. The spraying of

FIG. 160. The locust borer (*Megacyllene robiniae*). **A,** Larva. **B,** Pupa. **C,** Adult. (From Agricultural Research Service, U.S.D.A.)

trunks of shade trees before growth begins in the spring with a DDT-xylene emulsion spray will materially aid in the control of the pest.

The Twig Girdler (*Oncideres cingulata*). The twig girdler is widely distributed and may do considerable damage (Fig. 161) when it is abundant. A related form, *O. texana,* is found in the Southwest. Hickory, pecan, persimmon, elm, and other trees are attacked. Adults emerge in late summer or fall and girdle the branches with their powerful mandibles. Eggs are deposited in the girdled twigs, which provide conditions suitable for the development of the larvae. The branches are almost completely severed, leaving intact only a few strands of heartwood. Later, the branches drop, falling to the ground or lodging in the trees. Winter is passed in the larval stage. One generation develops annually. Severe injury may be caused, especially to nursery stock by the girdling of the terminal branches. The insect may be controlled, particularly in nurseries, by gathering and burning the severed branches during late fall and winter, provided there are no infested woodlands nearby. DDT and lead arsenate sprays applied when the adults are active in late summer and fall will destroy many of them.

FIG. 161. Twigs severed from a single pecan tree by twig girdlers (*Oncideres cingulata*). (From Florida Agricultural Experiment Station.)

Family *Chrysomelidae* (Leaf Beetles)

More than 1,000 species of this family are known to occur in North America. Leaf beetles are rather small; the Colorado potato beetle being one of the largest forms. Their bodies are rather short and more or less oval in shape with antennae of normal length. Color patterns of the adults are variable, but many common species are yellow with black markings. Both larvae and adults are foliage feeders, with the exception of the larvae of some species which attack the roots of plants. Eggs are yellowish, usually elongate, and are deposited on the food plants or in the soil. The larvae are usually short and grub-like, but some are elongate. Most chrysomelids hibernate in the adult stage.

The Colorado Potato Beetle (*Leptinotarsa decemlineata*).   The Colorado potato beetle (Fig. 162) is one of the best known of all American insects. It is a pest of the potato throughout most of the United States and eastern Canada, and it has been exported to Europe.

This insect is primarily a pest of the potato, but it also attacks tomatoes, eggplants, Jimson weeds, and other solanaceous plants. Both larvae and adults feed on the leaves and terminal growths of the plants. The Colorado potato beetle is an example of a native insect of no economic importance until the pioneer farmers brought to it a new food supply in the potato. The insect was first observed about 1823 on the eastern slopes of the Rocky Mountains feeding on a native weed known as the buffalo bur (*Solanum rostratum*). When the potato was planted in this area and became available as food, the beetle spread rapidly eastward over the United States. Entire

FIG. 162.   The Colorado po- tato beetle (*Leptinotarsa de- cemlineata*).

crops were often destroyed, for no efficient control of the pest was known until the efficacy of Paris green as a stomach poison was discovered about 1865.

The adults are about ⅜ inch in length, oval, and yellow with ten longitudinal black stripes on the wing covers. The insect over- winters in the soil as an adult. The adults emerge in the spring after potatoes are growing, and begin feeding and depositing yel- lowish eggs in clusters on the underside of the leaves. Each female lays an average of 500 eggs during a period of about five weeks. These eggs hatch in a week or less into soft, brick-red, humpbacked larvae or grubs. Following a feeding period of two or three weeks, the grubs enter the ground for pupation. The adult beetles emerge from the pupal stage one or two weeks later. There may be as many as three generations annually in the insect's southern range.

Although the Colorado potato beetle once was a formidable pest, both larvae and adults are now easily controlled by the use of modern insecticides. DDT, lead arsenate, dieldrin, and other insecti- cides are recommended for its control.

The Striped Cucumber Beetle (*Acalymma vittata*).   The striped cucumber beetle (Fig. 163A) is a very important pest of cucurbits east of the Rocky Mountains. The insect feeds on the plants throughout their growing season. The leaves, tender terminals, blossoms, and stems are fed upon; and, particularly in the fall, rinds of the fruits are attacked. The larvae attack the roots and underground portions of the stems of the plants. The adult is the vector of the bacterial wilt disease of cucurbits. This insect and the spotted cucumber beetle (*Diabrotica undecimpunctata howardi*) are the

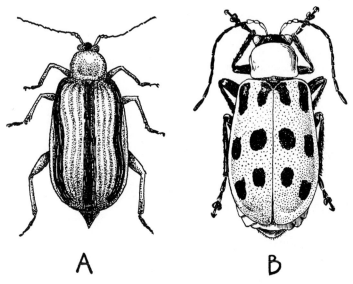

A   B

FIG. 163. **A,** The striped cucumber beetle (*Acalymma vittata*). **B,** The spotted cucumber beetle (*Diabrotica undecimpunctata howardi*). (**B,** from Agricultural Research Service, U.S.D.A.)

only known vectors of this important disease. They not only carry the disease from plant to plant, but the disease organisms live over the winter in their digestive tracts. The striped cucumber beetle is also a vector of the cucurbit mosaic disease.

Although the larvae are restricted to cucurbits, the adults also attack corn, beans, peas, and the flowers of many other plants.

The adults are about ⅕ inch long with three black stripes extending the length of the yellow wing covers. The elytra are minutely punctate. The larvae are white, elongate, and about ⅓ inch long when full-grown.

Unmated adults overwinter in protected places near fields where cucurbits were grown the previous season. They emerge in the spring, and egg deposition begins when their host plants are available. Eggs are deposited in the soil, and the larvae feed on the stems and roots of plants until completion of their development;

pupation is in the soil. A life cycle varies from four to eight weeks in duration, depending upon the climate. The number of generations varies from one in the North to four in the southern range of the insect.

The striped cucumber beetle may be controlled by dusting or spraying the plants with methoxychlor. Dusts or sprays of malathion, parathion, and sevin are also recommended for use. The first application of insecticide should be made when the first beetles are seen and further applications should be made as needed. Planting an excess of seed and thinning to a stand later is advisable.

A closely related species, the western striped cucumber beetle (*Acalymma trivittata*) is found on the Pacific Coast. The biology of this species is similar to the striped cucumber beetle and control measures are the same.

The banded cucumber beetle (*Diabrotica balteata*) is another species associated with the striped cucumber beetle in its southern range. The adult is yellowish-green with three transverse green bands across the wing covers. This insect is more general in its feeding habits than the striped cucumber beetle, attacking a number of crops other than cucurbits. It may be controlled by the same measures as recommended for the striped cucumber beetle.

The Southern Corn Rootworm or Spotted Cucumber Beetle (*Diabrotica undecimpunctata howardi*). This pest (Fig. 163B) is widely distributed through the United States east of the Rocky Mountains and its range also extends into Canada and Mexico. It is probably more destructive than the striped cucumber beetle and other species of *Diabrotica*. The insect is most injurious to corn; however, it also attacks cucurbits, oats, wheat, rice, rye, sorghums, alfalfa, beans, and many other plants. The adults are general feeders, and are frequently found feeding on flowers of many plants. The silks of corn are attacked, but the foliage is fed upon very little. Injury to cucurbits is the same as that caused by the striped cucumber beetle. The insect is also a disseminator of the bacterial wilt disease of these plants. The larvae feed on the roots of corn and drill into the stems, often destroying the stand of young corn which necessitates replanting. More mature plants are attacked in the North where the roots are eaten and the stalks may fall over. Injury is most severe to corn in years of heavy rainfall or the season following. Infestations are also greatest in lowland when corn is planted after a legume crop.

The adult is a familiar insect; it is about ¼ inch long and yellowish-green with black spots on the wing covers. The larva is ½ to ¾ inch long when full-grown, yellowish-white, wrinkled, with the head and the last abdominal segment brownish in color.

Winter is passed as an adult in protected places. In the extreme South the insect may be more or less active throughout the season. It is possible that reinfestation in the North may occur from flights of the adults from the southern states. This is one of the first insects to appear in late winter or early spring. Eggs are laid in the soil around the base of the host plants. The number of generations vary from one in the North to four in the South.

Delaying planting until the first generation of larvae has ceased feeding is recommended in some sections. However, weather conditions and other insects make it impractical to delay planting in many areas. Crop rotation is of no value in controlling the insect. The application of insecticidal dusts, as chlordane, aldrin, and BHC, to furrows just before planting has given promising results. Seed treatments with dieldrin and lindane have also proved effective in control of this pest. Control of the insects on cucurbits is the same as for the striped cucumber beetle. West of the Rocky Mountains, the above species is replaced by the western spotted cucumber beetle (*Diabrotica undecimpunctata*). The biology of this form is similar to that of the preceding species. The larvae are commonly found attacking the roots of corn, alfalfa, peas, and other plants. The native hosts are probably roots of grasses and weeds.

The Northern Corn Rootworm (*Diabrotica longicornis*). The northern corn rootworm (Fig. 164) has practically the same distribution as the southern corn rootworm, but it is best known as a pest of corn in the Upper Mississippi Valley. The larvae of this insect attack the roots of the corn, which results in stunted plants which may fall during wind and rainstorms. The full-grown larvae are about ½ inch in length, and white with brownish-yellow heads. It is believed that the larvae develop only on the roots of corn. The adults are about ⅕ of an inch long and are yellowish-green. They feed on the silks and the pollen of the tassels, as well as the pollen of a number of other plants.

This insect passes the winter in the egg stage in the ground. Eggs hatch in the spring, the larvae feed on the corn roots, and pupate in the soil. The adults emerge during the summer months.

Eggs for the next generation are laid in the corn fields in early fall. There is only one generation annually.

A closely related form, the western corn rootworm (*D. virgifera*), occurs principally in Colorado, New Mexico, Arizona, and Texas. It has a similar biology and causes the same injury.

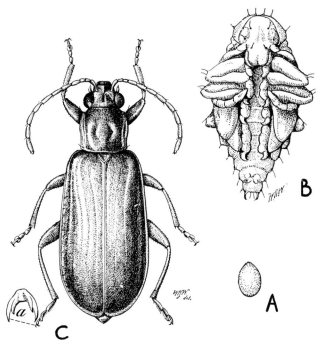

FIG. 164. The northern corn rootworm (*Diabrotica longicornis*). **A,** Egg. **B,** Pupa. **C,** Adult. (From Agricultural Research Service, U.S.D.A.)

Since the insect is known to develop only on corn and overwinters in corn fields in the egg stage, crop rotation will control it. Insecticidal control as recommended for the southern corn rootworm will afford effective control. Dusts of DDT control adults feeding on corn silks.

Flea Beetles. Flea beetles (Fig. 165) comprise a rather large group of small insects with enlarged hind femora which enable them to leap when disturbed. They injure plants chiefly by eating numerous small holes in the leaves, causing them to appear as if they have been perforated with small shot. Plants may be so heavily attacked that they die. These holes afford a means of entrance of plant disease organisms such as bacterial wilt of corn and early blight of potato. The larvae of some species feed on the roots, while others are foliage feeders. Both larvae and adults usually feed on one host or a group of related plants, but some are general feeders.

Some of the more common species are the pale-striped flea beetle (*Systena blanda*), the striped flea beetle (*Phyllotreta striolata*), the grape flea beetle *(Altica chalybea)*, the sweet-potato flea beetle (*Chaetocnema confinis*), the spinach flea beetle (*Disonycha xanthomelas*), and the potato flea beetle (*Epitrix cucumeris*). Flea bee-

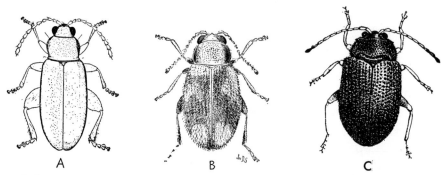

FIG. 165.   Flea beetles. **A,** The pale-striped flea beetle (*Systena blanda*). **B,** The tobacco flea beetle (*Epitrix hirtipennis*). **C,** The potato flea beetle (*Epitrix cucumeris*). (**A,** From Virginia Agricultural Experiment Station. **B** and **C,** From Agricultural Research Service, U.S.D.A.)

tles are oval and vary from $\frac{1}{16}$ to $\frac{1}{5}$ of an inch in length. They are bluish-black to yellowish-brown in color, and are frequently marked with yellow or red.

Life histories of flea beetles vary with the species. Generally they overwinter as adults in trash, leaves, grass, or rubbish. Adults emerge in the spring and attack weeds or other plants until cultivated plants are available. Frequently they seriously injure seedlings in seedbeds and young transplanted plants. Eggs are laid on the plants or in the soil near the base of the plants. These eggs hatch into tiny whitish elongate larvae which, when fully grown, are from $\frac{1}{8}$ to $\frac{1}{3}$ inch in length. The larvae usually pupate in the soil. There are one or more generations annually.

Several insecticides may be employed in the control of flea beetles. Toxaphene dusts or sprays give satisfactory results. DDT dusts and sprays are efficient in the control of the insects. If toxic residues on leafy vegetables are a concern, rotenone dusts are suggested for use. Repeated applications of these insecticides may be necessary.

Young plants may be protected by covering the seedbeds with tobacco cloth. Destruction of weeds in and around gardens and fields of truck crops is important as the insects often feed and reproduce on these plants.

The Elm Leaf Beetle (*Galerucella luteola*). This pest, introduced from Europe, is confined chiefly to the eastern states. Both larvae and adults feed on the foliage of the elm. Adults are about 1/4 inch long and greenish or yellowish colored with an indistinct black band along the margin of each wing cover. The insect overwinters as an adult in whatever protected places are available. Adults emerge in the spring and begin feeding and ovipositing on the young leaves shortly after they appear. Two or more generations occur annually. Effective control may be obtained by spraying the trees with lead arsenate.

Tortoise Beetles. These are interesting insects and many species are very beautiful with their green, golden, or iridescent colors. The bodies are convex above, with the margin of the wing covers and prothorax expanded and forming an oval outline suggestive of the shape of the tortoise. The larvae have spines around the margins of the body with the posterior pair about as long as the body. Cast skins and excrement collect on these posterior spines, causing the larvae to have the appearance of bits of animated dirt or filth.

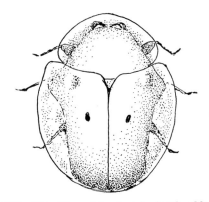

FIG. 166. The golden tortoise beetle (*Metriona bicolor*).

Tortoise beetles feed mostly on sweet potatoes, bindweeds, and morning glories. Among the more important species are the argus tortoise beetle (*Chelymorpha cassidea*), striped tortoise beetle (*Cassida bivittata*), and the golden tortoise beetle (*Metriona bicolor*, Fig. 166). Adults overwinter in protected places, emerge late in the spring, feed, and oviposit on the foliage of the host plants. They may be controlled with applications of DDT or lead arsenate either as dusts or sprays.

Family *Bruchidae* (Pea and Bean Weevils)

This is a relatively small family of beetles which feed, as larvae, chiefly on seeds of leguminous plants. The adults are chunky beetles, usually ⅕ inch or less in length. The head is prolonged into a short quadrate beak. The wing covers are short, leaving the tip of the abdomen exposed.

The Bean Weevil (*Acanthoscelides obtectus*). The bean weevil is the most injurious insect pest of garden beans of all varieties in

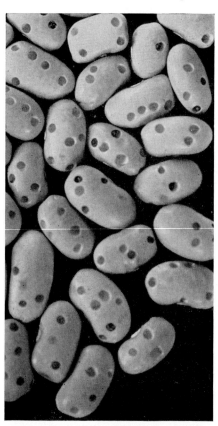

the United States (Fig. 167). It is also an important pest in other countries. The adults are brownish-gray or olive about ⅛ inch long. Injury is caused by the small footless larvae which feed in the seeds, destroying them completely or rendering them unfit for food or planting. Beans are attacked both in the field and in storage. In the field, eggs are laid in cracks in the pods or in holes gnawed by the females, but not on the outside of the pods as occurs with some other species. In storage, eggs are laid either on the beans or on the sides of the container.

This pest is quite prolific, each female laying an average of 85 eggs. A generation is produced in three weeks or longer, depending on locality and season. A number of generations may be produced annually. Breeding may continue throughout the winter if

FIG. 167. Beans showing exit holes of bean weevils (*Acanthoscelides obtectus*). (From Agricultural Research Service, U.S.D.A.)

the weather is sufficiently warm and food is available.

The bean weevil may be controlled in stored beans by fumigation or heating. Ethylene dichloride mixture is a safe and efficient fumigant for farm use. If beans are heated for three or four hours to a temperature of 135° F., all stages of the weevils will be killed. Beans intended for planting purposes and not for animal consumption may be protected from the depredations of weevils by mixing small amounts of DDT powder with the seed. Lime and dry road dust may be used to prevent further infestations, but will not prevent development of the immature stages already in the seed. Plant residues should be fed to livestock, plowed under, or burned to destroy overwintering weevils.

The Cowpea Weevil (*Callosobruchus maculatus*). The cowpea weevil (Fig. 168) is an important pest of cowpeas both in the field

 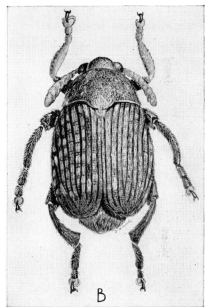

FIG. 168. **A,** The cowpea weevil (*Callosobruchus maculatus*). (From Agricultural Research Service, U.S.D.A.) **B,** The vetch bruchid (*Bruchus brachialis*). (From Texas Agricultural Experiment Station.)

and in storage throughout the South where the crop is grown. Damage is caused by the fleshy, grub-like larvae feeding in the seed. The adults are 1/8 to 1/5 inch long and dark colored with four pale brown spots on the wing covers. All varieties of cowpeas are attacked. It appears doubtful that the species can reproduce on any other host. Most damage occurs in storage, eggs are glued to the peas, and are laid on the pods at least to some extent in the fields.

Under favorable conditions a life cycle from egg to adult is completed in less than three weeks, with each female laying an average of more than 100 eggs. In warm climates reproduction continues throughout the winter with as many as nine generations occurring annually.

To protect cowpeas in storage, the bins should first be cleaned and the surfaces sprayed with malathion or methoxychlor. Then malathion as a protectant may be applied to the peas, and fumigation with the ethylene dichloride mixture as needed is advised.

The Pea Weevil (*Bruchus pisorum*). The pea weevil is a pest of garden and field peas of the genus *Pisum* only. This insect does not attack cowpeas and beans as is commonly believed. Injury consists of feeding on the contents of the seeds by the larvae. Heavily infested peas are reduced to mere husks. The round exit holes of adults are commonly observed. Only green peas are attacked; peas in storage are not attacked.

The adults are robust beetles about $\frac{1}{5}$ inch in length, brownish and spotted with light and dark areas. The larvae are white chunky grubs with short legs. Adults hibernate within the seeds or elsewhere in protected places. The beetles emerge in the spring when peas begin to bloom. They feed upon pollen and later lay eggs on the pods in all stages of development. The eggs hatch and each small larva bores into the pod and enters a pea in which it feeds and develops. Upon completion of larval growth, pupation occurs within the cavity of the seed. Normally, there is only one generation annually.

The application of rotenone or DDT dusts at weekly intervals, beginning when blooming starts is recommended for the control of the insect in the field. Other control measures are the same as for the bean weevil.

The Vetch Bruchid (*Bruchus brachialis*). The vetch bruchid is an important pest of vetch where the crop is grown for seed. As much as 50 to 90 percent of the seed may be destroyed. Such varieties as Hungarian and common vetch are not damaged, while purple vetch, smooth or hairy vetch are most heavily attacked.

Adults are about $\frac{1}{8}$ inch long, black with wing covers marked with light colored patches. The larvae are yellowish, fleshy, and grub-like. Biology of this weevil is similar to that of the pea weevil. The adults emerge from hibernation in the spring and oviposit on the seed pods. The larvae hatching from the eggs bore through the seed pods and enter the seeds, feeding on the contents of the seed throughout larval development. Pupation occurs within the seed, and the adults emerge through a circular hole during the summer and seek hibernation quarters. Only one generation occurs annually. The insect does not develop in dry seeds.

Dusting with DDT provides satisfactory control. Two applications of the insecticide are recommended, but one application made when the first pods set will provide considerable control. Weevils in the seeds may be killed by fumigation as for the bean weevil.

Family *Curculionidae* (Curculios, Weevils, or Snout Beetles)

The family Curculionidae is very large, more than 2,000 species having been recorded from North America alone. The adults of

FIG. 169. A weevil, *Curculio (Balaninus)* with a greatly elongated snout. (From Illinois Natural History Survey. Drawn by C. O. Mohr.)

this group are typified by the prolongation of the head into a distinct snout. This snout in some cases may be longer than the body (Fig. 169) and it is quite generally curved. Chewing mouthparts are located at its tip. The snout enables the insects to feed on the internal tissues of plants and provides places for egg deposition. Generally the larvae are internal plant feeders. As a rule these insects not only have specialized feeding habits, but also are quite specialized in their host plants. Each species has its particular plant or group of plants or plant products upon which it lives and reproduces. The larvae are light colored, fleshy, legless grubs.

The Boll Weevil (*Anthonomus grandis*). No insect has had a more profound influence on agriculture of the southern United States or has attained more notoriety than the boll weevil (Fig. 170). The original home of the insect was in Mexico or Central

America, where it fed on its wild host plants of those regions. Little is known of the pest prior to 1892 when it was found at Brownsville, Texas. From here it has spread over the entire Cotton Belt with the exception of California, Arizona, New Mexico, the western extension of the cotton belt of Texas, and possibly a few isolated areas along the northern edge of the cotton-growing belt.

The boll weevil is one of the most destructive of all agricultural pests. For all practical purposes, cotton is its only host. Both larvae and adults feed in and destroy the squares (flower buds) and later the bolls (developing fruit). The adult is generally grayish-brown or dark yellowish-brown in color. The average length is about ¼ inch with a snout about ⅓ the length of the entire body. The

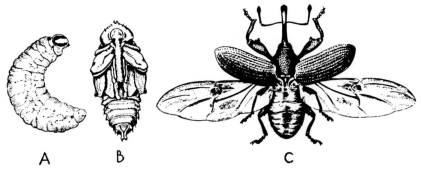

FIG. 170. The boll weevil (*Anthonomus grandis*). **A,** Larva. **B,** Pupa. **C,** Adult. (From Agricultural Research Service, U.S.D.A.)

most distinctive characteristic of the weevil is the presence of two spurs on the inner surface of the front femur. The larva is a white, wrinkled, fat, legless grub, found only in the squares or bolls. It attains a length of ¼ to ⅓ inch.

The adult overwinters in a state of diapause in all types of shelter such as ground and gin trash, seed houses, Spanish moss, and under bark of trees. Those individuals that are best protected, as in Spanish moss or in the deep recesses of woods, have the best chances for survival. Winter mortality is quite high as the average survival is only about 6 percent. Emergence begins in the spring when the mean air temperature reaches 64° F. and may extend over a period of several months. The first weevils to emerge from overwintering feed on the terminal portions of the young cotton plants. When squares become available, they puncture them and feed on the highly nutritious pollen sacs. Eggs are laid in punctures made by the females, one egg being deposited in each square as long as there is a sufficient supply. When the squares are punctured, they usually flare and later drop or else hang on the stalks where they wither and turn brown. Bolls are heavily attacked when squares are not available. Small bolls may drop, but large ones do not, although one or more locks (locules) may be destroyed. The length of life of adult weevils depends greatly upon conditions. During the summer months weevils live an average of 50 days, while some that hibernate in the fall may live into the next summer.

Female boll weevils oviposit an average of about 100 eggs. These are laid over a period of about one month. The length of the egg stage may be as short as one day, but the average is about three days during the growing season. The larvae feed on the contents of the squares and bolls usually for a period of seven to 12 days before the completion of growth and pupation. During this period two or three molts occur. The pupae are found within a pupal cell formed in the squares or bolls. The length of the pupal stage is three to five days. The adults emerge, and about a week later females begin oviposition. A life cycle may be completed in three weeks; however the seasonal average length is somewhat longer. The average number of generations is four to six annually. With the approach of cold weather in the fall, weevils seek overwintering quarters.

Climate is the most important check on the boll weevil. Extremely cold weather in the winter may destroy most of the adults in hibernation. Hot, dry weather is also a powerful check, especially on immature forms. The boll weevil has more than 50 insects and arachnids which attack it. Often they destroy large percentages of the immature forms. Natural factors, however, are not sufficient to keep the weevil in check. Other available control measures must be employed also. Overwintering quarters within the field, such as weeds and debris along fence rows, ditch banks, and roadsides, should be eliminated. The use of quick maturing varieties of cotton and planting of the crop reasonably early aid in maturing the crop before the boll weevil population increases to such large proportions. The destruction of cotton stalks as soon as the crop is harvested and as long before frost as possible eliminates late-season increases of weevils and forces the adults into a starvation period prior to the time of hibernation. This practice, when conducted on a community-wide basis, materially reduces the number of weevils to emerge the next season.

The boll weevil is difficult to control with insecticides because the adult is largely an internal feeder and the immature stages are found only in the squares and bolls. However, a number of insecticides will kill the adult if they are correctly applied. Recommendations for the control of the boll weevil and other cotton insects differ in various sections of the Cotton Belt. The cotton farmer should procure from his local agricultural authority current detailed recommendations for his state, and these should be carefully followed.

Except for early season control, applications of insecticides should begin when 15 to 25 percent of the squares are punctured. These applications should be repeated at intervals of five days until the weevil is controlled. In those sections where early season control is recommended, two or more applications of insecticides are made at weekly intervals beginning before any of the first squares are one-third grown, to prevent egg laying.

There is a choice of several insecticides and their combinations available for use in a boll weevil control program. The insecticides employed are dependent upon several factors, such as costs, and presence of resistant weevils or of other pests, such as bollworms, aphids and spider mites. Among the more generally used poisons are sevin, toxaphene, methyl parathion, Guthion, and endrin.

The Rice Weevil (*Sitophilus oryza*). The rice weevil (Fig. 171**A**) is believed to be the most destructive insect attacking stored grain. It is a small, reddish-brown weevil about $\frac{1}{8}$ inch in length with the wing covers marked with four lighter reddish spots. Corn, rice, wheat, maize, and other seed or seed products are attacked. Adults may feed upon flour, but larvae cannot develop on it unless the material is caked. The female chews a hole in each seed preparatory to egg deposition. Three hundred to 400 eggs may be laid during a period of four or five months by a single female. The eggs hatch into white legless grubs which feed upon the contents of the seed. The immature stages are never found outside of the seed. When conditions are most favorable, the adult stage may be reached in less than four weeks from the time the egg is laid. In Kansas, four or five generations occur each year. In the South grain is attacked in the field as soon as the kernels become hard, and development may continue throughout the winter. In colder climates the insect is primarily a stored grain pest and seldom attacks grain in the field. The granary weevil (*Sitophilus granarius,* Fig. 171**B**) is closely related to the rice weevil in hosts, habits, and life history. It is quite similar in appearance to the rice weevil, but lacks the light reddish spots on the wing covers; also, the wing covers are fused together and the insect cannot fly. This insect never attacks grain in the field and is strictly a stored grain pest.

Most of the loss caused by grain weevils may be prevented by the use of proper control measures. Much of the infestation in fields

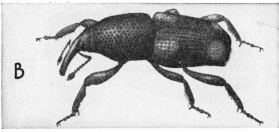

FIG. 171. **A,** The granary weevil (*Sitophilus granarius*). **B,** The rice weevil (*Sitophilus oryza*). (From the University of California Division of Agricultural Sciences.)

may be prevented by fumigating or disposing of infested grain in storage before the crops begin to ripen. Bins should be thoroughly cleaned, and the surfaces sprayed with either methoxychlor or malathion before the new crops is stored. The moisture content of the grain should not be more than 12 percent. Malathion may be employed as a grain protectant. Several fumigants are effective in control of stored grain pests if properly used. Among the more commonly used are mixtures containing carbon tetrachloride and either ethylene dichloride or carbon disulphide. Much rice in storage is fumigated with methyl bromide.

The Sweet-Potato Weevil (*Cylas formicarius elegantulus*). This is the most important insect pest of the sweet potato (Fig. 172). The

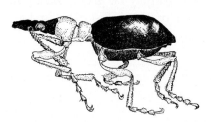

insect is widely distributed over the Gulf States; its native home is probably Asia.

Infested potatoes are honey-combed by the feeding of the grubs and their tortuous tunnels are filled with excrement. The grubs are legless, dirty-white with yellowish-brown heads, and about ¼ inch in

FIG. 172. The sweet-potato weevil (*Cylas formicarius elegantulus*).

length. Infested potatoes are bitter in taste and are unfit for human consumption. The larvae also feed in stems and roots.

The adult weevils are shiny snout beetles about ¼ inch in length and ant-like in appearance. The head, wing covers, and abdomen are blue-black, while the thorax and legs are reddish-brown. The adults feed on leaves, vines, sweet potatoes, and roots. In addition to sweet potatoes, the insect breeds to some extent in the roots of various species of morning glory.

Breeding is continuous during the year, with stored sweet potatoes being attacked throughout the winter. One overlapping generation follows another with a possibility of five or more annually. Under favorable conditions adults may live for several months.

Since flight is not important in the dissemination of the insect, most infestations begin through the use of infested slips or seed sweet potatoes. Quarantines are maintained to prevent the spread of the pest and to assist in eradication and control. In areas of light infestations, the insect may be eradicated if proper practices are followed. Only weevil-free slips or seed sweet potatoes should be used. Rotation and thorough cleanup of crop residues must be practiced. All infested sweet potatoes must be disposed of and storage places thoroughly sprayed with DDT.

In areas of general infestations, the same cultural control measures should be practiced. Also, stored sweet potatoes may be dusted with DDT or methoxychlor at the rate of ⅕ ounce per crate. Excess residue must be removed before marketing or consumption.

Sweet potato slips or draws may be fumigated with methyl bromide. Three pounds of methyl bromide per 1,000 cubic feet of space in a fumigation chamber with an exposure of five hours is recommended. Cured sweet potatoes may also be fumigated with methyl bromide. It is not advisable to hold sweet potatoes long following fumigation.

The Plum Curculio (*Conotrachelus nenuphar*). The plum curculio (Fig. 173) is a destructive pest of fruit, particularly plums, peaches, cherries, apricots, and apples. This native American insect is found east of the Rocky Mountains. The adult beetle is about $\frac{3}{16}$ inch long, dark brown, with mottlings of white and gray, and with four humps on its elytra. The larva is a whitish, crescent-shaped legless grub about $\frac{1}{3}$ inch in length.

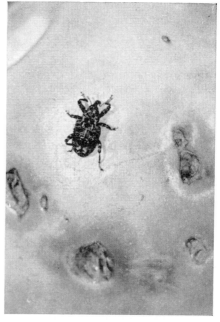

FIG. 173. The plum curculio (*Conotrachelus nenuphar*) and injury on section of fruit. (From Department of Entomology, A & M College of Texas.)

Injury produced by the curculio is in several forms. Much of the fruit may be destroyed by larval feeding on the pulpy tissues. Although it may not be destroyed, infested fruit is "wormy" and worthless. Feeding and egg-laying punctures of the adults cause knotted, gnarled, and misshapen fruit. The insect is also an important agency in the dissemination of brown rot of peaches.

Adults overwinter in leaves, bark, rubbish, grass, and other protected places. They emerge in the spring and feed first on buds, calyxes, and newly formed fruit. Females lay an average of less than 100 eggs. These are deposited in holes made by the snout through the skin of the fruit. After the egg is laid, the female cuts a crescent-shaped slit around it. This slit extends underneath the egg, leaving it in a flap of dead or dying tissues so that proliferating cells will not crush the egg or young larva. The eggs hatch in two to 12 days. In stone fruits, the young larvae tunnel to the center of the fruit and feed around the stone for two or three weeks. At the end of this time, the larvae leave the fruit and enter the ground to a depth of one to several inches. Here a pupal cell is formed and the insect transforms into the pupal stage. Thirty to 35 days after entering the soil, the adult emerges. The length of a life cycle from egg to adult is usually 50 to 55 days. In the North only one generation occurs annually, but in the South two full generations may develop in favorable seasons.

There are several orchard practices which aid in controlling the pest. Dropped and culled fruit should be gathered periodically and destroyed before the larvae have completed development and entered the soil for pupation. The ground underneath the spread of the trees should be disced at intervals to destroy the pupal cells. Most adults hibernate in the immediate environment of the orchards. The destruction of trash, leaves, and grass by burning or by other means will eliminate many of the overwintering insects.

In heavily infested areas, it is necessary to follow a definite spray schedule to control the pest satisfactorily. Spray schedules for various fruits differ, and schedules for the same fruits are not the same in different sections of the country. This necessitates obtaining correct spray information from the local or state agricultural authorities. Usually two or three well-timed combination sprays when the curculios are most active in feeding and oviposition will control the pest. Dieldrin or parathion in combination with a fungicide provides satisfactory control if the spray is thoroughly applied.

The Plum Gouger (*Anthonomus scutellaris*). The plum gouger is a pest primarily of native plums. Domestic plums, apricots, and prunes are also attacked. It is occasionally reported infesting peaches. Adults are reddish-brown with yellowish head and thorax. They are about ¼ inch in length. Larvae are legless grubs found in the pit of the fruit. Adults, in feeding and ovipositing, make small holes in the fruit. Upon hatching, the grubs tunnel into the pits and feed upon the kernels. Pupation occurs within the pits and adults emerge in late summer. Only one generation is produced each season. Control measures for the plum curculio are also recommended for this pest.

The Pecan Weevil (*Curculio caryae*). This insect (Fig. 174) is a pest of pecans in the southern states. Hickory nuts are also attacked. The adult is gray or light brown and its body is slightly less than ½ inch long. The snout of the female is somewhat longer than the body.

Adults usually emerge following rains during late summer. They feed first on the developing nuts which causes them to drop. When the kernels develop in the earliest varieties, females begin to lay eggs in the nuts. Early maturing varieties suffer the greatest damage. Eggs hatch in a week, and the larvae feed upon the kernels for about a month. Larvae emerge from the nuts through holes about ⅛ inch in diameter. Larval emergence extends from September through December, with the highest emergence in October. Larvae enter the soil to a depth of one to 12 inches where pupal cells are formed. The life history of the insect is imperfectly known; however, it is believed that pupation occurs the current fall, and in some cases the following fall. Thus, there may be a generation annually, or the life cycle may extend over a period of two years.

In those sections where the insect is a pest, checking for its presence should begin in early August. This is done by spreading a canvas under the trees and jarring the lower limbs. Control measures should begin when three or more weevils per tree are col-

FIG. 174. Pecan weevils (*Curculio caryae*) on nuts. (From Agricultural Research Service, U.S.D.A.)

lected. The trees should be thoroughly sprayed with DDT. If the infestation is severe, the spray should be repeated in two weeks. In orchards known to be infested, the nuts should be gathered as early as possible. The nuts should be placed in containers with tight bottoms or on tight floors so the emerging larvae cannot reach the soil and complete the life cycle.

Family *Scolytidae* (Bark Beetles)

Bark beetles (Fig. 175) are small to medium insects, measuring from one to nine millimeters in length. They are usually cylindrical in form and brown to black in color. The posterior end of the body

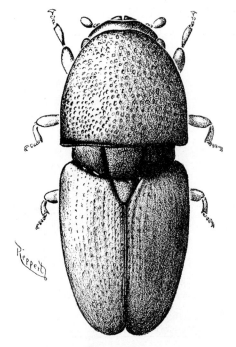

FIG. 175. A bark beetle. (From Department of Entomology, A & M College of Texas.)

of many species ends abruptly as if cut off. The antennae are elbowed and clubbed on the end. Larvae are small, whitish, legless grubs.

Most bark beetles are wood borers, living principally under the bark or burrowing in hardwood. Patterns made by the tunnels of adults and larvae on bark and sapwood and burrows in the heartwood are quite characteristic and a species often may be identified by these markings. Bark beetles spend almost their entire existence in their burrows. Adults usually leave their burrows only long enough to locate new hosts.

On the basis of tunneling habits and nature of food materials, bark beetles may be divided into three groups: (1) true scolytids which engrave the inner bark and sapwood; (2) wood-eating bark beetles which tunnel and feed on sapwood and heartwood; (3) Ambrosia beetles, found in sapwood and which feed, as both larvae and adults, on ambrosia (fungi) which they invariably grow in their burrows.

Hosts of most bark beetles are forest trees; however, some attack fruit trees and herbaceous plants. Dead, dying, or devitalized timber is usually attacked; but some species attack trees that are healthy or only slightly devitalized.

Habits of bark beetles vary with the species. In general, an entrance gallery is made through the bark. Then it is either widened into an irregular cavity or one or more branching galleries are constructed, extending in diagonal, longitudinal or transverse directions. Eggs are deposited in a mass in the irregular cavity or in one of several ways in the egg galleries, as in niches. Upon hatching, the larvae usually make separate tunnels at right angles to the egg gallery, but they may work together in a common chamber.

The Shot-Hole Borer (*Scolytus rugulosus*). This insect is a pest of importance of most deciduous fruit trees. Its presence is recognized by small holes in the bark (Fig. 176). These holes are made by the adults when they emerge and later reënter the trees. Injury results from the feeding and tunneling of both larvae and adults between the bark and the cambium.

The adult beetle is a small, black beetle about $\frac{1}{10}$ inch in length with the body quite blunt at each end. Adults emerge in the spring, mate, and the females search out new hosts for egg deposition. Usually healthy trees are not attacked if weak trees are available. Entrance holes are made in branches usually near lenticels or projections. The females excavate galleries extending in parallel directions with the branches. Eggs are deposited on the sides of the galleries. These eggs hatch in a few days into white grubs which tunnel directly away from the parent gallery. Later, these larval tunnels turn in various directions. Larval maturity is reached in six to eight weeks. Pupation occurs in the

FIG. 176. Holes made by the shot-hole borer (*Scolytus rugulosus*) in apple wood. (From Agricultural Research Service, U.S.D.A.)

burrows, from which the adults emerge to mate and begin a new generation. The insect hibernates as larvae underneath the bark. One to four generations occur annually.

The most satisfactory method of preventing and overcoming attacks of the insect is keeping trees in the best possible condition. In healthy, vigorous trees the flow of sap tends to prevent larval development. Proper fertilization, watering, cultivation, and pruning practices should be followed. Diseased trees and limbs should be removed during the dormant season. All prunings should be gathered and burned. Spraying in the spring with DDT will destroy many adults when they leave or re-enter the trees.

FIG. 177. Winding galleries of the southern pine beetle (*Dendroctonus frontalis*). The larger galleries are made by larvae of the southern pine sawyer (*Monochamus titillator*). (From Agricultural Research Service, U.S.D.A.)

The Southern Pine Beetle (*Dendroctonus frontalis*). The genus *Dendroctonus* contains several species of very destructive pests of coniferous trees. One of the most important is the southern pine beetle whose range extends from Pennsylvania to Florida and westward to Texas and Oklahoma. It infests and kills healthy pines when conditions are favorable, as well as devitalized and dying trees. Losses in the southern states due to this pest amount to millions of dollars. Usually the first indication of damage by this insect is the presence of dead or dying trees. The inner bark or wood surface will show S-shaped egg tunnels with short larval tunnels leading out from the sides (Fig. 177). The middle and upper portion of the trunks of the trees are most commonly attacked. The adult beetles are about ⅛ inch long, brownish or black, and with the posterior end of the body smoothly rounded. The insect reproduces rapidly, completing a generation in 30 to 40 days under favorable conditions. There are as many as five generations annually. Winter is spent in all stages.

Epidemics of the southern pine beetle follow droughts or severe storms which have damaged timber, and large scale logging operations. Cutting timber in dry weather should be avoided. The removal of infested and weakened trees is recommended.

Order STREPSIPTERA[2]

Stylopids or Twisted-Wing Parasites

Members of the order Strepsiptera are very small internal parasites, seldom observed even by entomologists. They are of little economic importance. Only about 300 species are known, yet they are
widely distributed. Their morphology is so unusual that they comprise a separate and distinct order.

The order is characterized as follows:

1. **Wings, present in the males only, four in number with the first
   pair reduced to paddle-like vestigial wings (elytra), and the second
   pair broad triangular, with reduced venation and folding fan-like.**
2. **Mouthparts in the male degenerate, in the female vestigial or
   wanting.**
3. **Metamorphosis complete.**
4. **Eyes stalked, antennae flabellate, and metathorax enlarged in the
   male. The female is worm-like with no legs, eyes, antennae, or
   wings.**

Stylopids are endoparasites of certain Hymenoptera, Homoptera,
Hemiptera, Orthoptera, and Thysanura. The largest males (Fig.
178) are not more than three millimeters in length. The presence
of the parasites is indicated by small disc-like or rounded and tu-
berculate objects extending between the abdominal segments of the

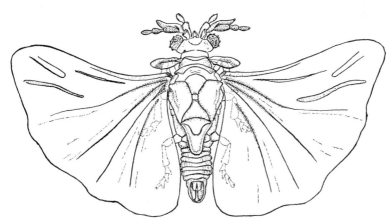

FIG. 178. An adult male of a stylopid or twisted-wing parasite. (After Essig, *College
Entomology*, 1942. By permission of The Macmillan Company.)

[2] *Strepis*, turning; *pteron*, wing.

host insect. The projected portions are the anterior ends of the parasites.

Biology of stylopids is imperfectly known and only an outline of their life activities can be given. The adult male is free-living and can fly. It lives only a short time. Copulation is effected by the male through an opening between the extruded head and thorax of the female. The young larvae escape to the outside of the host and seek the immature stages of other hosts. When a new host is found, the larva burrows through the body wall and becomes an internal parasite. Upon molting, the larva becomes grub-like and legless. Nourishment is thought to be taken from the body of the host by osmosis. Near the close of the larval stage the parasite works its anterior end out so that it extrudes between the abdominal segments of the host. The male pupates in a puparium formed by the last two larval skins. Escape of the adult male is effected by pushing off the operculum of the puparium. The female remains worm-like her entire life within the body of the host insect.

17

ORDERS NEUROPTERA
AND MECOPTERA

Order NEUROPTERA[1]

Dobsonflies, Lacewings, Ant Lions, and Others

The Neuroptera are chiefly predaceous insects, and some species are highly beneficial. Members of the order may vary greatly in size and appearance but body structure is quite similar in all forms.

The chief characteristics of the group are:

1. **Two pairs of large membranous wings, usually with many veins and cross-veins, similar in size and texture, and held roof-like over the body when at rest.**
2. **Mouthparts formed for chewing but modified into sucking organs in the larvae of several families.**
3. **Complete metamorphosis.**
4. **Cerci absent; tarsi with five segments.**

This is not a large order of insects, there being only about 4,000 known species. The biology of the group is quite variable. Most of the larvae are predaceous, but some are parasitic; no harmful species are known. Some species develop in water; most are found on land. Some of the larvae pupate in cells within the soil; most of them spin silken pupal cases, the silk for which is produced by the Malpighian tubes spun from the anus. Mouthparts are for chewing, but in several families the mandibles and maxillae of the larvae are modified for sucking the body fluids of the prey. In these larvae the

[1] *Neuron*, nerve; *pteron*, wing.

mandibles are long, curved, and fitted for grasping and piercing. Each mandible is ventrally furrowed and the corresponding maxilla underneath has a dorsal groove. The two furrows form a tube extending from the tip of the combined mandible and maxilla to the mouth cavity. Larvae are long, somewhat flattened, and with well developed legs.

Family *Sialidae* (Dobsonflies, Alder Flies, and Fish Flies)

The best known insect of this family is the dobsonfly or corydalus (*Corydalus cornutus*, Fig. 179), the larva of which is the dobson or

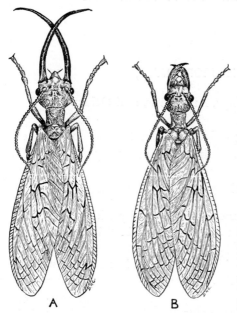

FIG. 179. Dobsonflies (*Corydalus cornutus*). **A,** Male. **B,** Female.

hellgrammite. The adult is quite large, with a wing expanse of four or five inches. The males have strikingly long curved mandibles, which are relatively short in the females. The larvae are predaceous on aquatic insects and are found under stones and chunks of hard earth in swiftly flowing water. They have paired lateral filaments with a tuft of tracheal gills at the base of each on the first seven abdominal segments. The mature larvae are about three inches in length. Hellgrammites are prized for use as fish bait by many fishermen. When mature, the larvae leave the water and pupate underneath stones and other debris. About a month later the adults emerge. Soon after emergence, the females lay eggs in masses on limbs, stones, and other objects overhanging the water. Upon hatching, the larvae drop into the water. Adults live for only a short time. Two or three years are required for a life cycle.

Alder flies (*Sialis*) and fish flies (*Chauliodes, Neohermes,* and *Nigronia*) occur in about the same environment as dobsonflies. They are smaller and darker in color. Only one year is required for a life cycle of these insects.

Family *Chrysopidae* (Lacewing Flies or Aphis Lions)

The lacewing flies (Fig. 180) are well known insects. Their larvae, called aphis lions, are among the more important beneficial insects.

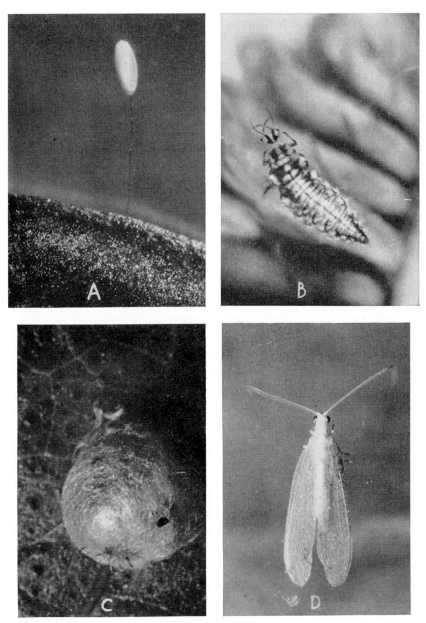

FIG. 180. Lacewing fly (*Chrysopa*). **A,** Egg on silken stalk. **B,** Larva. **C,** Cocoon. **D,** Adult. (From Department of Entomology, A & M College of Texas.)

They feed voraciously upon aphids; thrips; mites; young corn ear-worms; and other small, soft-bodied insects or eggs.

The adults are recognized by their usually greenish or yellowish-green color, delicate lace-like wings, and shining golden eyes of some species. They are rather delicate, soft-bodied insects and are less than one inch in length. Some species emit a disagreeable odor when handled or crushed, and for this reason are sometimes known as stink-flies.

The larvae have been named aphis lions because they prey chiefly upon aphids or plant lice. The aphis lions are elongate spindle-shaped (alligator-like) larvae with long sickle-like mandibles. These characteristic mandibles readily distinguish them from lady beetle larvae, which they resemble. The larvae are very active in seeking their prey and obtain their food by puncturing the body of the victim and extracting the body fluids with their unusual mouthparts.

Among the more common species of lacewing flies are *Chrysopa oculata*, *Chrysopa californica*, and *Chrysopa rufilabris*. Lacewing flies usually hibernate in their silken cocoons as prepupae. Some are reported to overwinter as adults. The adults emerge in the spring when the weather becomes sufficiently warm. Eggs are laid on silken stalks which project about $\frac{1}{2}$ inch above the surface of the leaves or stems to which they are attached. It is thought the stalks protect the eggs from the natural enemies, particularly larvae of their own kind. Females probably lay an average of several hundred eggs each under natural conditions. Eggs hatch in about a week. Larvae are voracious feeders upon aphids and other small insects. At the end of the third instar, the larvae seek sheltered places on leaves or else-where and spin cocoons in which they pupate. The larval period averages between two and three weeks; the pupal period is of similar duration. The completion of a generation averages about 40 days; there may be five or six generations annually in warm climates.

Family *Myrmeleontidae* (Doodlebugs or Ant Lions)

Doodlebugs or ant lions are known by almost everyone, yet few realize they are the larvae of graceful gauzy-winged insects (Fig. 181) which superficially resemble damselflies of the order Odonata. They may be readily distinguished from the latter by the antennae, which instead of being small and inconspicuous, are rather large and terminally enlarged. The joint-like structure, the nodus, on the front margin of the wings is also absent. Larvae are broad, spindle-shaped, and somewhat flat. The head bears large and powerful mouthparts of the grasping-sucking type previously described. Principal food consists of ants. The larvae spin spherical silken cocoons in which they pupate.

Food is captured in various ways. Larvae of most species probably do not make pits to trap their prey but conceal themselves in sand or trash, and await the passing of an unwary insect, or else actively search for their victims. The best known forms, however, construct cone-like pits. They are members of the genera *Myrmeleon* and *Hesperoleon*. The pits are constructed in sandy soil in protected places, such as at the base of trees, and near or underneath build-

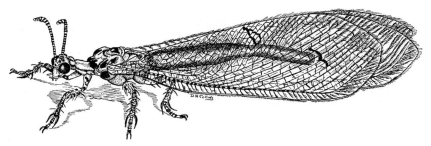

FIG. 181. Adult of doodlebug or ant lion.

ings. The pits are one to two inches in diameter with a depth consistent with the nature of the soil. The ant lion lies concealed in the sand at the bottom of the pit and waits for an ant or other small insect to fall into the trap where it is quickly seized and drained of its body fluids. When an insect attempts to crawl out of the trap, the ant lion flips sand upon it, which usually sweeps the victim within reach of his powerful jaws. A doodlebug or ant lion constructs a number of pits during its life. As the larva grows, progressively larger pits are constructed; and, also, many pits are destroyed by rains, winds, and other agencies. The length of development of these insects is imperfectly known but indications are that about two years are required for a complete life cycle.

The family *Ascalaphidae* is closely related to the *Myrmeleontidae*. Members of this family may be readily distinguished from those of the latter by their long antennae. Adults have the habit of remaining motionless when at rest on a branch or stem. At this time the antennae are held parallel to the resting surface with the head depressed, abdomen elevated, and wings drooping. Both larvae and adults are predaceous. Larvae resemble doodlebugs, but are commonly larger. They do not construct pits but lie in ambush partly concealed on the ground and wait for the prey to come near enough to be seized. The ascalaphids, such as the myrmeleontids, are commonly found in regions of sandy soils.

Adult members of the family *Mantispidae* are very unusual in appearance. They resemble praying mantids with their elongate prothorax and front legs fitted for grasping prey. The adults are predaceous, but the insects are not numerous enough to be of much benefit as predators. Little is known of the biology of the group. As far as is known, the larvae feed on spider eggs and in wasp nests.

Order MECOPTERA[2]

Scorpion Flies

Members of this order have the following characteristics:

1. **Wings, rarely absent, two pairs, long, narrow, and net-veined.**
2. **Mouthparts chewing, located at the end of an elongated deflexed beak.**
3. **Complete metamorphosis.**
4. **Larvae resemble caterpillars.**

The ordinal name of this group of insects is derived from wing characteristics. The pincer-like organs, resembling the sting of a scorpion, on the end of the abdomen of the males (Fig. 182) of the most common forms have given rise to the common name. This is a small order, both in species and numbers, but its members are found in most parts of the world.

FIG. 182. A male scorpion fly (*Panorpa*).

The most distinctive characteristic of the order is the elongation of the head on the underside, which forms a deflexed beak with chewing mouthparts at the tip. Wings are long and narrow with a number of cross-veins. In one group, wings are lacking or vestigial. Antennae are long and slender; the tarsi are five-segmented.

[2] *Mecos*, length; *pteron*, wing.

Most scorpion flies belong to the genus *Panorpa*. The wings are marked with yellow and black. The adults, which appear in late summer and fall, are commonly found in moist places where there is a growth of rank vegetation. Larvae resemble caterpillars but have more abdominal legs. They live on the ground in rotten vegetative material or moss in wooded, damp environments. Both adults and larvae are scavengers, feeding on dead insects and other animal matter. The biology of these insects is imperfectly known.

Certain species are known as hanging flies. This name has been applied to them because they hang by their long legs from a supporting object when at rest. In flight they may be mistaken for crane flies. Adults catch their prey while in the resting position. When a small insect comes within reach, it is seized by the hind legs and transferred to the mouthparts where it is quickly devoured. Larvae of hanging flies are found in the same habitat as those of the genus *Panorpa* and have similar food habits.

18

ORDERS TRICHOPTERA AND LEPIDOPTERA

Order TRICHOPTERA[1]

Caddisflies

Characteristics of the order may be summarized as follows:

1. **Two pairs of membranous wings, usually covered with long hairs, and held roof-like over the body when at rest.**
2. **Mouthparts of the adults rudimentary, except the palpi.**
3. **Metamorphosis complete.**
4. **Larvae are aquatic (rare exceptions) and construct either cases or nets in which they live.**

The order Trichoptera is rather small both in number of species and size of the individuals. Caddisflies (Fig. 183) are moth-like in appearance, and most of them are somber in color. Their bodies are somewhat soft and clothed with long hairs. They are not strong fliers and are found most frequently in the vicinity of the aquatic environment of the larvae. They are nocturnal in habit. The wings are membranous with the front pair longer and usually narrower than the hind pair. They are generally clothed with long hairs but sometimes are almost naked; in rare exceptions, scales are present. When the insects are at rest, the wings are held over the abdomen like the roof of a house. Antennae are long and bristle-like. Mouthparts are rudimentary with the exception of the palpi which are quite well developed. Legs are long and the tarsi have five segments.

[1] *Trichos,* hair; *pteron,* wing.

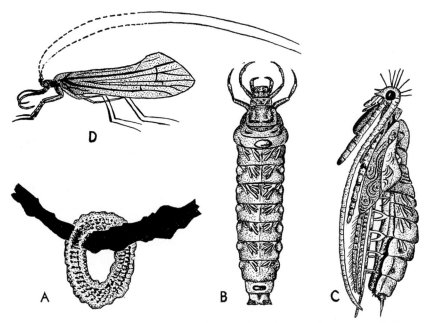

FIG. 183.   Developmental stages of a typical caddisfly. **A,** Eggs of *Phryganea*. **B,** Larva. **C,** Pupa of *Halesus*. **D,** Adult of *Leptocerus*. (After Frost, *General Entomology,* 1942. By permission of McGraw-Hill Book Company.)

Female caddisflies lay from several hundred to 1,000 eggs either in the water or upon objects above its surface. They are usually laid in a gelatinous mass which absorbs water and swells. Often species may be identified by the form of the egg mass and the arrangement of eggs in the gelatinous matrix.

The larvae, known as caddisworms, resemble caterpillars but lack prolegs, except the anal pair. Thoracic legs are well developed and mouthparts are for chewing. They respire by means of tracheal gills, blood gills, or a combina-

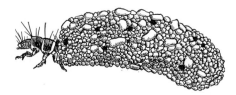

FIG. 184.   Caddisworm and its case. (After Ross, from Illinois Natural History Survey.)

tion of both. Caddisworms feed upon both animal and vegetable materials; however, some are predominantly predaceous and feed on small insect larvae. Most caddisworms build portable cases (Fig. 184) in which they live, while others construct nets. Those larvae living in portable cases crawl partly out of the cases which are dragged along wherever they go. Larvae of those species which construct nets to catch food, live in tubes constructed of silk and debris. Cases differ in form and construction with the species. Silk is spun from the modified salivary glands through an opening in the labium, usually in a sheet-like mass. The cases of some species are constructed only of silk. Usually other materials, such as small pebbles, grains of sand, bits of leaves, or wood, are incorporated in the case and bound together with the silk. The cases are varied in shape, ranging in form from a straight tube to the coiled case of *Heliopsyche* which is quite like a snail shell. The interior of the case is lined with silk, which protects the soft abdomen of the larva.

The net-spinning species are found in swift water or along shores of lakes. The nets are funnel-like and are held open by the current. In the bottom of the funnel a strainer is constructed to capture food. The tube in which the larva lives opens into this strainer.

Mature caddisworms do not leave the water for pupation since the pupae are also aquatic. Pupae are of the exarate type with legs and wings free. Before the larva pupates, a cocoon is spun which, in the case-making forms, is simply made by lining the interior of the case with silk and closing the ends. The net-building forms spin special pupal cases of silk, sand, pebbles, or other materials. These cases are firmly cemented to stones or other objects in the swift water. Following pupation, the wings of those species that emerge from swift water expand instantly upon reaching the surface and the adults fly away immediately to prevent their being swept away by the current.

The complete life cycle of the caddisfly usually requires a year, most of which is spent in the larval stage. The egg stage is short; the length of the pupal stage is two or three weeks; and the adult lives for about a month. About 800 species are found in the Nearctic fauna.

Caddisflies are of little economic importance; however, they must be regarded as beneficial since the larvae are important sources of food for fish. In river towns the adults are occasionally pestiferous since great numbers may be attracted to lights.

Order LEPIDOPTERA[2]

Moths, Skippers, and Butterflies

The Lepidoptera are one of the largest and most important orders of insects. They are exceeded in numbers of species only by the

[2] *Lepis,* scale; *pteron,* wing.

Coleoptera (Beetles). The number of species in the order is estimated to be almost 150,000, of which 10,000 species are thought to occur in North America.

The chief distinguishing characteristics of the Lepidoptera are summarized as:

1. **Two pairs of membranous wings (rarely absent) covered with overlapping scales.**
2. **Mouthparts formed for sucking.**
3. **Complete metamorphosis.**
4. **Larvae, known as caterpillars, with chewing mouthparts.**

Members of the order are readily recognized by the scales on the wings and body. When a section of a wing is examined under magnification, the scales in the more specialized groups will be seen to be arranged like shingles on the roof of a house. The scales provide strength and rigidity for the wings and are also the source of color. The brilliant, striking colors of these insects are produced by pigmentation, and by diffraction of light by the striae on the scales or by the thin film-like plates which make up their walls.

Insects of this order are commonly known as moths (Fig. 185), butterflies, and skippers. Moths have stout bodies, and the wings when at rest are held in a horizontal position, roof-like over the

FIG. 185. A giant silkworm moth (*Hyalophora calleta*).

abdomen, or wrapped about the body. The antennae of moths are variable in form but are usually filamentous or feather-like in appearance. They fly chiefly at night. Bodies of butterflies are slender, the wings are held vertically when at rest, and the antennae are slender and club-like at the tips. They are day-fliers. Skippers dart or skip through the air in flight during the day. Their bodies are intermediate in form between the moths and common butterflies, and their wings are held erect when at rest. The antennae of skippers are club-like at the tips but usually a hook-like process is present on the end of the club or knob.

Wings of lepidopterous insects are usually broad and somewhat triangular in form with the front pair larger. Venation (Fig. 186) in the more generalized forms closely resembles the hypothetical type. In the more specialized groups there is a reduction of the wing veins, especially in the hind wings. Special structures are often present to synchronize the front and hind pairs of wings in flight. These may be (1) an enlargement of the humeral angle of the hind wing to extend well underneath the front wing; (2) a group of bristles (one stout bristle in the male), the frenulum, arising from the humeral angle of the hind wing, extending underneath the front wing, and fitting into a pocket or clasp; or (3) rarely, a finger-like process (jugum) extending from the base of the front wing underneath the hind wing.

Mouthparts of most adults are specialized for sucking. In typical mouthparts the palpi and maxillae are well developed. When only one pair of palpi is present, it is the labial palpi. If the maxillary palpi are present, they may be recognized by the attachment to the maxillae. If mouthparts are not vestigial, a long, sucking tube (the proboscis) is found coiled underneath the head like a watch spring. This tube is formed by the elongate galeae of the maxillae fused together on the inner margins. Each of the galeae is grooved on the inner surface; and when the two are brought together, a sucking tube is formed. The proboscis is adapted for feeding on nectar of flowers and plant juices. In some species spines are present on the tip of the proboscis. These enable the insect to lacerate the thin skin of some fruits and suck the juices. As an example, the cotton leafworm moth may damage figs and late peaches. However, this type of injury by moths is quite rare. In visiting flowers, moths and butterflies perform some service in the pollination of plants. Small moths are frequently pestiferous around lights during warm seasons.

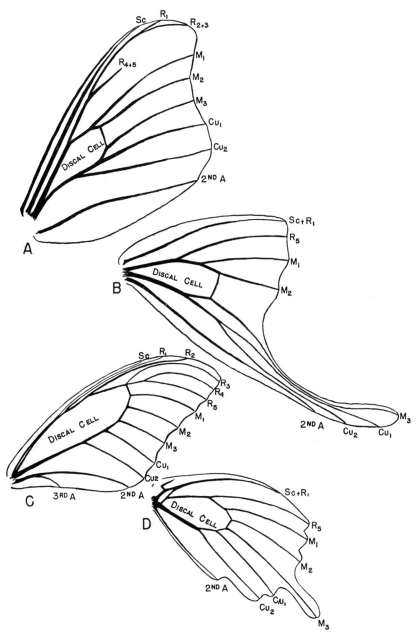

FIG. 186. Wings of Lepidoptera showing venation. **A** and **B,** Wings of the luna moth (*Actias luna*). **C** and **D,** Wings of the giant swallowtail butterfly (*Papilio cresphontes*).

Larvae are commonly known as caterpillars (Fig. 187). They do not have the least resemblance to the adults into which they develop. Caterpillars are worm-like, usually cylindrical and vary much in form and appearance. In addition to the three pairs of thoracic legs, there are two to five pairs of abdominal legs, termed prolegs, which are thick, fleshy, membranous and not segmented. They are

FIG. 187.   A common caterpillar, the armyworm *(Pseudaletia unipuncta)*. (From Department of Entomology, A & M College of Texas.)

shed with the last larval molt. The pair of prolegs on the last (10th) abdominal segment is termed the anal prolegs. When all pairs of prolegs are present, they are borne by the 3rd, 4th, 5th, 6th, and 10th abdominal segments. The tip of a proleg is called the planta upon which are borne hooks or claws known as crochets. The crochets are an aid in crawling and clinging to surfaces. The arrangement and form of the crochets are of much value in the identification of lepidopterous larvae.

Most caterpillars have relatively few inconspicuous setae or hairs on their bodies. However, some are woolly in appearance. All graduations in density of setal vesture occur. With the exception of highly specialized forms, setae on the segments of the bodies of the larvae are quite definite in number and arrangement. The number and position of the setae differ, thus affording valuable characters for identifying caterpillars. The head is usually well developed and bears short antennae, ommatidia (simple eyes), and chewing mouthparts. Caterpillars feed, with the exception of the larvae of clothes moths and a few others, upon plants or their products. Almost every plant has some species of caterpillar feeding upon some part of it or its products. Inasmuch as many of the most important insect pests are caterpillars, the order is of much economic importance.

When larvae are mature they usually spin silken cocoons in which they pupate. The silk is secreted by silk glands (modified salivary glands) and spun from a spinneret located on the tip of the labium. Hairs, leaves, or soil may be incorporated with the silk in the formation of the cocoon. Some cocoons are very elaborate, e.g., the cocoons of silkworms, while others may be quite simple. Larvae of butterflies form naked pupae, known as chrysalids, which have the tip of the abdomen secured to a branch, stem, or other object by a pad of silk—some are held in an upright position by a silken belt placed around the body.

Lepidopterous pupae are of the obtect type which have developing antennae, legs, wings, and mouthparts firmly cemented to the body. This characteristic, together with the long slender sclerites, which form the maxillae, located along the midventral surface of the body, identifies most pupae of the order.

KEY TO SOME COMMON FAMILIES OF LEPIDOPTERA

1. Wings absent or reduced to pads. This group applies only
    to females. All males have well developed wings   2
    Wings well developed   4
2. Adult females grub-like, footless, and seldom leave the
    larval case (Bagworms)   **Psychidae,** p. 312
    Adult females not in a case; legs present   3
3. Body of adult clothed with fine hairs; eggs deposited on or
    near cocoons (Tussock Moths)   **Lymantriidae,** p. 346
    Body of adult densely clothed with scales or spines, or with
    dark gray hairs; female active and deposits eggs removed
    from cocoons (Measuring Worms)   **Geometridae,** p. 343
4. Antennae varied in form, but rarely, if ever, ending in a
    club. If antennae are clubbed, frenulum is always present   5
    Antennae terminating in a club; frenulum wanting   34
5. Hind wing often linear or lanceolate; hind wing narrower
    than anal fringe of hairs   6
    Hind wing much broader than the anal fringe of hairs,
    not lanceolate   15
6. Second segment of labial palpi bristled on outer side
    (Clothes Moths)   **Tineidae,** p. 310
    Labial palpi scaled or clothed loosely with silky hairs   7
7. Maxillary palpi well developed and folded when in resting
    position   8
    Maxillary palpi vestigial, or projecting forward   9
8. Front wing with R_5 extending to the outer margin (Fig.
    186)   **Plutellidae,** p. 320
    Front wing with R_5 absent or extending to the costa
    (Clothes Moths)   **Tineidae,** p. 310

9. Upper face and vertex clothed with dense bristly hairs; third segment of labial palpi spindle-shaped, equal in length to the second (Clothes Moths)   **Tineidae,** p. 310

  Face covered with smooth and short scales; third segment of labial palpi short with a rough heavy vestiture, or long and pointed   10

10. Hind wing narrowly lanceolate and pointed or linear   11

  Hind wing broad with well-developed anal region, apex usually rounded   12

11. Hind wing sinuate or emarginate below the pointed apex (Gelechiid Moths)   **Gelechiidae,** p. 314

  Hind wing lanceolate, much narrower than the fringe; front wing with only 4 veins extending from the discal cell to the costa   **Plutellidae,** p. 320

12. Cu_2 of the front wing arises from a point before the outer fourth of the discal cell is reached; front wings usually truncate (Tortricids)   **Tortricidae,** p. 324

  Cu_2 of the front wing arises from a point on the outer fourth of the discal cell   13

13. Front wing with 1A missing   **Gelechiidae,** p. 314

  Front wing with 1A present   14

14. Hind wing with R_s and M_1 fused, stalked, or close together   **Plutellidae,** p. 320

  Hind wing with R_s and M_1 well separated (Bagworm Moths)   **Psychidae,** p. 312

15. Wings, especially hind wing, largely devoid of scales; width of front wing about $\frac{1}{4}$ the length; moths day-flying (Clear-wing Moths)   **Aegeriidae,** p. 321

  Wings fully scaled, or if with areas devoid of scales, front wing triangular in form   16

16. Hind wing with 3 anal veins   17

  Hind wing with 1 or 2 anal veins   23

17. $Sc + R_1$ and R_s of the hind wing fused or closely parallel for a considerable distance beyond the apex of the discal cell (Pyralid Moths)   **Pyralididae,** p. 329

  $Sc + R_1$ and R_s of the hind wing more widely separated beyond the apex of the discal cell   18

18. Fringe of hairs on the anal angle of the hind wing conspicuously longer than elsewhere; spurs of the tibiae much longer than the width of the tibiae   6

  Fringe of hairs on the anal angle of hind wing not conspicuously longer than elsewhere; spurs of the tibiae approximately the same length as the width of the tibiae   19

19. $Sc + R_1$ and R_s of the hind wing at least fused to a point beyond the middle of the discal cell; moths densely clothed with light colored or brown woolly hairs (Flannel Moths)   **Megalopygidae,** p. 308

$Sc + R_1$ and R_s of hind wing separate from base or grown together for only a short distance along basal half of discal cell 20

20. 1A and 2A of front wing joined by a cross vein 21

1A and 2A of the front wing not joined by a cross vein 22

21. Front wing with any intercalary cell (formed by M forking in discal cell) (Carpenter Moths) **Cossidae,** p. 307

Front wing with no intercalary cell (Bagworms) **Psychidae,** p. 312

22. Moths with strong narrow wings and heavy spindle-like bodies (Carpenter Moths) **Cossidae,** p. 307

Moths with ample wings and slender bodies 6

23. Front wing with 2 anal veins but partly fused so as to appear as a branched vein (Bagworms) **Psychidae,** p. 312

Front wing with only 1 anal vein 24

24. Frenulum present 25

Frenulum absent 32

25. Anal angle of the hind wing with a fringe of hairs much longer than elsewhere (Owlet Moths)

Noctuidae or **Phalaenidae,** p. 349

Anal angle of the hind wing with a fringe of hairs not much longer than elsewhere 26

26. Basal part of R_1 of the hind wing appears as a cross vein between R and Sc; Sc and R_1 are closely parallel to end of discal cell or further; moths with narrow wings, stout and usually large bodies (Sphinx Moths) **Sphingidae,** p. 340

Basal part of R_1 of hind wing seldom appearing as a cross vein; if this occurs then Sc and R_1 and R_s are widely separated from where Sc and R_1 are joined 27

27. Base of M_2 of front wing not joined more closely to Cu than to R; Cu appears to be 3-branched 28

Base of M_2 of front wing joined more closely to Cu than to R; Cu appears to be 4-branched in most cases 29

28. Basal part of Sc of hind wing prominently bent forward into the humeral area and connected by a usually strong cross vein to the humeral angle. Slender moths with broad delicate wings (Measuring Worms or Geometrid Moths) **Geometridae,** p. 343

Basal part of Sc of hind wing not prominently bent forward and extends parallel with R. Moths usually stout (Prominents or Notodontid Moths) **Notodontidae,** p. 344

29. $Sc + R_1$ and R_s of hind wing separated along discal cell, and then grown together for a short distance beyond. Small moths (Pyralid Moths) **Pyralididae,** p. 329

$Sc + R_1$ and R_s of hind wing not as described above. Moths medium to large in size 30

30. Sc and R_1 of hind wing coalesced along the anterior margin of the discal cell for usually ½ of its length. Stout-

Heterocera (Moths)

Family *Incurvariidae* (Yucca Moths)

Of chief interest in this family of small moths are the yucca moths, *Tegeticula* (*Pronuba* spp.). A remarkable biological relationship exists between these moths and the yucca plant. The flowers are pollinated only by these insects (Fig. 188) and the larvae feed exclusively on their seeds. Each is dependent upon the other for perpetuation of the species.

The female of these small white moths has maxillae modified for the collection of pollen. Balls of pollen are collected and deposited on the stigmata of flowers, in the ovaries of which eggs have been laid. This insures development of seed as food for the pinkish larvae that hatch from the eggs. Only enough larvae are provided to eat part of the seeds and thus permit some to mature so the plant species may be perpetuated. Most species of these insects are confined to the South, Southwest, and Mexico.

The bogus yucca moths of the genus *Prodoxus* are closely related to the yucca moths. The larvae develop in the flower stems, base of the seed capsules and main stems of the yucca and century plants. The bogus yucca moth is dependent, at least in part, on the yucca moth for a source of food for its larvae, inasmuch as the seed capsules and flower stems of the yucca plant would not develop without fertilization of the yucca flowers.

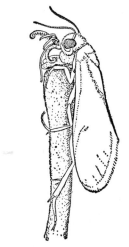

FIG. 188. The female yucca moth (*Pronuba yuccasella*) collecting pollen from the yucca flower. (After Folsom, *Entomology*, Blackiston, 1906, from Metcalf and Flint, *Fundamentals of Insect Life*, 1932. By permission of McGraw-Hill Book Company.)

Family *Cossidae* (Carpenterworm Moths)

This is a small family of moths; the larvae are wood borers and often do considerable injury to trees. The larvae are almost devoid of hairs; are grub-like in appearance; but may be distinguished readily from beetle larvae by the presence of prolegs. Pupation occurs within the feeding tunnels of the larvae. The pupa works its way partly out of the tunnel before the emergence of the adult. After the adult has emerged, the empty pupal case may be seen projecting partly out of the tunnel. These moths are stout-bodied and large or medium in size. The shape of the body and wings in some species resembles the sphinx moths. Mouthparts are vestigial.

Several species are common. The best known of these is the carpenterworm or goat moth (*Prionoxystus robiniae,* Fig. 189). This is a widely distributed insect in the United States and Southern Canada. The larvae attack a large number of forest and shade trees, especially oaks. Eggs are laid in crevices of the bark. The size of the pinkish-white larvae varies, but they may attain a length of two inches or more. The larvae tunnel in the trunks and larger branches of trees. Some of the tunnels extend to the outside from which frass may be eliminated and sap exudes. Winter is passed in the larval stage and the adults emerge during the summer months. The moths are large, with a wing expanse of as much as three inches in the female. The wings are gray with light and black markings,

FIG. 189. Carpenterworm (*Prionoxystus robiniae*). Stages of development and type of injury. (From Agricultural Research Service, U.S.D.A.)

and the hind wings are slightly tinged with yellow. Probably three years are required for the development of the larvae. In valuable shade trees, the larvae may be killed by injecting small amounts of carbon disulphide in the tunnels and closing the hole with putty or mud.

The pecan carpenterworm (*Cossula magnifica*) is found only in the southern states. The larva attacks pecans, hickories, and oaks. Infested trees may be recognized by the presence of coarse sawdust at the base of the tree where it has dropped from the entrance of the larval burrows.

Fully grown larvae are more than one inch in length and are pinkish-white. The moths, which appear in late spring or early summer, deposit eggs on small branches. The larvae tunnel in successively larger branches. Before cold weather, the partly grown larvae crawl down and tunnel into the trunks of the trees to pass the winter. There appears to be one generation annually. Control measures are the same as recommended for the carpenterworm.

Family *Megalopygidae* (Flannel Moths)

Wings of the moths of this family are clothed with loose scales mixed with long hairs which produce a flannel-like appearance. Bodies of the larvae are heavily clothed with fine hairs or setae, with which are intermixed venomous setae.

The best known member of the group is the puss caterpillar (*Megalopyge opercularis*). This caterpillar is frequently abundant in the South and often becomes a pest in shade trees around homes, schools, and in parks. They are of little importance as enemies of shade trees, but they are capable of inflicting rather severe stings to man. When the body of a caterpillar is pressed against tender skin, it is pricked by the venomous setae which are hollow and supplied with a poison. Some of the setae are pulled out and others are broken off, resulting in severe dermatitis and other symptoms. Larvae are short, thick set, and woolly in appearance. Color is variable, being yellow, gray, reddish-brown, or a mixture of colors. The mature larva is about one inch in length and possesses seven pairs of prolegs.

Winter is passed as a larva within a cocoon. Following pupation, the adults emerge, and several hundred eggs are laid by each female in late spring or early summer. The larvae feed on foliage of hack-

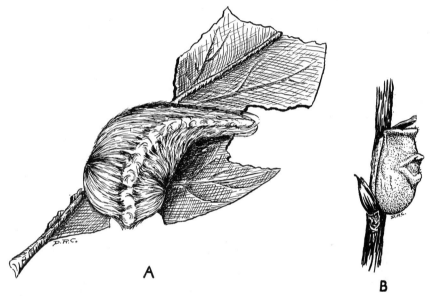

A   B

FIG. 190. **A,** The puss caterpillar (*Megalopyge opercularis*) . **B,** Cocoon, showing trap door for escape of the moth.

berry, elm, oak, and other trees. The mature larva constructs a rather unique cocoon (Fig. 190) on the trunk or branches of the host plant in which to pupate. At one end of the cocoon a trap door is provided for the escape of the adult as it emerges from the pupal case. The dorsal surface of the cocoon is marked by a structure similar to a leaf scar. The color of the cocoon is about the same as that of the larva, because the larval hairs are incorporated in the silk. Adults are yellowish-brown with wings clothed with long wavy hairs. Wing expanse of the moths ranges from one to 1½ inches. One or two generations of the puss caterpillar occur annually. Should the puss caterpillar appear in numbers large enough to be pestiferous, the insect may be controlled by spraying the trees with lead arsenate, toxaphene or DDT.

The crinkled flannel moth (*Megalopyge crispata*) is found in the North. The sting of this larva is not so severe as that of the puss caterpillar. The caterpillar feeds on foliage of elm, oak, apple, and many other trees. The larva is short, thick set, and densely clothed with long brown hairs. The adult is yellowish-white with the front wings crossed by irregular lines formed by brown and black hairs. The species is somewhat larger than the puss caterpillar.

Family *Tineidae* (Clothes Moths)

This family is composed of a large number of small moths; however, only a few species, the clothes moths, are of economic importance. The two most common species are the webbing clothes moth (*Tineola bisselliella*) and the casemaking clothes moth (*Tinea pellionella*), both of which are native to Europe. The moths do not feed on clothing since their mouthparts are imperfectly developed. Damage is caused by the larvae feeding upon wool, feathers, furs, hair, and products made from them. They will also feed upon beef meal, casein, skins, dead insects, and other animal matter. The larvae do not feed upon products of vegetable origin, such as cotton, linen, and rayon; silk is rarely attacked.

The webbing clothes moth (Fig. 191) is the more important

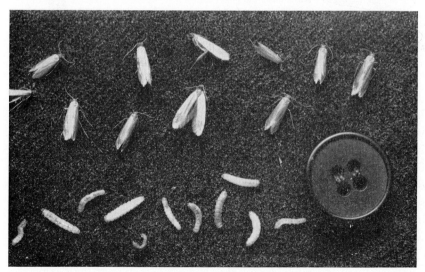

FIG. 191. Webbing clothes moths and larvae (*Tineola bisselliella*). (From Agricultural Research Service, U.S.D.A.)

species. The adult has a wing expanse of about ½ inch, and is uniformly pale yellow. The larvae are small white caterpillars about ½ inch in length. The webbing clothes moth takes its name from the habit of the larvae which spin transparent tubes as they feed, and produce a web-like mass of silken threads upon the food materials. When maturity is reached, the larvae spin silken cocoons in which are incorporated bits of excrement and food materials. Within the cocoon, the larvae transform into pupae from which the adults emerge later.

The adult of the casemaking clothes moth (Fig. 192) is about the same size as the webbing clothes moth. The front wings are grayish-yellow, marked by indistinct dark spots while the hind wings are

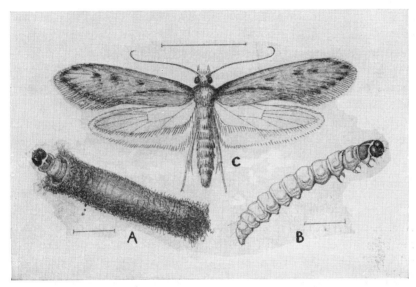

FIG. 192.   The casemaking clothes moth (*Tinea pellionella*) . **A,** Larval case. **B,** Larva. **C,** Adult. (From Agricultural Research Service, U.S.D.A.)

lighter in color. The larvae spin small portable cases which they seldom leave. The biologies of the two species are quite similar.

The adult females each lay 100 to 150 small white eggs on the food materials of the larvae. The eggs hatch in four to eight days during warm weather. In colder weather the egg stage may be prolonged to as much as three weeks. Length of the period of larval development is most variable, ranging from six weeks to four years. The pupal period is one to four weeks in duration, depending upon the temperature. A life cycle of clothes moths may be completed in two or three months or be prolonged over a period of several years.

Frequently, small moths of various species are seen in the home and are mistaken for clothes moths. Many of these are attracted to lights from the outside, while others may be breeding in foodstuff. The Angoumois grain moth is most often mistaken for clothes moths. A characteristic which readily distinguishes this insect from clothes moths is the decidedly narrowed and pointed apex of the hind wing. (See Fig. 195, p. 318.)

Control of clothes moths is similar to that of carpet beetles. Control begins with good housekeeping. It is advisable to dispose of all old woolen clothing and scraps, or place the materials in tight boxes or chests and spray with DDT household spray, or sprinkle liberally with paradichlorobenzene or naphthalene crystals. Frequent vacuum cleaning of rugs, carpets, and floors will remove lint, hair, and bits of other materials upon which the larvae feed. Woolen clothing may be sprayed with DDT. With precautions, rugs, carpets, and upholstered furniture may be sprayed also. Spraying with commercial products containing fluorine compounds is another means of protection against the insects. Brushing and sunning articles will remove the pests; dry cleaning destroys all stages. The latter two measures do not prevent reinfestation of the materials. Cedar chests, while new, afford some protection against damage.

Family *Psychidae* (Bagworm Moths)

Larvae of members of this family construct bags in which they live. Adult females are wingless, while the males bear wings which are sparsely covered with scales. Members of the family are rather widely distributed over the world.

The most important species of this family in the United States is the common bagworm (*Thyridopteryx ephemeraeformis*). This insect (Fig. 193) is found from Massachusetts to Kansas and south to Central Texas and Florida. The common bagworm attacks a long list of trees and shrubs, but its feeding is most destructive on arbor vitae and cedars. Many beautiful ornamental plants around homes, public buildings, in parks and cemeteries are defoliated and killed each year by the feeding of these larvae.

Winter is passed as eggs in the female bags which remain suspended by silken strands on the host plants. The eggs hatch in the spring and the young larvae disperse in search of food, some of them being blown by the wind to other plants. The young larvae immediately construct small bags of silk in which are incorporated bits of leaves or twigs. As the larva grows, the size of the bag is in-

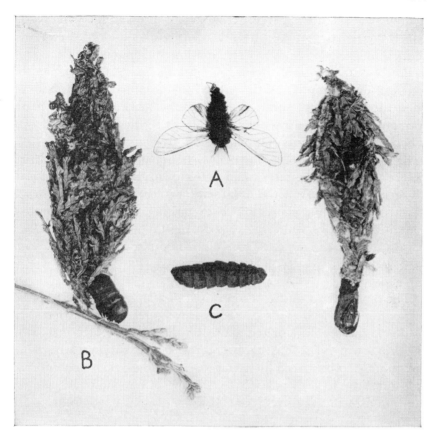

FIG. 193. The common bagworm (*Thyridopteryx ephemeraeformis*). **A,** Adult male; **B,** Typical bag with head and thorax of larva protruding. **C,** Pupa removed from bag. (From Agricultural Research Service, U.S.D.A.)

creased correspondingly. In feeding, the larva protrudes the head and thorax and carries the bag with it as it crawls. Pupation occurs within the bag in the latter part of summer or September.

Prior to pupation the larva reverses its position in the bag and hangs with its head downward. Before emergence of the male moth, the pupa pushes its way partly out of the small opening at the lower end of the bag. The pupal case then splits and the male moth emerges. The moth is medium in size, dark colored, and the wings are almost devoid of scales. The female does not emerge completely from the pupal case, pushing only the head and part of the thorax out of a T-shaped slit. The mature female is grub-like, devoid of wings, functional eyes, legs, and antennae. She remains concealed in the bag and hangs head downward.

Males are attracted to receptive females by odor. The end of the abdomen of the male is inserted in the lower opening of the bag in which the female is found until the entire abdomen of the male is hidden in the bag. Following fertilization, the abdomen of the male is slowly retracted from the bag. Soon after mating, the female begins egg deposition. Eggs are packed in the pupal case with down from the body. After the eggs are laid, the female moth forces her way out of the pupal case and bag, drops to the ground, and dies. There is one generation annually.

Bagworms are readily controlled by spraying with lead arsenate before the larvae are more than half-grown. Toxaphene sprays are also recommended. When the infestation is localized on small shrubs, effective control may be obtained by picking and burning the bags containing the overwintering eggs during the winter months.

Family *Gelechiidae* (Gelechiids)

The family *Gelechiidae* is comprised of a large number of species of small moths. Many of the species may be recognized as members of this family by the pointed apex and the sinuate outer margin of the hind wing. Feeding habits of the larvae vary greatly. Some are miners; others feed in stems or rolled leaves; some produce galls; and the food of many is seed. Some of our most serious pests are found in this family.

The Pink Bollworm (*Pectinophora gossypiella*).   The pink bollworm (Fig. 194) is the most destructive insect pest of cotton in many parts of the world. In Egypt, India, China, and Brazil it has been an important pest for many years. Indications are southern Asia, probably India, is the native home of the insect. It has spread to distant parts of the world, such as Egypt, Brazil, and Mexico, through shipments of infested cotton seed. In 1917, the insect was first found in Texas. Eradication measures were successful in East Texas and Louisiana, but failed in the western districts along the Mexican border. Indications are that these districts were reinfested periodically by moths drifting in from infested areas in Mexico, for the moths are known to be carried long distances by winds. Extensive spread of the insect was prevented for many years by quarantine and control measures in the infested areas. In recent years, unfavorable weather conditions greatly hampered the practice of control measures in the infested areas, and the insect has spread rapidly, especially in Texas.

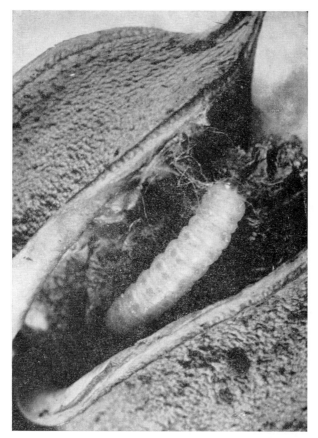

FIG. 194. The pink bollworm (*Pectinophora gossypiella*) in cotton boll. (From Department of Entomology, A & M College of Texas.)

Primary damage of the pink bollworm is caused by feeding on the seeds of green bolls. Seeds from infested bolls are of low viability, light in weight, and their oil content is low and of inferior quality. In making pathways through the immature lint, it is cut and stained, and of inferior quality. Bolls may be completely or partially destroyed and much of the lint produced is not worth picking. Squares and blooms are also attacked, but this damage is not significant.

In addition to feeding on cotton, the pink bollworm attacks okra, hollyhock, species of native *Hibiscus, Thurberia,* and other malvaceous plants. Infestations in okra and hollyhock depend chiefly on the proximity of fields of infested cotton.

The moths, or adults, are small, with a wing expanse of about ¾ inch, grayish-brown, and resemble clothes moths or Angoumois grain moths in general appearance. They are nocturnal in habit and are not attracted to ordinary lights. Eggs may be laid on stems, squares, and buds; but when large green bolls are available, most of them are deposited in masses underneath the calyx at the base of the bolls. Eggs are white, oval, and about $\frac{1}{50}$ inch in length with the surface finely reticulated by longitudinal and irregular cross-veins. Each female lays 100 to 200 eggs.

The fully grown caterpillar is about $\frac{1}{2}$ inch in length and is pinkish or light cream colored. Other larval characteristics are: crochets of abdominal prolegs uniordinal and arranged in a penellipse (horse-shoe shape) opening to the outside; four denticles are present on each mandible; and three triangularly arranged setae are located on the prespiracular shield of the prothorax. Several habits of the larvae are also helpful in recognizing the insect. Infested bolls are rarely filled with frass and excrement. The larvae make clean cut "shot holes" through the partitions and carpels in their feeding activities, and in making their exit from the bolls.

Another characteristic of the larvae is the frequent webbing together of seed late in the season prior to hibernation. The seed-feeding and seed-inhabitating characteristics of the larvae are also valuable in recognizing the insect.

Immediately following emergence from the eggs, the larvae begin searching for food. If suitable food is not found soon, they die. Larvae may feed slightly on foliage, but squares or bolls are essential for development. Cotton is attacked as soon as squares are found. Larvae, feeding in squares, may web the tips of the corolla together prior to blooming so that the petals will not unfold normally and the blooms have a rosetted appearance. Larvae, developing in squares, may drop to the ground and pupate in trash or the soil.

When large bolls are attacked, the newly hatched larvae tunnel through the carpels to the inner membrane. When the membrane is reached, a small, brown, tortuous tunnel is made before the lint is entered in search of seed. The formation of this small tunnel or mine is a characteristic habit of this insect. Upon reaching maturity within green bolls, larvae may cut small holes through the carpels and drop to the ground to pupate—or pupation may occur within the bolls. Pupae are about $\frac{2}{5}$ inch in length, brown, and covered with a fine pubescence. They are usually found in cocoons.

There may be four to six generations of the pink bollworm annually, a generation being completed in 25 to 30 days during warm weather. Duration of the egg stage averages about five days, while the feeding period of the larvae is ten to 14 days. Pupae transform into moths in about eight days. Three or four days following emergence, female moths begin oviposition. Larvae of the summer or warm season generations are known as short-cycle larvae, while the overwintering forms are termed long-cycle larvae.

The pink bollworm overwinters as larvae in cocoons. The overwintering or long-cycle larvae are found in old bolls, dropped squares, trash, and surface soil of the cotton field. Gin trash and seed in heavily infested areas contain many hibernating larvae. A larva may hibernate in a single seed or in two seeds webbed together forming what is known as "double seeds." Larvae pupate and moths emerge in the spring; however, emergence may be prolonged into the summer months.

Quarantine measures are maintained in infested districts, and movements of all products in those areas which may harbor the pest are regulated. In heavily infested districts, sterilization of the seed with heat is a part of the ginning process. Burning or mechanical treatment of the gin trash is also required. Fumigation with methyl bromide may be required before seed can be shipped to areas free of the pest.

Good cultural practices materially aid in control of the pink bollworm and other insects. The planting of early maturing varieties is advisable. In those areas where the crop is harvested before frost, the cotton stalks should be destroyed with a shredder and the residue later plowed under. Insecticidal control of the pink bollworm consists of the use of DDT, Guthion, or sevin applied at weekly intervals either as dusts or as sprays.

The Angoumois Grain Moth (*Sitotroga cerealella*). The Angoumois grain moth (Fig. 195) is second in importance to the rice and granary weevils as a pest of stored grains. It was given this common name because its destructiveness as a grain pest was first reported from the old province of Angoumois, France. The insect has a wide distribution but it is most destructive in warm climates. The larvae feed in and destroy seeds of corn, wheat, oats, sorghum, barley, and other crops.

Adults are small yellowish moths with a wing spread of about ⅗ inch. They may be seen flying in infested bins or crawling on the surface of the grain. Each female normally deposits about 40 small, white or reddish eggs on tips of ears of corn or heads of small grain or grain sorghums in the field, or on grain in storage. The newly hatched larvae bore into the kernels where they feed upon either the endosperm or the germ. Prior to pupation, each larva constructs a tunnel to the outside but keeps it closed with a thin layer of the seed coat. The larva then changes to a reddish-brown pupa within a silken cocoon. The adult later emerges from the

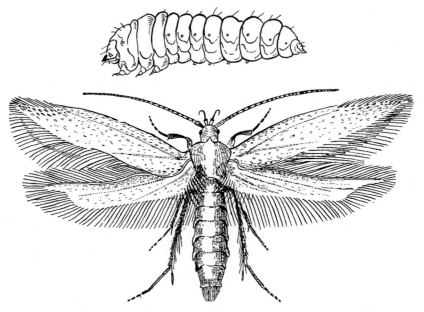

FIG. 195. Larva and adult of the Angoumois grain moth (*Sitotroga cerealella*). (From the University of California Division of Agricultural Sciences.)

pupal case, pushes aside the thin layer of the seed coat, and escapes to the outside. A generation of the Angoumois grain moth may be completed in about five weeks. There may be as many as six generations in warm climates. If temperature conditions permit, breeding continues in stored grains throughout the winter months; otherwise, the insect hibernates in the larval stage.

Before storage of a new crop of grain the bins should be thoroughly cleaned and the surfaces sprayed with either methoxychlor or malathion. Field infestations may be reduced to a minimum by harvesting as soon as the grain is sufficiently dry for storage. Malathion as a grain protectant may be applied as a spray or dust during the process of storage. Several fumigants are effective in control of the pest. Those most commonly employed are mixtures of carbon tetrachloride and ethylene dichloride or carbon disulphide. Methyl bromide is an effective fumigant, but its use requires a recirculation system built into the storage facilities. Drying' systems often may be adapted for this type of fumigation.

The Peach Twig Borer (*Anarsia lineatella*). The peach twig borer is an important pest of peaches in several sections of the country, particularly on the Pacific Coast. This is an old European insect which was first found in this country in 1860. Injury is caused by the feeding of the larvae in the fruit and tunneling in the twigs (Fig. 196); damage to fruit is important. Peaches, almonds, apricots, cherries, and prunes are attacked.

Winter is passed as immature larvae in hibernacula closely attached to the bark. The over-wintered larvae emerge, tunnel out, and kill the young succulent shoots in the spring. Pupation occurs in cracks, pruning scars, and rough places of the bark. Small, gray moths with a wing expanse of ⅓ to ½ inch later emerge from the pupal cases and deposit eggs on the twigs. Larvae of the summer generations prefer fruit to the twigs. The majority of fruit are attacked at the stem end, where the fruit touch or where the leaves are in contact with the fruit. Most of the worms penetrate only a small distance; however, large larvae sometimes feed to the pit. The mature larvae are about ⅜ inch long and chocolate brown. The number of generations annually are one to four, with the

FIG. 196. Damage to early spring growth of almond by the peach twig borer (*Anarsia lineatella*). (From the University of California Division of Agricultural Sciences.)

larger number occurring in warm climates.

In the central states, delayed dormant sprays of lime-sulphur or oil emulsion are the most effective control measures. The spray kills the larvae in their hibernacula. These sprays, however, have not proved effective in all sections of the country. Sprays containing basic lead arsenate, applied in the spring, provide satisfactory control on the Pacific Coast. The use of DDT sprays has shown promise. Dust mixtures of basic lead arsenate and sulphur are recommended for use on mature fruit to avoid poisonous residues.

Family *Plutellidae*

About 50 species of this family are known to occur in North America. The diamond-back moth (*Plutella maculipennis,* Fig. 197) is the best known member of the family. It is a pest of some economic importance on cruciferous plants and attacks certain ornamental and greenhouse plants such as stock, candytuft, and sweet alyssum. The larva feeds on the underside of the leaves, eating out small areas but leaving the thin epidermis intact. This produces a transparent spot on the leaf surface. Upon drying, the thin epidermis breaks, producing characteristic holes in the leaves. Young plants may be rather severely injured. The full-grown larva is about 1/3 inch in length and pale green with small black setae on its body. When the larva is disturbed, it wriggles actively or drops from the plant on a silk thread.

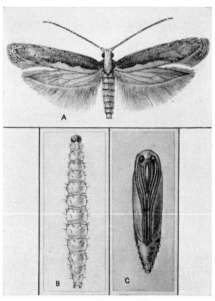

FIG. 197. Diamond-back moth (*Plutella maculipennis*). **A,** Adult. **B,** Larva. **C,** Pupa. (From Agricultural Research Service, U.S.D.A.)

This habit aids in distinguishing this caterpillar from small cabbage worms. Prior to pupation, the larva spins a transparent gauzy cocoon which is attached to a leaf or some other part of the plant. Adults are small, grayish moths with a wing expanse of about 1/3 inch. The front wings of the male have an irregular yellow stripe along each inner margin. When the wings are folded the two yellow stripes are brought together and form three diamond-shaped yellow spots which have suggested the common name. Females lay the small, yellowish-white eggs on leaves of the host plants. The length of a generation is relatively short; there are probably two to six or more generations annually. Winter is usually spent as adults, hidden beneath cabbage leaves or other cover in the fields. However, all stages may be found during the winter in the insect's southern range. Dusts and sprays of DDT, malathion and methoxychlor are recommended for home gardens. Parathion, toxaphene, endrin, and Guthion may be used on commercial crops.

Family *Aegeriidae* (Clear-Wing Moths)

The most striking characteristic of most members of this family is that one or both pairs of wings are relatively free of scales. Many of the adults are wasp-like in general appearance. The moths are moderate in size with the front wings exceptionally narrow. They are active during the day. The larvae are borers, infesting a number of plants. More than 100 species are known in this country. Several are important pests.

The Peach Tree Borer (*Sanninoidea exitiosa*). The peach tree borer (Fig. 198) ranks with the San Jose scale and plum curculio in importance as a pest of the peach. Many trees die each year as

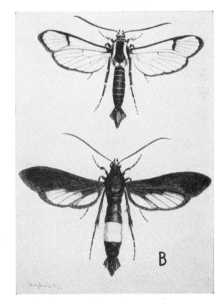

FIG. 198. The peach tree borer (*Sanninoidea exitiosa*). **A,** Larvae feeding in young peach tree. **B,** Adults; above, male; below, female. (From Agricultural Research Service, U.S.D.A.)

a direct or indirect result of the attacks of the larvae of this insect. Larvae tunnel and feed in the cambium or inner layer of the bark, usually in the base and occasionally in the larger roots. Masses of gum mixed with frass, soil, and bits of bark are usually seen around the base of trees infested by the borers. The presence of gum does not always indicate the presence of borers, however, as injury, sun scald, and other agencies may cause the exudation of gum. Other hosts of the peach tree borer are plum, apricot, almond, nectarine, and related plants. The range of distribution of the insect is east of the Rocky Mountains from Canada to the Gulf Coast.

Winter is passed as larvae. All the larger larvae remain in their tunnels but some of the smaller forms hibernate in a protective covering on the bark of the tree. Feeding and growth is resumed when the weather becomes warm. Upon completion of larval development, brownish cocoons in which the larvae pupate are formed either in the soil near the tree trunk or at the exit of the tunnels. The fully grown larvae are about one inch long and yellowish-white with brown heads.

The length of the pupal stage is three or four weeks. A few moths may emerge during May in the southernmost range of the insect; however most moths emerge in July and August in the North, and June through September in the South. The female moth is blackish-blue with clear hind wings and one or two orange bands around the abdomen. The male is lighter colored than the female with both pairs of wings clear and the abdomen ringed with several narrow yellow bands. The wing expanse of the adults is slightly more than an inch.

The females usually lay 500 to 600 eggs each, most of which are deposited on the tree trunks. In warm weather, eggs hatch in nine or ten days. The newly hatched larvae find their way to the base of the trees and enter near the ground level. They bore into the cambium and inner bark layers where they feed until cold weather. Normally only one generation is completed each year.

Several control measures may be employed in combating this pest. DDT, parathion, EPN, or BHC may be sprayed on the lower parts of the large branches and trunks of the trees during the time the moths are emerging and ovipositing. Recommended strength of the sprays and time of applications vary in different parts of the country. Paradichlorobenzene treatment has been successfully used for more than 30 years. Crystals of the compound are applied in a ring around the base of the tree. A gas is formed, as the crystals vaporize, which penetrates the bark and tunnels, and kills the larvae. The paradichlorobenzene treatment should be made at the close of the oviposition period in the fall. Ethylene dichloride treatment is efficient and relatively safe for use on young trees when properly applied. Applications may be made with this insecticide in the fall or spring, or warm periods of weather during the winter in the South. Most satisfactory results are probably obtained by fall treatments. Worming the trees is an old control measure. If the worming is carefully done, reasonable control will be obtained. The time of application of control measures and dosages vary so much in different sections of the country that the grower should consult the local state agricultural experiment station or extension service, or refer to available USDA publications for local recommendations and details of control.

The Lesser Peach Tree Borer (*Synanthedon pictipes*).   This insect is quite similar to the peach tree borer in appearance. Its injury is confined chiefly to the trunks and limbs. The larvae work in crotches, under old bark, and in places injured by mechanical means (freezes, sun scald, or disease).

Overwintered larvae change to pupae in the spring. Shortly after emergence from the pupal cases the female moths lay their eggs on trunks and limbs. One and a partial second generation occur annually in the South but only one is completed in colder climates.

Proper care of orchards is important in preventing infestations of the lesser peach tree borer. Care should be taken to prevent mechanical injuries. Wounds and areas killed by sun scald and disease should be treated. The removal of dead and broken limbs is advisable.

In the North, sprays of parathion and EPN are recommended for the control of the lesser peach tree borer. The insecticides should be applied about one month before the initial spray application for the peach tree borer. Subsequent applications should be made as recommended for the peach tree borer.

The Squash Vine Borer (*Melittia cucurbitae*).   This insect is an important pest of squashes and pumpkins. Usually the first indication of the presence of the borer is the sudden wilting of leaves and masses of yellowish excrement pushed out of holes in the vines. Examination of an infested vine will show it to be tunneled out by white, brown-headed larvae which may measure up to one inch in length. Heavily infested plants are killed. In addition to squashes and pumpkins, gourds, cucumbers, and melons are attacked. The insect is found from Canada to Brazil, westward to the Rocky Mountains.

Larvae mature in four to six weeks. They leave their tunnels in the plant, enter the ground, and spin silken cocoons which are covered with particles of soil. In the North, larvae remain in the cocoons until spring before transforming into pupae. In warmer climates, the larvae change to pupae from which moths soon emerge and eggs are laid for a second generation.

The moths are medium in size. The fore wings are opaque and olive-brown; the hind wings are transparent. The abdomen is ringed with red or orange, black, and bronze; and long hairs fringe the hind legs. Each female deposits singly 150 to 200 eggs chiefly on the stems, but also on other parts of the plant.

Vines should be raked and destroyed following harvest to destroy the larvae remaining in them. Fall, winter, or spring plowing will destroy many of the larvae and pupae in the cocoons. As the larvae are internal feeders, insecticidal control is difficult. Heavy dust applications of rotenone, DDT, or chlordane will destroy many of the young larvae before they enter the stems. The dusts should be applied at weekly intervals during the growing season. DDT and chlordane may cause plant injury under certain conditions.

Family *Tortricidae* (Tortricids)

This is a large family of rather small moths. There are probably more than 1,000 North American species. The front wings are broad and truncate at the outer margins. The larvae feed on a wide variety of plants. Many species are leaf-rollers; others feed in the fruits, buds or stems. A number of important pests are found in this group. This family is considered a superfamily, *Tortricoidea*, and subdivided into several families by a number of authorities.

The Codling Moth (*Carpocapsa pomonella*). The codling moth (Fig. 199) is the most serious insect pest of apples, causing most of the wormy fruit which is so familiar to everyone. The core of the fruit is eaten out by the pinkish-white caterpillars which have brown heads and are about 3/4 inch long when fully grown. Apples, pears, English walnuts, and occasionally other fruits are attacked. This insect is found wherever apples are grown.

The winter is passed as mature larvae in tough silken cocoons underneath the bark of trees, in crotches, crevices, pruning scars, debris on the ground, and similar environments. Many larvae over-winter in packing sheds or other places where apples have been

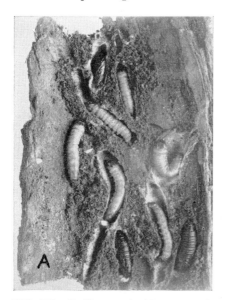 

FIG. 199. Codling moth (*Carpocapsa pomonella*). **A,** Larvae and pupae in cocoons underneath bark. **B,** Moth on apple leaf. (From Agricultural Research Service, U.S.D.A.)

stored. In the spring the larvae transform within the cocoons into brownish pupae. Three or four weeks following pupation, grayish moths with a wing spread of about ¾ inch emerge from the pupal cases. Near the tip of each front wing is a copper brown spot which is bordered internally by a cross-band of chocolate brown. The moths are active mainly at twilight in warm weather. They are not strong fliers.

Moths that develop in the spring from overwintered larvae emerge over a period of several weeks. Egg deposition is usually heaviest about four weeks after the petals of the apple blooms have fallen. Each female moth deposits 50 to 75 eggs on the leaves, twigs, and fruit. Eggs hatch in about a week. Many of the young larvae of this generation enter the fruit by way of the calyx cup or blossom end and eat their way to the core. Larvae of later generations enter the fruit at almost any point and commonly produce a type of injury known as codling moth stings. Larvae complete development in three to five weeks. Then they leave the fruit and seek suitable places for pupation, such as underneath bits of loose bark and other protected places on the tree, and in debris on the ground. Here cocoons are spun and pupation occurs. In the New England States a small number of the larvae of the first generation pupate before the next spring, so there is a partial second generation. Farther south the size of the second generation increases. Two full generations occur in the middle Atlantic states. In warmer climates there may be three or four generations annually.

Recommendations for the control of the codling moth vary somewhat in different sections of the country. This insect is difficult to control, and correct timing of the sprays, thorough applications, and the use of proper materials are essential. So it is necessary for the grower to obtain detailed information on the most satisfactory spray program and materials for his section of the country from the local state experiment stations and extension service entomologists. A number of insecticides and combinations of these are employed to control this insect. DDT, diazinon, Guthion, sevin, parathion, malathion, lead arsenate and methoxychlor are commonly used. In most sections three to four sprays applied at ten- to 14-day intervals are recommended in control of the first-brood larvae. Their application should begin ten to 14 days after petal fall. For control of subsequent broods one to three applications of spray should be made at the same intervals.

In the Pacific Northwest the spray program usually begins three weeks after petal fall. Two to four applications of spray should be applied at three-week intervals as needed. Lead arsenate is used only in control of light infestations or in those sections where it has proved satisfactory. Sevin and Guthion are recommended to control DDT-resistant strains, and sevin also, for use in late applications to prevent excessive residues of other insecticides. Guthion and parathion should not be used on small plantings around homes, and where used they should be applied only by trained applicators. Parathion should not be used on such varieties as the McIntosh.

Several minor practices help in the control of the codling moth. Cleaning up and removing trash and rubbish in the orchards, and scraping loose bark from all old trees aid in the elimination of places of pupation and hibernation. The removal of cull apples is advised. Packing sheds and their immediate surroundings should be cleaned up and the rubbish destroyed.

The Oriental Fruit Moth (*Grapholitha molesta*). The oriental fruit moth (Fig. 200) is believed to have been imported into the

United States from the Orient prior to 1915. It is now found in most of the peach-producing sections of the country. The injury produced by the insect ranges from slight to heavy, varying with the locality and the season. The larvae feed on both twigs and fruit. Injury to the twigs is similar to that done by the peach twig borer. Damage to fruit is suggestive of the feeding of the plum curculio in peaches and the codling moth in apples. Peaches, plums, apples, and pears are the fruits chiefly attacked. The larvae are pinkish-white, not chocolate or reddish-brown as is the peach twig borer, and about ½ inch long. The last segment of the abdomen bears a plate with five teeth.

FIG. 200. Oriental fruit moth (*Grapholitha molesta*) on leaf. (From Agricultural Research Service, U.S.D.A.)

Winter is passed as larvae in cocoons which are found in such protected places as cracks in the bark of the tree, mummied fruit, or rubbish on the ground. In the spring the larvae transform to pupae, from which stage the moths emerge about the time peach trees are in bloom. The grayish adults have a wing spread of about ½ inch and resemble codling moths, except they are smaller.

Eggs are usually laid on the underside of the leaves, but occasionally they may be deposited on the twigs. While the new growth is tender in spring and early summer, the larvae bore into the twigs and eat out the centers. This twig injury may seriously interfere with the growth of young trees. Fruit is attacked in the summer when the twigs become tough and fibrous. There are three to seven generations of the insect annually. In those sections where fruit is not available after midsummer the insect is rarely an important pest. In the absence of fruit, the larvae must feed on hardened twigs which are not satisfactory food material.

Properly timed sprays containing DDT, EPN, or parathion will control the oriental fruit moth. Sprays should not be applied later than 30 days prior to harvesting. A small wasp, *Macrocentrus ancylivorus,* is an important parasite and has provided effective control of the pest in some sections of the country.

Destruction of dropped and culled fruit will aid in reducing infestations. The paradichlorobenzene treatment for the control of the peach tree borer will destroy many hibernating larvae around the base of the trees. The application of fertilizers late in the season is not advised, because new twig growth may be promoted which could then provide food for the larvae at this season.

The Grape Berry Moth (*Paralobesia viteana*). The grape berry moth (Fig. 201) is distributed over most of the eastern part of the United States where it is frequently a pest of importance of both wild and cultivated varieties of grapes. In early season the larvae feed in the blooms or the young berries. The second and third generations attack the green or ripening fruit. They are greenish and 1/3 to 1/2 inch long when fully grown. Prior to pupation the larvae leave the berries and each cuts out a bit of leaf which is folded over, and a cocoon is spun within this shelter. The moths are grayish, with a wing expanse of about 1/2 inch. About five weeks are required for development from egg to adult. There are two or three generations of this insect annually. Hibernation is in silken cocoons which are usually found in the fallen leaves. Some of the cocoons, however, may be found in the loose bark or trash on the ground.

FIG. 201. Grape berry moths (*Paralobesia viteana*). (From Agricultural Research Service, U.S.D.A.)

Cleaning up and burning fallen leaves and trash in the fall or winter will destroy many of the hibernating pupae. DDT, methoxychlor, and parathion are among the insecticides recommended for the control of this pest.

Family *Pyralidae* (Pyralid Moths)

This is a very large family of moths; more than 1,000 species occur in North America. The family is considered by many authors as a superfamily with four or more families which are divided further into a number of subfamilies. The members of the family are a diverse group with much variation in appearance and habits. Most of the moths are small or moderate in size with the labial palpi often projecting snout-like. Larvae of the family may be recognized by the presence of two setae in the prespiracular group of the thorax, by setae IV and V of a proleg-bearing segment located close together below the spiracle, and by the arrangement of the crochets of the prolegs in a circle or a penellipse. A number of important pests are found in the family.

The European Corn Borer (*Ostrinia nubilalis*).   This serious pest of corn (Fig. 202) was probably brought into this country in shipments of broom corn from Europe about 1908 or 1909. Its presence here has been known since 1917. The insect is now found in most of the major corn-producing sections of the country. Its distribution extends from the Atlantic seaboard westward to North Dakota, South Dakota, and Nebraska, and southward to Kentucky and North Carolina. Some conception of the destructiveness of this insect may be obtained

FIG. 202. Adult of the European corn borer (*Ostrinia nubilalis*). (From Agricultural Research Service, U.S.D.A.)

from the estimate that it caused a loss of 85,000,000 bushels of corn in 1948. Primary injury of the larvae is by tunneling through the stalks and ears (Fig. 203). Injury is sometimes so severe that the plants break and fall in the fields.

There are two biological races of the European corn borer. A one-generation race is predominant in the North Central States. This race does not generally attack plants other than corn. In eastern and southern regions of the insect's range a multiple-generation race

FIG. 203. European corn borer damage; a contrast between undamaged and damaged ears of sweet corn. (From Agricultural Research Service, U.S.D.A.)

predominates. The number of generations annually of this race may vary from one in colder climates to three in Virginia, and five in Guam. These larvae are more destructive because of the greater number of generations and the wider range of host plants. More than 200 different kinds of herbaceous plants are attacked.

The insect hibernates as larvae in stems of the food plants. The larvae are brownish or pinkish with the body marked by small dark spots, and they attain a length of almost one inch when fully grown. When the weather becomes warm in the spring the larvae construct flimsy cocoons for pupation within the tunnels in the host plants. The moths, which emerge from June until August, have a wing spread of about one inch. They are yellowish to pale brown with dark wavy lines extending across the wings. The male moths are darker than the females. They are rather strong fliers and are most active at night. Females lay an average of 500 to 600 eggs, which are usually deposited on the underside of the leaves of the food plants in groups of five to 50. The duration of the egg stage is about one week. On corn the young larvae feed in the whorls of developing leaves, between the leaf sheaths, or between the ears and the stalks. Tassels, which frequently break over, are heavily attacked until ears are formed. When the larvae are about half grown they become borers and tunnel into the stalk and ears. Here they feed until they complete their development. Dry weather destroys many larvae before they enter the stalks. Cold weather and heavy rainfall also are beneficial in checking the insect.

Since the insect hibernates as larvae in the tunnels of the food plants, utilization or destruction of the plant residues before emergence of the adults will appreciably reduce the population for the next season. Plowing plant residues under deeply and completely is a very effective control measure. Residues that cannot be plowed under should be raked together and burned. The planting of resistant varieties of corn is advisable. If corn is utilized for silage or fodder, the plants should be cut as close to the ground as possible; no stubble should be left more than two inches high. Correctly timed applications of insecticidal dusts and sprays will greatly reduce corn borer injury. DDT was the first insecticide generally used. Ryania as a dust has been recommended. Recently, DDT, endrin EPN, and toxaphene are the chief insecticides used.

The Southern Cornstalk Borer (*Diatraea crambidoides*).   This is often a corn pest of importance in the South, but because of the nature of its attacks, the full extent of its damage is not generally realized. Injury is caused by the yellowish-white larvae which are about one inch in length and marked with brown spots when fully grown. The insect overwinters as mature larvae which are generally found in the tap roots of the cornstalks. In the spring the larvae change to pupae from which the moths emerge ten or more days later. The moths are light yellow with a wing expanse of barely more than one inch. Each female usually lays 300 to 400 eggs on the undersurface of the leaves. Eggs hatch in seven to ten days. The young larvae feed first on the surface of the leaves but later tunnel into the stalks and feed as borers until their development is completed. They may leave and reënter a stalk several times or change to other plants in the course of their development. The length of the larval stage in the summer is 20 to 30 days. There may be as many as three generations annually. Although corn is the principal host, sorghums and Johnson grass are attacked also.

Cultural practices are the most effective control measures in combating this insect. Cleaning up and destroying cornstalks and stubble following harvest are the most satisfactory measures. Fall and winter plowing will destroy many of the hibernating larvae. Crop rotation is also of value in decreasing the injury caused by the pest.

The Southwestern Corn Borer (*Zeadiatraea grandiosella*). Larvae of the southwestern corn borer (Fig. 204) are not readily distinguished from those of the southern cornstalk borer. The two species also

FIG. 204. A southwestern corn borer (*Diatraea grandiosella*) in base of a corn stalk. (From Texas Agricultural Experiment Station.)

have similar life histories and habits. Their habits differ in that the southwestern corn borer may girdle the stalk internally prior to hibernation in the tap roots. This injury results in lodging as the stalks are readily blown over. The southwestern corn borer is a native of Mexico. It spread into Arizona, New Mexico, and Texas prior to 1913. In addition to those states, the insect is now found in Oklahoma, Colorado, Kansas, and Nebraska.

Corn is the primary host of this insect. As sorghums are not heavily attacked it is advisable to substitute planting of these crops for corn, at least in those areas where borer damage is the heaviest.

In those regions where extremely cold winter weather normally prevails, plowing out the corn stubble is recommended. This practice exposes the larvae to low temperatures and most of them will be killed. Other practices, such as those recommended for the southern cornstalk borer, are suggested for the control of this insect.

The Sugarcane Borer (*Diatraea saccharalis*). The sugarcane borer (Fig. 205) is the most important insect pest of sugarcane in Louisiana. Annual loss due to this insect amounts to several million dollars. It is also a serious pest of rice. In addition to sugarcane and rice, the larvae attack corn, sorghums, sudan grass, and native grasses. Biology, habits, and general description of the insect are quite similar to those of the southern cornstalk borer. The life cycle of the insect is somewhat shorter and four to five generations may be completed annually. The insect, which is of tropical or subtropical origin, was introduced into Louisiana about 100 years ago and is now found in Texas, Louisiana, Mississippi, and Florida.

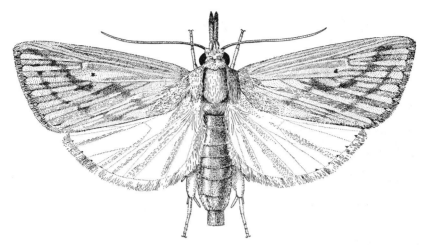

FIG. 205. Moth of the sugarcane borer (*Diatraea saccharalis*). (From Agricultural Research Service, U.S.D.A.)

Since the larvae overwinter in crop residues it is important that this material be destroyed. Cane tops, pieces of stalks, leaves, and other trash should be thoroughly burned or plowed under (wrapped) between the rows. Infested rice fields should be burned, grazed, or flooded following harvest. The destruction of stalks and stubble of infested corn fields during the winter months will reduce the number of hibernating larvae. The growing of resistant varieties of sugarcane is recommended. Insecticides recommended for control of this pest are ryania, endrin and cryolite.

The Lesser Cornstalk Borer (*Elasmopalpus lignosellus*). This insect is often a troublesome pest of corn, peanuts, cowpeas, beans, sorghum, and several other crops in the South. Injury is caused by the larvae tunneling into the stalks or stems of the plants. The lower portions of the stalks or stems are attacked. Injury is most severe where the plants are grown in sandy soils. The larvae (Fig. 206) are bluish-green with darker markings, rather slender, and about ¾ inch long.

Winter is passed in the larval, pupal, or adult stages, but most commonly as larvae in its southern range. Moths emerge in the spring, and eggs are deposited on the foliage and stems of the food plants. The moths are brownish-gray with a wing spread of less than one inch. Larvae hatching from the eggs feed first on the leaves and roots and later tunnel into the stems of the plants. Larval development is completed in two or three weeks. The larvae pupate in silken cocoons which are found under trash on the surface of the

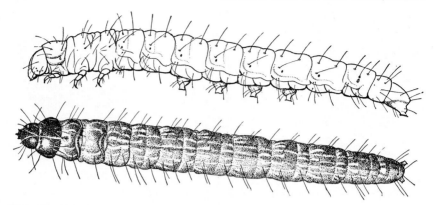

FIG. 206. The lesser cornstalk borer *(Elasmopalpus lignosellus)*. (From Agricultural Research Service, U.S.D.A.)

ground. There may be as many as four generations annually in the South with a lesser number occurring in cooler climates. The most effective control measures are clean-up schedules after harvest and crop rotation. Fall and winter plowing is also helpful in reducing the numbers of the insect.

The Garden Webworm *(Loxostege similalis)*. The foliage of cotton, alfalfa, clover, cowpeas, beans, and other plants (including a number of weeds) are fed upon by the larvae of this insect (Fig. 207). Because the most common native host is the careless weed *(Amaranthus* spp.) the larvae are often referred to as "careless

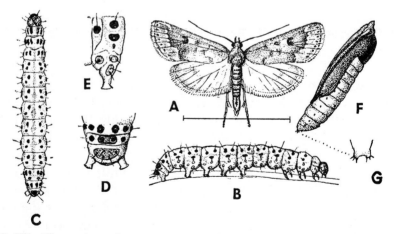

FIG. 207. The garden webworm *(Loxostege similalis)*. **A**, Moth. **B**, Lateral view of larva. **C**, Dorsal view of larva. **D**, Anal segment. **E**, Lateral view of abdominal segment. **F**, Pupa. **G**, Cremaster on end of abdomen of pupa. (From Agricultural Research Service, U.S.D.A.)

weed worms." Frequently infestations on cultivated crops are caused by migrations from weeds which have become overpopulated or destroyed. The larvae usually spin webs over the leaves upon which they are feeding.

The insect hibernates as larvae or pupae in the soil where the host plants grow. Adults emerge in the spring and lay their eggs on foliage of the host plants of the larvae. The moths are small and yellowish or grayish-brown with irregular shading on the wings. They are nocturnal in habit and often collect around lights in numbers. The fully grown larvae are about one inch in length, greenish-yellow with three conspicuous black spots arranged in a triangle on the side of each abdominal segment. Larvae complete development in three to five weeks, and then enter the soil to transform into the pupal stage. The insect may complete as many as five generations in the South, with probably two or three occurring in its northern range.

The garden webworm may be controlled with a number of insecticides. Both dusts and sprays are effective. Dusts of DDT and toxaphene are most commonly employed in controlling the pest. Arsenicals and cryolite are also used. Rotenone may be dusted on vegetable crops. The alfalfa webworm (*Loxostege commixtalis*) and the beet webworm (*Loxostege sticticalis*) are two related insects with similar biologies, and the same insecticides may be used in their control.

The Greater Wax Moth (*Galleria mellonella*). This widely distributed insect is most destructive to colonies of bees in warm climates. The larvae burrow through honeycombs and construct silken tunnels as they feed (Fig. 208). They feed on wax, pollen, cocoons, and impurities in the combs. Old, dark combs are preferred to those that are new and light colored. The combs in a heavily infested colony of bees may be reduced to a mass of webs, fragments, and excrement. Damage and destruction of combs occur in weak colonies when the bees are unable to adequately police the hives and keep out the intruders, and when combs are stored. The fully grown larvae are rather plump, dirty gray, and about 1½ inches in length. Pupation occurs in a tough silken cocoon within the hive or in other protected places. The adults have a wing expanse of about 1¼ inches and are grayish-brown. There are two or three generations of the insect annually. Winter is passed either in the larval or the pupal stage, although moths may emerge during

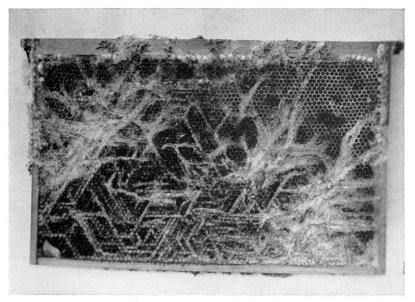

FIG. 208. Damage to comb of the honey bee by larvae of the greater wax moth (*Galleria mellonella*). (From the *American Bee Journal*.)

the winter months in the South during periods of warm weather.

Control of the wax moth consists essentially of good beekeeping. With adequate care of the colonies, broken combs and cappings, and stored combs, wax moth injury may be kept to a minimum. Stored combs should be fumigated with hydrogen cyanide, methyl bromide, or paradichlorobenzene.

The Mediterranean Flour Moth (*Anagasta kuhniella*). This insect is very troublesome in flour mills. As the larvae feed they spin silken threads which result in masses of flour being webbed together. This matted material clogs the flour machinery and impedes operations. Flour is the principal food material, but the larvae may be found also feeding on corn, wheat, wheat bran, buckwheat flour, cornmeal, cottonseed meal, cereals, and other grain products. The fully grown larvae are whitish or pinkish and about ⅗ inch long. Pupation occurs in silken cocoons which are found in flour, meal, and mill machinery. The moths have a wing spread of less than one inch and are blackish-gray with wavy black lines crossing the wings near the tips. Eggs are laid in the food materials, on containers, carton walls, floors, or in milling machinery. A generation may be completed in nine or ten weeks. When temperature conditions are favorable, breeding is continuous throughout the year.

Elimination of accumulations of flour, meal, and grain in flour mills, bins, loading docks and other places will aid in minimizing infestations. General fumigaton with methyl bromide or hydrogen cyanide is a highly effective treatment. Sprays of methoxychlor or malathion applied as a residual treatment to woodwork of flour mills, warehouses, and storage bins aid in controlling the pest.

The Rice Moth (*Corcyra cephalonica*).   This moth is similar in appearance to the Mediterranean flour moth. It commonly attacks rice in the South and is found occasionally in other farinaceous products. It is not usually found in flour mills. The pest may be controlled by the recommendations given above.

The Indian-Meal Moth (*Plodia interpunctella*).   The larvae (Fig. 209) feed on a wide variety of materials such as grains, grain prod-

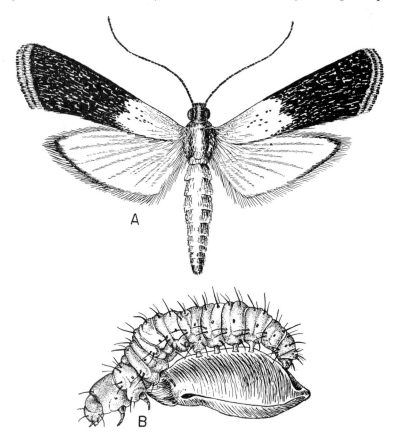

FIG. 209. Indian-meal moth and larva (*Plodia interpunctella*). **A,** Adult. **B,** Larva. (From Agricultural Research Service, U.S.D.A.)

ucts, dried fruits, nuts, roots, herbs, and powdered milk, but the insect is seldom a pest in flour mills. Infested materials become fouled with cast skins, excrement, webbing, and cocoons. The larvae are dirty white, and are frequently marked with pinkish or greenish hues. The mature larvae are about ½ inch in length. The cocoons in which the larvae pupate are found on the surface of the food materials or in cracks and crevices. The moths are readily recognized by the markings of the front wings, the bases of which are grayish-white and the apical ⅔ reddish-brown. The wing expanse is almost ¾ inch. The Indian-meal moth may pass through its developmental stages in six to eight weeks. Breeding is continuous throughout the year under favorable conditions. As many as five generations may develop annually. The insect may be controlled by the same measures recommended for the Mediterranean flour moth.

The Pecan Nut Casebearer (*Acrobasis caryae*). This is the most important insect pest of the pecan which is its only known host. Injury is caused by the larvae which bore into and destroy the nuts (Fig. 210). Larvae of the first generation are the most destruc-

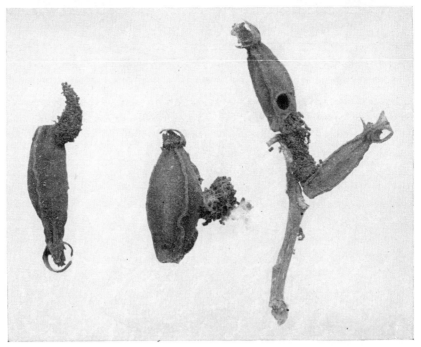

FIG. 210. Pecan nuts destroyed by the pecan nut casebearer (*Acrobasis caryae*). (From Agricultural Research Service, U.S.D.A.)

tive. They are active in May and early June when the nuts are small, and one larva may destroy several nuts in a cluster. Second generation larvae also tunnel into the nuts, but the nuts are larger at this time and fewer are destroyed. Later generations usually feed in the shucks of the nuts, buds, or axils of the leaf stems. The larvae are olive green and are about 1/2 inch long when fully grown.

The insects hibernate as partly grown larvae in small silken cases, or hibernacula, attached to buds of the trees. In the spring, the overwintered larvae feed first on the buds to which the hibernacula are attached, and later tunnel into the young growing shoots. Development is completed in the shoots and the larvae transform into the pupal stage within their tunnels.

The moths that have developed from the overwintered larvae emerge in largest numbers when the nuts are setting. These moths are small with a wing expanse of about 3/5 inch. They are gray with a ridge of dark scales extending across the front wings, 1/3 the distance from the base. Pupation of the first and second generations is within the nuts. Larvae of the third and fourth generations usually pupate within the shucks of the nuts. There are two to four generations of the pecan nut casebearer annually.

The most effective control of the nut casebearer is obtained by spraying soon after the nuts have set in the spring when eggs and young larvae are found. DDT, parathion, malathion, and toxaphene are recommended for control of the insect.

The Pickleworm (*Diaphania nitidalis*). The larvae of this insect bore in the underside of the fruit of cantaloupes, squashes, and cucumbers. Before fruit is formed the larvae feed in blooms, buds, leaf stalks, and stems. This widely distributed insect is particularly destructive in the South. The young larvae are whitish or greenish with small black spots on the body. When fully grown the larvae are coppery or greenish and about 3/4 inch in length.

Winter is passed as pupae in silken cocoons which are usually found in the leaves of the host plants. Adults emerge in late spring or early summer. The moths have a brown body with a brush of black hairs on the end of the abdomen and a wing expanse of about one inch. The wings are brownish with yellow areas in the middle of the front wings and basal half of the hind wings. Each female moth deposits 300 or more eggs upon those parts of the plants which are used as food by the larvae. The size of the first generation of larvae is small but the numbers increase rapidly as the season advances. A generation may be completed in four weeks during the summer. There may be as many as four or five generations during the year.

Cultural control measures are valuable in reducing infestations for the next season. Following harvest, crop residues should be collected and burned to destroy larvae feeding in them. In the fall the land should be plowed to eliminate the pupae on the ground. Trap crops of squash are often recommended as preventive measures since the insect prefers this plant as food. When these plants become infested the blossoms and fruit may be picked and destroyed or the entire plant removed and burned. Insecticides most commonly used in control of the pest are malathion (for home garden use), lindane, parathion, and sevin.

The Melonworm (*Diaphania hyalinata*).   This insect is similar to the pickleworm in its biology, habits, and hosts. Since the larvae feed on foliage, at least in part, the insect can be controlled by using cryolite, methoxychlor, or parathion, should control measures be justified.

Family *Sphingidae* (Sphinx Moths)

The moths of this family are recognized by the spindle-shaped bodies, narrow wings, and the long sucking tube coiled like a watch spring underneath the head. They usually fly at dusk and are often seen poised in the air over flowers, like hummingbirds, feeding on the nectar. Their feeding habits have suggested the name of hummingbird moths. The caterpillars feed on the foliage of plants. They are large, cylindrical, naked, and usually bear a horn on the eighth abdominal segment. The horn is not provided with a sting and serves no purpose unless it terrifies enemies. Some of the larger and more conspicuous moths and caterpillars are found in this family.

The Tobacco Hornworm (*Protoparce sexta*) **and the Tomato Hornworm** (*Protoparce quinquemaculata*).   These two closely related insects are the most common tomato pests. The caterpillars feed voraciously on the foliage; green tomatoes are also attacked. They are also pests of importance on tobacco, eggplant, potato, and other solanaceous plants. The two species are distributed over most of the United States, and larvae of both may be found feeding on the same plant. However, the tobacco hornworm is more common in the South and the tomato hornworm occurs more frequently in the North. The larvae are large, green (sometimes brownish-black) worms about three or four inches long with white stripes on the side of the body and a horn on the end of the abdomen. The larger larvae of the two species may be readily distinguished. (See Fig. 211.) The tobacco hornworm is green with seven white stripes extending obliquely along each side; the horn on the end of

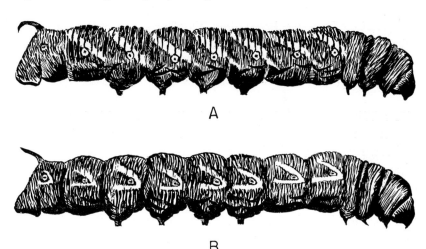

A

B

FIG. 211. **A,** The tobacco hornworm *(Protoparce sexta)*. **B,** The tomato hornworm *(Protoparce quinquemaculata)*. (From the University of California Division of Agricultural Sciences.)

the abdomen is red and curved. The tomato hornworm is green or brownish-black with eight white V- or L-shaped markings along each side; the horn on the end of the abdomen is black and usually almost straight.

The pupae, which are about two inches long, dark brown, and spindle-shaped, hibernate in the soil. The case within which the proboscis develops arches from the head and is bent downward like a pitcher handle. The moths emerge in the spring. They are large and gray, with a wing expanse of about four inches. Moths of the tobacco hornworm are dark gray, with the front wings marked by a group of white dots at the base, and the hind wings blackish and crossed by more or less broken diagonal white bands. The abdomen is marked with six pairs of more or less rounded orange-yellow spots. The tomato hornworm adult is light gray; the front wings bear no white dots at the base; and the hind wings are ash gray crossed by black and whitish diagonal bands. The abdomen bears five pairs of quadrangular orange-yellow spots.

The greenish-yellow eggs, which are deposited on the underside of the leaves, hatch in a week. The larvae reach maturity after five molts in three or four weeks. The fully grown larvae enter the soil to a depth of three or four inches, form cells and pupate. The number of generations varies from one in the North to possibly three in the Gulf States.

Small larvae may be readily poisoned with lead arsenate, calcium arsenate, DDT, or methoxychlor. The large caterpillars are more difficult to kill. Hand picking is often resorted to as a control measure. The insect has a number of natural enemies such as insect parasites, birds, and diseases.

The White-Lined Sphinx (*Celerio lineata*).   This is one of the most common sphinx moths (Fig. 212). The body and front wings are brown with six light lines on the thorax and a yellowish-white stripe extending from the inner margin of the base to the apex of each front wing. The hind wings are black with a broad rosaceous band across the middle of each. Wing expanse of the moths varies from 2½ to three inches. The larvae are nearly three inches in length with the characteristic horn on the end of the abdomen. Markings and coloration of the larvae are extremely variable, the

FIG. 212.   **A,** Moth. **B,** Caterpillars of the white-lined sphinx (*Celerio lineata*). (From Department of Entomology, A & M College of Texas.)

most common color being greenish-yellow with black markings. Some larvae are almost black and marked with yellow lines.

This insect has a biology similar to the tomato and tobacco hornworms. There are two and possibly three generations annually. Larvae feed on the foliage of a wide range of plants such as purslane, chickweed, cotton, vegetable crops, roses, apple trees, watermelons, and buckwheat. On rare occasions the larvae become so abundant that they swarm over the plants like armyworms. When control measures are needed the larvae may be killed by the insecticides recommended for the control of the tomato and tobacco hornworms.

The Pandorus Sphinx (*Pholus pandorus*). This is a large and beautiful moth with a wing expanse of about four inches. The color of the wings consists of shades of olive and gray with inner margins marked with yellow and rose. The larvae feed on Virginia creeper. *Pholus labruscue* is a related species but more tropical in its habitat.

One group of sphinx moths has the central portion of the wings transparent. The hummingbird clear-wing (*Hemaris thysbe*) and the snowberry clear-wing (*Hemaris diffinis*) are examples of this group. Larvae of the former feed on the virburnums; those of the latter are found on bush honeysuckle and snowberry.

Family *Geometridae* (Geometrid Moths or Measuring Worms)

Moths of this large family are rather delicate and are usually medium in size. They are weak fliers and are ordinarily found around woods. The larvae are known as measuring worms or loopers because they crawl by means of looping movements. They do not have the full complement of prolegs; the first three pairs are usually absent. The larvae feed primarily on the foliage of trees. Pupae are found in flimsy cocoons or cells in the ground. More than 1,000 species of this family are found in North America.

Cankerworms. The spring and the fall cankerworms are the best known of the geometrids. The caterpillars of these two species defoliate many fruit and forest trees such as elm, apple, oak, hickory, and maple. Maximum injury occurs in the spring as the new foliage is completing its growth.

The moths of spring cankerworms (*Paleacrita vernata*) emerge and lay eggs in the spring. The fully grown caterpillars are dark greenish or blackish measuring worms with only two pairs of prolegs and about one inch in length. They feed for three to five weeks and then enter the soil where they transform into pupae in earthen cells. Here they remain until the next spring when the adults emerge. The female moths are wingless with a gray, spider-like body. The male moths have functional wings and are gray in color. Only one generation occurs annually.

Infestations may be prevented by banding the trunks of trees with sticky materials, such as tanglefoot, to prevent the wingless females from ascending to lay eggs. This must be done early, for the moths emerge in February or March. The caterpillars are easily killed by applications of lead arsenate or DDT.

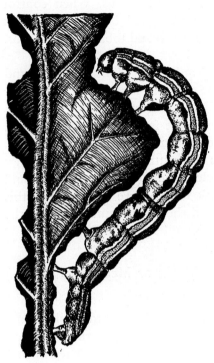

The fall cankerworm (*Alsophila pometaria*) has a biology similar to the spring cankerworm. It differs from the latter in that the moths emerge and the females lay eggs in the fall instead of the spring. Winter is passed in the egg stage. The larvae are similar in appearance to the spring cankerworm but they have three pairs of prolegs (Fig. 213) instead of two pairs. This insect can be controlled by following the recommendations given for the spring cankerworm, except that trees need to be banded in the fall instead of the spring if this control measure is employed.

FIG. 213. Fall cankerworm (*Alsophila pometaria*). (From Agricultural Research Service, U.S.D.A.)

Family *Notodontidae* (Notodontid Moths)

Moths of this family are of moderate size, with a wing expanse of usually less than two inches. They are stout in form, and the body is densely clothed with hairs. Many resemble the owlet moths. Some species have a posteriorly projecting lobe or prominence on the inner margin of the front wings, and this character has suggested the common name "prominents" for the group. Larvae feed on the foliage of trees and shrubs. Pupation is in flimsy cocoons or in the soil.

The Handmaid Moths (*Datana* spp.). Members of this genus are the most common insects of the family. The moths are brown with the front wings marked by transverse stripes of a different color (Fig. 214). Most species have a dot on the discal cell.

The larvae are gregarious in habit and feed on the leaves of a number of forest and fruit trees, such as apple, oak, pecan, and hickory. They are black or reddish with longitudinal stripes of white or yellow (Fig. 215). Winter is passed as pupae in the ground.

The yellow-necked caterpillar (*Datana ministra*) is generally distributed over the United States and Canada. The mature larvae are about two inches long with a black head, immediately behind which is a yellow band. The body is black with yellow

FIG. 214. Datana moths and egg cluster. (From Texas Agricultural Experiment Station.)

stripes and is sparsely clothed with hairs. Eggs are laid in clusters on the leaves. Only one generation occurs annually in the cooler climates. A related species (*Datana robusta*) is double-brooded in its southern range. Colonies of the walnut caterpillar (*Datana integerrima*) often defoliate small walnut and pecan trees. The species has two broods in the South. Datana caterpillars are rather easily controlled by the use of lead arsenate or DDT sprays.

The Red-Humped Caterpillar (*Schizura concinna*). The caterpillars of this widely distributed insect feed on the leaves of elm, apple, cherry, rose, and other plants. When fully grown the larvae are about one inch in length. The head is red; the body is marked by black and yellowish lines with a prominent red hump on the

FIG. 215. Datana caterpillars showing tachinid parasite eggs deposited on their bodies. (From Texas Agricultural Experiment Station.)

dorsal surface of the first abdominal segment; the adults are dark brown. The insect hibernates as larvae in cocoons found in debris or in the topsoil. There are one or two generations annually depending on the climate. Control measures are the same as for the Datana caterpillars.

The Saddled Prominent (*Heterocampa guttivitta*). The larvae of this insect feed on the foliage of beech, apple, and sugar maple. Mature larvae are about 1½ inches long, and are usually yellowish-green or light green. The body is quite devoid of hairs and a brownish or purplish saddle-shaped patch is usually present on the back. The moths are grayish with a wing spread of 1½ to two inches. Only one generation occurs annually in the northern states. *Heterocampa manteo* and *H. umbrata* are related species. These caterpillars may be controlled by lead arsenate or DDT sprays.

Family *Lymantriidae* (Tussock Moths)

The common name of this family refers to the characteristic tufts of brightly colored hairs with which the larvae are clothed. The larvae are feeders on the foliage of deciduous trees and may do serious damage. The female moths of many species are practically wingless.

The Gypsy Moth (*Porthetria dispar*). This is the best known insect in the family. The insect was brought from Europe to Medford, Massachusetts, about 1869 by a naturalist who was investigating the possibility of silk production of this and other caterpillars. Some of the experimental insects escaped and became established in adjacent woodlands. The caterpillars feed on the foliage of both deciduous and evergreen trees. The insect is known to attack more than 500 species of plants. The larvae are hairy, dark colored, and attain a length of two or more inches (Fig. 216). On the dorsal surface of the body is a double row of five pairs of blue spots followed by six pairs of red spots. The insect is found in the northeastern part of the United States and Canada. In 1954 an infestation was discovered in Michigan where eradication measures were undertaken.

Hibernation is in the egg stage. Eggs are laid in masses of 400 to 500 and are covered with hairs from the body of the female moth. The eggs hatch in the spring as the young leaves are expanding. Most of the larvae reach maturity by midsummer and spin flimsy cocoons within which they change to dark brown pupae. Duration

FIG. 216. Larvae of the gypsy moth (*Porthetria dispar*). (From Connecticut Agricultural Experiment Station, New Haven.)

of the pupal stage is ten to 14 days. The male moths are brownish and have a wing expanse of about 1½ inches. The females are somewhat larger, almost white, and have dark irregular markings across the wings. Fortunately the females are unable to fly. Soon after mating the females lay their clusters of eggs on trunks of trees, stones, buildings, and other objects. Only one generation occurs annually. The insect is spread chiefly in the larval stage. Egg masses may also be transported on lumber, boxes, nursery stock, and other materials.

Several control measures are used against this pest. Its spread has been restricted by strict quarantine measures. Egg masses may be destroyed by brushing them with coal-tar creosote. Spraying infested trees with DDT or lead arsenate is the most effective control measure.

The Brown-Tail Moth (*Nygmia phaeorrhoea*).   The larvae of the brown-tail moth are important pests of fruit trees, such as apple and pear, and deciduous shade trees; evergreens are not attacked. The insect is found in New England, New Brunswick, and Nova Scotia. The fully grown caterpillars are about 1½ inches in length, dark brown, hairy, and have a row of white tufts along each side of the body. The body bears barbed nettling hairs which produce a dermatitis on contact with the skin, not unlike that caused by poison ivy. The larvae pupate the latter part of June in flimsy cocoons which are found in sheltered places. Two or three weeks following pupation the moths emerge. The moths (Fig. 217), which have a wing expanse of slightly more than 1½ inches, are white with a tuft of golden brown bristles on the end of the abdomen, which

FIG. 217. Brown-tail moths (*Nygmia phaeorrhoea*). (From Agricultural Research Service, U.S.D.A.)

has suggested the common name. The females lay 200 to 400 eggs each on leaves in an elongate mass. The eggs hatch in about three weeks and the young larvae feed gregariously on terminal leaves which they soon web together to form hibernation shelters. Only one generation occurs annually. Destruction of the hibernation webs or tents and spraying with lead arsenate or DDT are recommended as control measures.

The White-Marked Tussock Moth (*Hemerocampa leucostigma*). The caterpillars of this moth are frequently a pest of deciduous shade and fruit trees, particularly in the eastern United States. The mature larvae (Fig. 218) are yellowish-black, hairy, and about 1¼ inches long. They are recognized by a red head, by tufts of long black hairs on either side of the head with a third tuft on the eighth abdominal segment, and by two reddish spots near the end of the abdomen. Outbreaks of this insect may be controlled by the use of DDT or lead arsenate sprays.

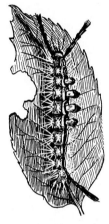

Family *Phalaenidae* or *Noctuidae* (Noctuids or Owlet Moths)

FIG. 218. Larva of the white-marked tussock moth (*Hemerocampa leucostigma*). (From Illinois Natural History Survey.)

This is the largest family of the Lepidoptera in North America. More than 2,500 species are known in America north of Mexico. From an economic viewpoint this is also the most important family of the order in this country, as many agricultural pests are found here.

A majority of moths seen around lights are members of this family. Most of the adults are inconspicuously colored and of average size. Typically, the body is large in relation to the size of the wings. The front wings are rather narrow and somewhat elongate. A triangular body outline is formed when the wings of the moths are folded upon the abdomen. The caterpillars are ordinarily dull in color, naked, and usually provided with the full complement of prolegs. They generally feed on foliage of plants but some are borers in stems and fruits. The larvae may be identified by the presence of two setae in the prespiracular group of the prothorax; by the proleg-bearing segments of the abdomen with setae III above, IV behind, and V below the spiracle; and by the arrangement of the crochets of the prolegs in a longitudinal mesoseries.

The Cotton Leafworm (*Alabama argillacea*). The cotton leafworm (Fig. 219) is one of the oldest and best known of the cotton insects. The caterpillars feed on the leaves of the plant, and vast areas of cotton may be defoliated late in the growing season. The fully grown larvae are about 1½ inches long and rather slender in form. The anal prolegs stand out quite prominently, and in crawling

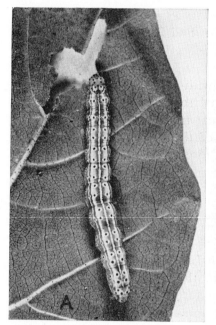 

FIG. 219. **A,** Cotton leafworm. **B,** Moth (*Alabama argillacea*). (From Department of Entomology, A & M College of Texas.)

the larvae move in a semilooping manner. The caterpillars of the first generations are lighter colored than those found at the end of the season. The lighter forms are yellowish-green with three narrow white stripes down the back and a white line along each side. There are four equally spaced black spots on the dorsum of each abdominal segment. Each spot bears a black seta and is surrounded by a light ring. With the exception of the first instar, there are 30 black dots on the head. There is an increase of pigmentation between the white stripes in the dark specimens. In extreme cases the caterpillars are almost black. Length of the larval period varies from one to three weeks.

The mature larvae pupate in slight cocoons protected by a folded corner of a leaf. Pupae range in color from chestnut brown to almost black. When conditions are favorable the adults may emerge in a week. They are light brown, tinged with olive green and wine. The wing expanse varies from 1⅛ to 1¼ inches. The adult females deposit singly 400 to 600 bluish-green eggs on the underside of the leaves during a period of seven to ten days. The eggs hatch in two or three days in warm weather. A life cycle may be completed in three or four weeks and there may be three to seven generations annually. Wet weather favors outbreaks of the insect.

Here is an exceptional case of a moth capable of causing injury. The tip of the proboscis is armed with many sharp stout spines by means of which skins of fruit may be lacerated. Considerable damage may be done to figs and ripening peaches.

The cotton leafworm is a tropical insect; it does not overwinter in the United States. With the advent of cold weather in the fall all stages of the insect die. In the spring moths drift into the cotton belt from the tropics. The first leafworms are generally reported from southwest Texas near the coast. The moths are strong fliers and may be found as far north as Canada by the end of the season.

The production of earlier crops of cotton and the widespread use of insecticides for the control of the boll weevil and other insects have eliminated most of the injury caused by this pest. The caterpillars may be controlled by several poisons, such as calcium arsenate, parathion, toxaphene, DDT, Guthion and sevin.

Corn Earworm (*Heliothis zea*). This species (Fig. 220) is widely distributed in both North America and South America, and also occurs in Hawaii where it was probably introduced from this country. The insect is listed as a pest of importance throughout its range of distribution, but it is most destructive in southern United States. Other common names of the insect are cotton bollworm, tomato fruitworm, vetch worm, and false tobacco budworm. The corn earworm is a general feeder, attacking many plants, particularly corn, cotton, tomato, tobacco, vetch, and cowpea.

The corn earworm is most destructive in feeding in the fruits of plants, such as ears of corn, flower buds (squares) and bolls of cotton, and fruit of the tomato. However, foliage and tender stems

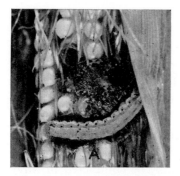

FIG. 220. **A,** Corn earworm. **B,** Moth (*Heliothis zea*). (From Department of Entomology, A & M College of Texas.)

may be attacked. Early in the season the larvae feed in the whorl of terminal leaves of young corn plants, damaging leaves and developing tassels. When silks develop, numbers of eggs are laid on them. The larvae which hatch from these eggs tunnel into the ears and feed on the kernels. On cotton, newly hatched larvae feed on the squares. Older larvae tunnel out large green bolls. Leaves and succulent stems of the cotton plant are sometimes attacked. On the tomato plant, the larvae feed first on the foliage and later tunnel into the fruit. Both foliage and seed pods of alfalfa and vetch are attacked. Often foliage of the peanut is severely riddled by the feeding of the larvae in the Southwest.

Eggs of the corn earworm are waxy white and about $\frac{1}{50}$ inch in diameter. They have a flat base, are dome-shaped and ribbed. The mature larvae are about $1\frac{1}{2}$ inches in length. Their color is quite variable, ranging from very dark to light green or pink. Their bodies are marked by alternating longitudinal dark and light stripes, but these markings are not dependable. The most distinctive characteristics are the presence of short, sharp microspines with which the skin is covered, except on the dorsal abdominal tubercles, and the feeding habits. The brown pupae, which are quite simliar to those of cutworms, are found in the soil. Color and markings of the moths are variable. One of the most common forms is tan or buff. In another form, the front wings are grayish-brown marked with dark gray irregular lines and darker spots.

Moths feed on nectar of flowers and other sweet liquids. They are strong fliers and are active at dusk. Eggs are deposited singly on host plants of the larvae. A moth may deposit a maximum of 3,000 eggs, with an average number of eggs probably in excess of 1,000.

The length of the life cycle depends upon weather conditions.

Eggs may hatch in two or three days during the summer. The length of the egg stage is increased in cooler weather in the spring and fall. The length of the larval stage varies from two weeks in the summer to a month or longer during spring and fall. When larval maturity is reached, the insect leaves the plant and enters the ground for pupation. The depth to which the soil is entered varies from one to seven inches, depending upon the type of soil and moisture. The pupal stage ranges in length from less than two weeks in warm weather to more than six months in the period of hibernation. A generation may be completed in one month under warm conditions, while in cool weather it may extend over a period of two months. There are four to seven generations annually in the southern states with only one or two occurring in the insect's northern range.

The corn earworm has many natural enemies. One of the most important natural checks is cannibalism of the larvae. Cannibalism is more marked in corn than in other crops because of the proximity of the larvae in feeding in the ears. Birds, toads, spiders, the insidious flower bug, larvae of lacewing flies, lady beetles, wasps, and other insects prey upon the pest. *Trichogramma evanescens* is an important egg parasite.

Control measures depend upon the crops attacked. Strains of corn are being developed which show a measure of resistance to corn earworm attacks. No insecticidal control on field corn is practicable. The corn earworm may be controlled in sweet corn with several applications of a spray mixture of DDT emulsifiable concentrate, white mineral oil, and water applied to new silks at two-day intervals. The corn earworm may be controlled on cotton if applications of insecticides are correctly made at the proper time. The pesticides and their combinations most commonly used are DDT, toxaphene, toxaphene-DDT, endrin, endrin-DDT, sevin, and sevin-DDT. Both dusts and sprays are used in combating the pest. Dust or spray applications of DDT, TDE, or endrin provide control of the insect when infestations develop on tomatoes.

The Armyworm (*Pseudaletia unipuncta*). Somewhere in the United States east of the Rocky Mountains outbreaks of this insect occur almost every year. The hordes of the greenish-brown caterpillars feed on leaves and stems of grains and grasses and other plants. (See Fig. 187, p. 302. The larvae are about 1½ inches long when fully grown. On each side of the body are three stripes of approximately equal width. The upper stripe is pale orange; the middle one, dark brown; and the bottom stripe, pale yellow. The skin is smooth, the spiracles are black, and the mandibles are devoid of denticles.

The larvae feed at night and hide underneath clods or other protection during the day. When the host plants have been destroyed, the caterpillars crawl in great numbers to adjacent fields in search of more food. This habit of travel has suggested the name "armyworm." The length of the larval stage is three to four weeks in the northern states. The caterpillars enter the ground to transform into pupae. About two weeks later the moths emerge from the pupal cases. The moths, which have a wing spread of about 1½ inches, are brownish-gray with a white spot near the middle of each front wing. Each female lays 500 or more eggs in rows of ten to 50 on the lower leaves of the host plants. There are usually two or three generations each year; however, it is possible for more generations to occur in the South. Hibernation is chiefly as immature larvae, but indications are that adults or pupae also may survive the winters in southern regions.

Applications of DDT or toxaphene will effectively control the armyworm. The use of poison-bran mash, as recommended in grasshopper control, also provides satisfactory control of the pest.

The Fall Armyworm (*Laphygma frugiperda*). Feeding habits of the fall armyworm are similar to those of the armyworm. Grain and grass crops are most generally attacked, but the range of host plants is greater than for the latter species. Peanuts, alfalfa, potato, tomato, cotton, cowpeas, and a number of other plants may also serve as hosts. The larvae may feed in the buds and ears of corn like the earworm. In parts of the West Indies the insect is commonly known as the corn earworm. The caterpillars (Fig. 221) are greenish or brownish and are about 1⅓ inches in length when fully grown. They have three yellowish-white, hair-like stripes down the back, a conspicuous inverted Y on the head and prominent black tubercles on the body from which the body hairs grow.

When serious outbreaks of the insect occur, the larvae exhaust the food supply and begin crawling, literally by the thousands, seeking more plants to devour. The first generations are well defined and do not overlap as the later broods. The larvae mature and suddenly disappear, having gone into the ground for pupation. The length of the larval period is dependent upon climatic conditions

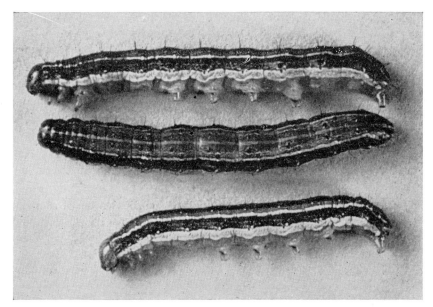

FIG. 221. Fall armyworms (*Laphygma frugiperda*). (From Department of Entomology, A & M College of Texas.)

and may vary from 12 days to more than a month. In warm weather the pupal stage may not be more than eight to ten days in duration.

The moths resemble the adults of cutworms. The wing expanse is about 1½ inches. The hind wings are grayish with the front pair dark gray, mottled with light and dark areas, and with a light spot near the tips. The life span of the moths is ten to 14 days, but in this brief period they may fly hundreds of miles and the females lay an average of 1,000 eggs. The eggs are laid in clusters on or near the food plants. In hot weather the egg stage may be as short as two days. The length of a generation may vary from less than a month to two months, dependent upon climatic conditions.

The biology of the insect is similar to that of the cotton leafworm in many respects. The insect is of tropical origin and, through flight of moths, tends to spread over the United States east of the Rocky Mountains each season. But, unlike the cotton leafworm, it is able to overwinter in the United States along the Gulf coast. All stages may be found there during the winter months. As with the cotton leafworm, wet seasons are favorable for outbreaks of the insect. The number of generations completed annually depends upon the section of the country in which the insect is found. Only one generation may occur in the North; there may be as many as nine to 11 completed in the southernmost range of the insect.

Sprays and dusts containing DDT, toxaphene, or chlordane will control the fall armyworm. The use of poison-bran mash as in grasshopper control is also effective in control of this insect.

The Yellow-Striped Armyworm (*Prodenia ornithogalli*). This caterpillar feeds on the leaves of a wide range of plants, such as corn, wheat, cabbage, turnip, potato, tomato, and cotton. Also, it may tunnel into cotton bolls in much the same manner as the bollworm. The mature larvae are 1½ to 1¾ inches in length. The head is quite small in relation to the size of the body and the color is quite variable, some specimens being much darker than others. Typical specimens are readily recognized by the presence of three light lines down the back with a double row of triangular dark spots lying between the outer lines (Fig. 222). The front wings of

FIG. 222. The yellow-striped armyworm (*Prodenia ornithogalli*). (From Department of Entomology, A & M College of Texas.)

the moths are dark velvety brown marked with black and light yellow with the hind wings lighter colored. The wing spread is about 1½ inches.

The life history of this insect is not very well known. Hibernation is usually in the pupal stage, but some moths may overwinter also. Two generations may be produced annually in the North with the possibility of four completed in the southernmost states. Should infestations become large enough to warrant control measures, applications of toxaphene and DDT are recommended for use either as dusts or as sprays.

Cutworms. Cutworms are inconspicuously marked, dull colored caterpillars. The color and markings of the body harmonize quite well with the soil, with which they are usually associated. They range in length from 1½ to two inches when fully grown. This is a rather large group of noctuid larvae with diverse feeding habits. The most commonly observed injury is the severance of the stems of young plants at the ground level. Based on feeding habits, cutworms may be classified into (1) surface feeders, (2) tunnel makers, (3) climbers, and (4) subterranean feeders. Most species of cutworms attack a wide range of plants including all common farm and garden crops. Feeding usually at night, the larvae hide in the soil, under clods, trash, or in other protected places during the day. Transformation is within pupal cells in the soil. Cutworms have one to five generations annually, depending upon the species and climatic conditions. They hibernate as larvae, pupae, and in some cases as adults. The moths are dark and the front wings are usually rather inconspicuously marked with darker or lighter narrow bands and spots. The hind wings are lighter than the front wings. The armyworm, fall armyworm, yellow-striped armyworm, cabbage looper, and the corn earworm are cutworms also, but because of their importance they are discussed separately. Only a few of the more common species can be mentioned here.

Surface-Feeding Cutworms. The granulate cutworm (*Feltia subterranea*) is a widely distributed form and is an important pest in the South. Three types of feeding by this cutworm have been reported; namely, cutting off small plants near the surface of the soil, feeding on the foliage, and tunneling into the fruits of tomatoes and eggplants. The caterpillars are dark gray with many small dark granules over the surface of the body. This species may produce five complete generations annually in the South. A related species, the dingy cutworm (*Feltia subgothica*), produces only one generation annually. This species has a wide distribution and is a common pest. The larvae are dull brown with a yellowish-gray dorsal stripe.

The army cutworm (*Chorizagrotis auxiliaris*) is found in the Great Plains region. Winter wheat and alfalfa are chiefly attacked. The larvae may assume the habit of armyworms and migrate to adjacent fields when they become extremely abundant and exhaust the food supply.

Tunnel-Making Cutworms. The black cutworm (*Agrotis ipsilon*) is a widely distributed and well-known species. It is most destructive east of the Mississippi River. The larvae make burrows in the soil into which the food is dragged. They are very destructive as they cut off many more plants than they consume. The caterpillars are greasy gray or brown with indistinct stripes. Four generations of this insect may be completed annually. The pale-sided cutworm (*Agrotis malefida*) also lives in a tunnel into which food is pulled. This is also a multiple-generation species. It is found most generally in the southern United States, Mexico, and Cuba.

Climbing Cutworms.   The variegated cutworm (*Peridroma saucia,* Fig. 223) is probably the most widely distributed and most important cutworm. This species is not only found through North America and South America, but it occurs in Europe and Asia

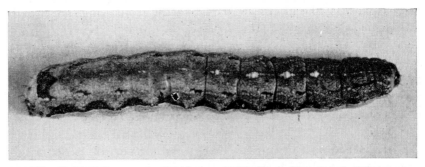

FIG. 223.   Variegated cutworm (*Peridroma saucia*). (From Department of Entomology, A & M College of Texas.)

Minor also. The caterpillars are feeders on most kinds of plants but they show some preference for vegetable and forage crops. Feeding activity is chiefly during the night, but the larvae may be active on cloudy days.

The mature larvae are pale yellow or brown and about two inches long. They are differentiated from other noctuid larvae by the presence of a row of dull yellow spots down the middorsal line and a more or less distinct black or brownish W on the eighth abdominal segment. Larvae, pupae, and adults may be found throughout the winter in the South. In the North the insect hibernates in the pupal stage. As many as four generations may be completed annually in southern climates.

The spotted cutworm (*Amathes c-nigrum*) is one of the most important species in the northern United States. The caterpillars are general feeders but prefer garden plants. These insects overwinter as immature larvae and complete two generations a season,

The caterpillars are brownish or grayish with a row of triangular spots along each side of the dorsal surface of the body.

Subterranean Cutworms.   The pale western cutworm (*Agrotis orthogonia*) is the most important of the subterranean forms. It feeds almost entirely under the surface of the ground and cuts off the plants slightly above the crowns. Wheat and barley are the most important food plants. The caterpillars are grayish without spots or other markings. The insect overwinters as larvae within the eggs. There is only one generation annually. This insect is confined to the arid and semiarid sections of the United States and Canada.

Control of Cutworms.   Dusting or spraying plants and the ground around them with DDT, toxaphene, or chlordane will control most species of cutworms. The use of poison-bran mash as recommended in grasshopper control provides effective control also. The baits should be spread in the late afternoon. Rotation of crops in such a manner that corn does not follow sod land is advised, unless the land is plowed the previous summer or fall. Cultural control is usually employed in combating the subterranean cutworm, but recent investigations have shown that applications of dieldrin to the soil will control the insect.

The Cabbage Looper (*Trichoplusia ni*).   This caterpillar (Fig. 224) is the common green looping worm found feeding on the leaves of cabbage, turnip, lettuce, pea, cotton, and a number of other plants. It is frequently mistaken for a measuring worm. In some sections the insect is a more destructive pest of cruciferous plants than the imported cabbageworm. The caterpillar attains

FIG. 224.   Cabbage looper (*Trichoplusia ni*). (From Department of Entomology, A & M College of Texas.)

a length of more than one inch, is naked, and green in color. There is a noticeable narrow white line along each side of the body. Other less distinct lines appear on the back. The larvae have only three pairs of prolegs in contrast with the imported cabbageworm and most other caterpillars which have five pairs. The larvae feed for a period of two to four weeks and then spin a flimsy cocoon, usually on the underside of the leaf of the host plant, in which transformation to the pupal stage occurs. During the summer months the adults emerge ten to 14 days following pupation. The moths have a wing spread of about 1¼ inches, and are grayish-brown with the front wings marked near the center by a silvery spot which is shaped somewhat like the figure 8. Eggs are laid singly on the upper surface of the leaves of the host plants. Hibernation is in the pupal stage. The number of generations varies from two in the northern range of the insect to four or more in the South. Quite a few insecticides have been recommended for control of this pest on various crops. Those compounds most commonly used are parathion, toxaphene, phosdrin, malathion, and endrin. Precautions must be taken to avoid harmful residues on vegetable crops.

The Stalk Borer (*Papaipema nebris*).   The common stalk borer is widely distributed east of the Rocky Mountains. The caterpillars bore or tunnel in the stems of giant ragweed, corn, cotton, and numerous other plants. Cultivated plants are usually injured around the weedy margins of fields. The brownish larvae are found within the stalks or stems and reach a length of about 1½ inches when fully grown. There are five white lines on the back and sides. The two lines on either side fade out between the first and fourth abdominal segments and produce an injured appearance of the body. The body lines disappear completely prior to the pupation of the caterpillars. The adults are grayish-brown in general color, with considerable variation in markings. The wing spread of the moths is more than one inch.

The insect passes the winter as eggs attached to the stems of the wild hosts. Eggs hatch in the spring and the larvae mature the latter part of the summer. Pupation is within the larval burrows. There is only one generation each year. Cutting and burning of wild host plants, and cleaning up the margins of fields and gardens by early spring are the most effective control measures in combating this insect pest.

The Green Cloverworm (*Plathypena scabra*). The green clover-worm frequently infests alfalfa, clover, cowpeas, and related crops. The caterpillar may be readily differentiated from the alfalfa cat-erpillar by the presence of four pairs of prolegs, whereas the latter possesses the full complement of five pairs. The larvae are green with two white lines along each side of the body and are about 1¼ inches long. The adults are dark brown and the front wings have a mottled appearance. The larvae pupate in light cocoons under lit-ter or slightly underneath the surface of the soil. Three or four generations develop annually in southern climates. There are prob-ably two generations in the North. The insect hibernates as pupae or adults. Cutting the alfalfa or clover of infested fields is usually the only control measure needed. This eliminates the food supply and exposes the larvae to bright sunlight and natural enemies. Insecti-cides suggested for control are Dylox, methoxychlor, and phosdrin. Phosdrin should be applied only by a trained operator.

The Underwings or Catocalas (*Catocala* spp.). The underwings or catocalas (Fig. 225) are an attractive group of moths, specimens of which are prized by all amateur collectors. Some of the moths are quite large with a wing expanse of as much as three inches. The front wings are generally gray or brown and marked with wavy lines. The hind wings are often bordered by yellow, red, or white.

FIG. 225. An underwing (*Catocala*). **A,** Larva. (From Florida Agricultural Experi-ment Station.) **B,** Adult.

The conspicuously marked hind wings have suggested the common name of underwings. The larvae feed on the foliage of forest trees such as oak, hickory, and pecan. They are rarely numerous enough to cause much injury to the foliage.

The Black Witch (*Erebus odora*). This species is the largest of the noctuids; some specimens have a wing spread of as much as six inches. The moths are dark brown. The front wings have an eye spot near the middle and the hind wings are marked by double eye spots near the anal angles. This insect is a native of the West Indies, but there are reports that it may breed in the extreme southernmost part of the United States. Certain leguminous trees serve as hosts of the larvae. These moths are strong fliers and are sometimes found as far north as Canada in the late summer or fall.

Family *Arctiidae* (Tiger Moths or Arctiids)

The common name of tiger moths has been suggested by the prominently striped or spotted wings of a majority of the adults of this family. The larvae are generally densely clothed with hairs. Most of the common woolly caterpillars are the larvae of tiger moths.

The Salt-Marsh Caterpillar (*Estigmene acrea*). The common name of this insect (Fig. 226) is misleading, for it is widely distributed throughout the country and is not confined to coastal regions as the name implies. The larvae feed on the foliage of most garden and field crop plants in addition to numerous weeds, grasses, and other uncultivated hosts. The caterpillars are about two inches long when fully grown and are clothed in long black, brownish or yellowish hairs. The moths have a wing spread of about two inches. They are predominantly white with a number of black spots on both the upper and lower surfaces of the wings. In the female the wings are white on both surfaces and the abdomen is brownish-yellow with the exception of the first and last segments which are white. The males are brownish-yellow on the underside of the front wings, on both surfaces of the hind wings, and on the abdomen excepting the tip, which is white. The thin brownish cocoons which the larvae spin have incorporated in them many body hairs. These are found under trash and in loose soil. Eggs are laid in clusters, usually on the underside of the leaves of the host plants. Winter is passed either as larvae or pupae. In the insect's northern range there is only one

FIG. 226. Salt-marsh caterpillar (*Estigmene acrea*). Larvae, pupa (removed from cocoon), and adult. (From Department of Entomology, A & M College of Texas.)

generation annually, while there may be as many as four in the South.

Control should begin with the destruction of weeds and trash where the insect hibernates. This insect is rather difficult to control with insecticides, especially when the caterpillars are almost grown. Applications of toxaphene at the rate of three pounds of the technical product per acre, however, have proved to be fairly satisfactory in its control.

The Fall Webworm (*Hyphantria cunea*). The unsightly webs of the fall webworm are most commonly observed in late summer and fall. The webs enclose the leaves of the twigs and smaller branches; occasionally small trees are almost completely enveloped by them. The larvae are gregarious and feed upon the upper and lower surfaces of the leaves within the webs (Fig. 227). As the food requirements increase, the webs are enlarged to enclose more foliage. Hickory, persimmon, pecan, elm, and numerous other forest, shade, and fruit trees serve as hosts of the caterpillars. Evergreens are not attacked. Winter is passed as pupae in cocoons secreted underneath scales of bark, debris on the ground, or in loose soil. The moths emerge in the spring. They are pure white, except that in some

FIG. 227. Fall webworms (*Hyphantria cunea*) on tent. (From Agricultural Research Service, U.S.D.A.)

specimens the front wings are marked with black or brown dots. The eggs are greenish-white and are laid in clusters on the leaves of the host plants.

The fully grown larvae are slightly more than one inch in length and are clothed with long black and white hairs. In its northernmost range of distribution the insect has only one generation annually, while in the South there are two generations. When infestations are light it is practical to remove the webs by pruning and burning them. Sprays of DDT, lead arsenate, or toxaphene will control the pest.

The Yellow Woollybear (*Diacrisia virginica*).   These caterpillars are about two inches long and are clothed with long yellowish hairs. They are seen most commonly in the fall crawling across highways and pathways in search of suitable hibernation quarters. Hibernation is in the pupal stage enclosed in silken cocoons. The moths are white except for a few small black spots on the wings.

The Banded Woollybear (*Isia isabella*).   These caterpillars are clothed with hairs of even length, which are black on the ends of the body and brown in the middle. The adults are grayish-yellow with a few small black spots on the wings. The insects hibernate as larvae in protected places.

Family *Nolidae*

This is a small family of moths which is frequently classified as a subfamily of the Arctiidae. Less than two dozen species are known to occur in the United States.

The Sorghum Webworm (*Celama sorghiella*).   This is the best known and most important insect of the family. It is an important pest of grain sorghums. The larvae feed in the heads on the developing seeds (Fig. 228). Late-planted and late-maturing crops tend to suffer the heaviest losses. In the United States the insect occurs in the Gulf and South Atlantic States, and the Great Plains region as far north as Nebraska. The mature larvae are sluggish caterpillars about ½ inch long, clothed with bristly spines of varying lengths. The basic color of the body is green with four red to blackish dorsally located stripes. The adults are whitish and have a wing expanse of about ½ inch. The insect passes the

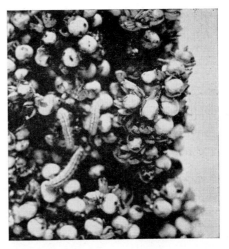

FIG. 228. Sorghum webworms (*Celama sorghiella*) on head of grain sorghum. (From Department of Entomology, A & M College of Texas.)

winter as larvae in crop residues. There may be six complete generations annually in its southern range. Control consists chiefly in destruction of crop residues, growing early crops, and the use of Phosdrin or Dibrom sprays as soon as the infestation is found.

Family *Citheroniidae* (Royal Moths)

This family contains a limited number of species of medium to large moths. Their bodies are stout and hairy and they are provided with strong wings. The basal half or two-thirds of the antennae of the males are strongly pectinate, and the head is sunken into the prothorax. The larvae bear long, curved horns or spines on the second thoracic segment and sometimes on the third also. The larvae pupate within earthen cells in the ground.

The Regal Moth (*Citheronia regalis*). This moth has a wing spread of 4½ to six inches. The front wings are olive gray with reddish veins and yellow spots. The hind wings are orange-red with yellow markings. The larvae, which are known as hickory horned devils or persimmon-bulls, attain a length of four to five inches. Their bodies are greenish, bluish, or reddish-brown. They are recognized by the long horns on the body, particularly those on the mesothorax and metathorax which are much longer than the

others. Food plants consist of hickory, persimmon, cotton, black walnut, and deciduous plants of other species. Hibernation occurs as
pupae in the ground. The moths emerge by early summer. Larvae
may be found in late summer and early fall.

The Imperial Moth (*Eacles imperialis*).   The wing expanse of this
moth (Fig. 229) is four to six inches. It is yellow with markings of
purplish-yellow. The larvae, which attain a length of four inches,
are usually green but may have a red or brown cast. The body is

FIG. 229. The imperial moth (*Eacles imperialis*) .

lightly covered with long whitish hairs. The second and third thoracic segments bear noticeable spiny horns. The larvae feed on the
foliage of a large number of shade and forest trees. The insect overwinters in the pupal stage in the soil. There is only one generation
annually.

Anisota spp.   There are several species of common moths in this
genus. The moths are brownish or dark yellow with the front wings
marked by a white discal spot. The larvae are cylindrical in form
and bear two conspicuous, slender, recurved horns on the mesothorax; the other dorsal and lateral spines are small. Their bodies
are conspicuously striped and are 1½ to two inches in length. They
feed chiefly on the foliage of various species of oak.

Family *Saturniidae* (Giant Silkworm Moths)

These large moths and their silken cocoons are known to almost all naturalists. The moths are stout and hairy, with broad wings; the heads are more or less sunken into the prothorax. Members of the family may be distinguished from regal moths by the antennae of the males which are pectinate to the tips. The caterpillars commonly feed on the foliage of shade and forest trees; however some species feed on grass. They are large and are more or less armed with tubercles and spines. Most larvae pupate in dense, silken cocoons which are frequently found attached to trees or enveloped within a leaf.

The Polyphemus Moth (*Antheraea polyphemus*). This is one of the more common moths (Fig. 230) of the family. The adults are brownish or yellowish with a transparent window-like spot on each wing. A grayish border is present on the costal margin of the front wings and there is a dark band near the outer margin of both pairs of wings. The wing spread may be between five and six inches. Larvae are about three inches long, light green, and marked by silvery white lines on each side of the abdomen. They feed on the leaves of hickory, oak, maple, birch, and a number of other trees. The cocoons are dense and usually wrapped in a leaf. Hibernation is in the pupal stage. Two generations of the insect develop in the South and one in the North each season.

The Cecropia Moth (*Hyalophora cecropia*). The cecropia moth (Fig. 231) is the largest member of the family; the wing spread of large specimens slightly exceeds six inches. The wings are dusky brown, margined with gray, and marked beyond the middle by a white band which is bordered on the outer edge by red. Near the center of each wing is a crescent-shaped light spot. Fully grown larvae are three to four inches in length and are bluish-green. Their bodies are armed with tubercles. Those located on the dorsal surface of the second and third thoracic segments are larger than the others and are coral red. The remaining dorsal tubercles are yellow except those on the first thoracic segment, the last abdominal segment, and those on the sides of the body, which are blue. The tubercles are armed with black spines. The larvae feed on the leaves of a number of trees and shrubs, among them, members of the *Rosaceae*, willow, and maple. The cocoons are quite large and are fastened length-

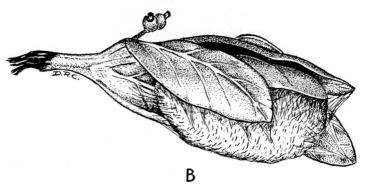

FIG. 230. **A,** Polyphemus moth (*Antheraea polyphemus*). **B,** Cocoon.

wise to branches or other objects. Winter is passed in the pupal stage.

The Luna Moth (*Actias luna*). The wings of the luna moth are light green with the costal margins of the front wings marked by a purplish-brown band. Each wing has a transparent spot and the anal angle of the hind wings is extended into a tail-like prolongation. Larvae attain a length of three inches. Their color is bluish-green with a pale yellowish stripe along each side and yellowish marks between the abdominal segments. The larvae feed on

FIG. 231. The cecropia moth (*Hyalophora cecropia*).

hickory, pecan, sweet gum, and other forest trees. The cocoons are somewhat similar to those of the polyphemus moth, but are considerably thinner in texture. The insect overwinters in the pupal stage.

The Io Moth (*Automeris io*). Adults (Fig. 232**A**) of this species have a wing expanse of three to four inches. The color of the sexes differs; the color of the male is a deeper yellow, and the front wings of the female are purplish-red. Near the center of each hind wing of both sexes is a large, circular, dark spot. Larvae are about two inches in length when fully grown. They are green and have a reddish stripe bordered below with white along each side of the body.

FIG. 232. **A,** The io moth (*Automeris io*). **B,** The Nevada buck moth (*Hemileuca nevadensis*).

The body is clothed with venomous spines which produce nettling of tender skin on contact. The larvae feed on many shade and forest trees and are also known to feed on cotton. Cocoons are found among leaves on the ground during the winter.

The Promethea Moth (*Callosamia promethea*).   This species is probably the most common of the giant silkworm moths. The moths have a wing spread of about four inches. The sexes differ so much in their coloration and markings that the males and females may be mistaken for different species. The male moths are dark brown or black except for the outer margin of the wings which is grayish. The female moths are brown and each front wing is marked with a white triangular discal spot. The outer margin of the front wings is clay-colored. The larvae attain a length of about two inches and are bluish-green. The body is armed with longitudinal rows of shining tubercles which are black, except the four on the second and third thoracic segments which are larger and coral red, and a yellow one located near the end of the abdomen. The larvae feed on the foliage of many forest and fruit trees but appear to prefer cherry, ash, and sassafras. The elongate cocoons are partially enveloped in a leaf of the host plant. Winter is passed as pupae within the cocoons.

The Range Caterpillar (*Hemileuca oliviae*).   The range caterpillar is one of a number of species of the genus *Hemileuca* found in the United States. Other common species are the buck moth (*H. maia*) and the Nevada buck moth (*H. nevadensis,* Fig. 232**B**). The range caterpillar feeds on grasses and is a serious pest of the range in parts of the West. The larvae are black, gray, or yellow and are densely clothed with venomous spines. Hibernation is as minute larvae within the eggs, which are attached in masses to the stems of plants. The adults have a wing spread of two to 2½ inches. The body is black, brown, or reddish, and the wings are buff with the front wings crossed by two lighter colored bands.

Family *Bombycidae* (Silkworm Moths)

This family is quite small in number of species and none are native to North America. The silkworm (*Bombyx mori*) is the only member of this group represented in this country. It was introduced many years ago in an attempt to establish a silk culture industry here, which never proved economically feasible. The silk of commerce is obtained from the cocoons of this insect. Although synthetic fibers are replacing the use of silk and the industry is not so important as it was previously, it still provides an important source of income in Japan, China, and other parts of the world.

Silkworms are carefully raised on mulberry leaves. Three or four weeks after hatching, the creamy white larvae are full-grown and are about three inches in length. Soon after the formation of the cocoons the insects are killed; the cocoons are then soaked in water, and the silk is unwound by skillful operators.

The moths are cream colored with two or three ill-defined brownish lines across the front wings. Several generations are produced each season.

Family *Lasiocampidae* (Tent Caterpillars)

Adults of this family are stout-bodied, hairy, and of average size. The larvae, which are covered with hairs, feed on the foliage of a number of deciduous trees, including fruit trees. Periodical outbreaks of the caterpillars occur, and serious damage may result if these insects are not controlled.

The Eastern Tent Caterpillar (*Malacosoma americanum*). This insect makes its tents (Fig. 233) in the crotches of haw, wild cherry, plum, apple, peach, and other trees and shrubs in early spring. Within the tents are found many brown, hairy caterpillars. When fully grown the caterpillars (Fig. 234A) are about two inches in length. They are marked by a white stripe down the back, which is bordered by reddish-brown. On either side of the body are blue and white spots.

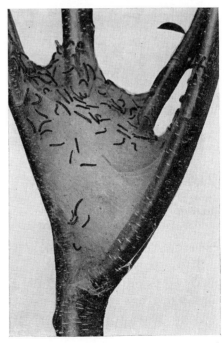

FIG. 233. Eastern tent caterpillars (*Malacosoma americanum*) on tent. (From Agricultural Research Service, U.S.D.A.)

This insect is found throughout the United States and Canada east of the Rocky Mountains. Closely related species are found on the Pacific Coast. Winter is passed as small larvae within the eggs. Eggs are laid in brown masses which form varnish-like rings around small limbs of the host plants. The larvae emerge from the eggs as the leaves begin to unfold in the spring, and crawl to a convenient crotch where the tent is made. They travel back and forth from the tent to the feeding areas.

Length of the larval stage is four to six weeks, at the end of which time the caterpillars disperse and seek protected places to spin co-

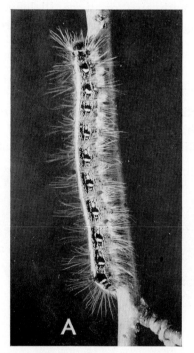 

FIG. 234. **A,** Eastern tent caterpillar (*Malacosoma americanum*). (From Agricultural Research Service, U.S.D.A.) **B,** Forest tent caterpillar (*M. disstria*). (From Department of Entomology, A & M College of Texas.)

coons in which they pupate. The cocoons are white and tough, and have a yellowish powder intermingled with the silk. Two or three weeks following pupation the moths emerge. They are brown, and each front wing is marked by two oblique lines. Shortly after eggs are deposited the larvae develop but do not emerge from the eggs until the next spring. The life cycle may be completed and eggs deposited by late spring in the South, and during the summer in colder climates. There is only one generation each season. These caterpillars are readily controlled with applications of lead arsenate or DDT sprays.

The Forest Tent Caterpillar (*Malacosoma disstria*). This species (Fig. 234**B**) is closely related to the eastern tent caterpillar, has a similar biology, but does not make a tent. The larvae feed on the foliage of oak, maple, gum, ash, birch, and other trees. The larvae are somewhat larger than the eastern tent caterpillars, the body is generally a pale bluish color, and there is a row of diamond or keyhole-shaped light spots down the back. These insects may be controlled by the same measures suggested for the eastern tent caterpillar.

Rhopalocera (Skippers and Butterflies)

Family *Hesperiidae* (Skippers)

Skippers are stout-bodied and moderate in size. The name has been given this group of butterflies because of the erratic and fast mode of flight. They may be separated from other butterflies by the tips of the antennae which in most cases are recurved and form a hook, and by their stout bodies which resemble the moths more than the butterflies. The larvae are characterized by their large heads and strongly constricted necks. They are usually naked and are found concealed by the leaves of the host plants. The pupae are rounded and resemble those of moths more than the chrysalids of butterflies. This stage of development is passed in slight silken cocoons protected by leaves fastened together with silken strands.

The Bean Leaf Roller (*Urbanus proteus*). The wings of this skipper are chocolate-brown with the front pair marked by silvery white spots. The hind wings have tail-like prolongations like those of the swallowtail butterflies. The wing expanse is about $1\frac{3}{4}$ inches. In the southern states the larvae are sometimes pests of beans, turnips, and other plants. They cut and roll the leaves around themselves and feed within the rolls that are formed.

The Larger Canna Leaf Roller (*Calpodes ethlius*). This insect is also known as the Brazilian skipper. The larvae live in folds of leaves of the canna. The body is greenish and semitransparent and has the characteristic large head and constricted neck (Fig. 235). The fully grown larvae are about $1\frac{3}{4}$ inches in length. The adults have a wing expanse of more than one inch, are dark brown, and both

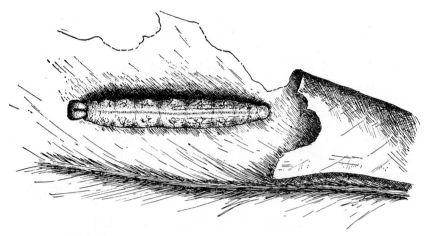

FIG. 235.   The larger canna leaf roller (*Calpodes ethlius*).

front and hind wings are marked by several small, white spots near the middle. Cannas may be severely injured by the feeding of the larvae if control measures are not taken. Hand picking of the larvae and the application of lead arsenate, either in the form of dusts or sprays, are recommended for control.

Family *Papilionidae* (Swallowtails)

Most members of this family are large. They are usually identified by the tail-like prolongations of the hind wings. The wings are basically black and are usually marked with yellow, and frequently with green and blue. Species of this group may be found in almost every section of the country, but they are seldom of any economic importance, as the larvae do not feed on a wide range of economic plants and are rarely abundant. The larvae are naked or very sparsely clothed with fine hairs. All of the caterpillars of this unusual family are provided with an organ known as an osmeterium. This is an orange colored, forked, and eversible tubular process which is projected through a slit on the dorsal surface of the prothorax when the caterpillar is disturbed. An unpleasant odor is diffused which is thought to be repellent to its enemies. The chrysalids are suspended on convenient objects by an attachment of silk on the end of the abdomen and a silken belt around the middle of the body. They are angular in outline and bear two conspicuous projections on the sides.

The giant swallowtail butterfly or orange-dog (*Papilio cres-*

phontes, Fig. 236) is the largest of this group of butterflies, with a wing spread of four to 5½ inches. The wings are mostly yellow underneath and black above. The dorsal surface of the front wings is crossed by a broken band composed of yellow spots. The costal area of the hind wings is yellow and there is a broken yellow band near the outer margins. The larvae attain a length of 2½ inches and

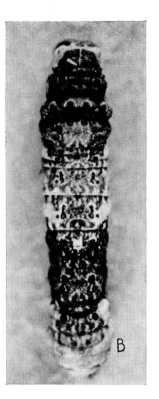

FIG. 236. **A,** The giant swallowtail butterfly (*Papilio cresphontes*) and **B,** its caterpillar.

are grayish-brown with lighter colored patches. Larvae feed on the leaves of prickly ash, citrus, poplar, and other plants. They are a minor pest of citrus trees in the Gulf coastal regions where they are known as orange-dogs.

The black swallowtail butterfly (*Papilio polyxenes asterius*) has two rows of yellow spots crossing its black wings. (See Fig. 240**A**, p. 379.) The larvae of this species feed on celery, dill, parsnip, caraway, and other umbelliferous plants. They are green, ringed with black, and marked with yellow. There are two or three generations each season. If control measures become necessary, the use of rotenone is suggested.

The tiger swallowtail butterfly (*Papilio glaucus,* Fig. 237), appears in two color phases. The *turnus* phase has yellow wings with a broad black margin in which is a row of yellow spots. The front wings are marked with four black bars. Both sexes are represented in this form. In the *glaucus* phase the wings are entirely black with a marginal row of yellow spots. Only the female is found in this

 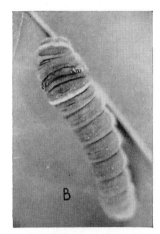

FIG. 237. **A,** The tiger swallowtail butterfly (*Papilio ajax turnus*) and **B,** its caterpillar.

phase. The larvae of the tiger swallowtail are quite striking. They are dark green and bear on either side of the thorax an eye spot which is greenish-yellow margined with black. Larvae feed on the leaves of birch, poplar, ash, wild cherry, and other trees.

The bodies of the larvae of the pipevine swallowtail (*Battus philenor*) are dark brown with coral red dots and bear fleshy filaments. The larvae feed on Dutchman's pipe, Virginia snakeroot, and related plants. The wings of the adults are black with a greenish cast. The hind wings are somewhat lighter than the front wings and bear a row of whitish spots along the outer margins.

Family *Pieridae* (Whites and Sulphur Butterflies)

These are our most abundant butterflies, and are seen commonly in fields and along roadsides. They are ordinarily medium in size; however, some are quite small. Their wing colors are almost always yellow, orange, or white, usually marked with black. The larvae are green and clothed with fine, short hairs. Some species are pests of cultivated plants.

The Imported Cabbageworm (*Pieris rapae*). This (Fig. 238) is the best known member of the family. The larvae are the velvety green caterpillars that feed on the leaves of cabbage, mustard, turnips, and related plants. The adults are the common white butter-

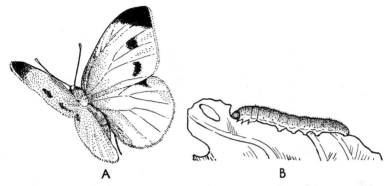

FIG. 238. **A,** The imported cabbage butterfly (*Pieris rapae*) and **B,** its larva. (From Agricultural Research Service, U.S.D.A.)

flies with the black-tipped front wings seen flying around gardens and truck farms. The female butterfly has two black spots on the front wings and one on the hind wings, while the male has one spot on both the front and hind wings. The yellowish, ribbed, and bullet-shaped eggs, which are laid on the underside of leaves, hatch into small green caterpillars which are voracious feeders. They attain a length of about 1¼ inches in about two weeks and pupate.

Three to six generations may be completed in one season. Hibernation is as a pupa. Malathion, parathion, rotenone, and other toxicants are used in control.

The Alfalfa Caterpillar (*Colias philodice eurytheme*). This is another common insect. It is a pest of alfalfa, particularly in the Southwest. In addition to al-

FIG. 239. The southern cabbage butterfly (*Pieris protodice*).

falfa, the caterpillars feed on the foliage of other legumes. They attain a length of about 1½ inches when fully grown and are green with a white stripe along the side of the body through which passes a fine red line. The butterflies are yellow with a wing spread of about two inches. The wings are solid yellow on the underside; the dorsal surface is trimmed in black. This insect may complete two to seven generations annually. Winter is passed in the pupal stage throughout most of its range of distribution. Cutting alfalfa closely and removing the hay is an effective control measure as this eliminates the food supply of the caterpillars and exposes them to the natural enemies and the effects of the sun. Sprays of methoxychlor, Phosdrin, and Dylox are recommended in control of the larvae.

The roadside butterfly (*Eurymus philodice*) is quite common. This yellow butterfly is often seen around damp places. The larvae feed on clover and related plants. The orange sulphur (*Eurymus eurytheme*) and the dog's head (*Zerene caesonia*) are other common yellow butterflies.

Family *Nymphalidae* (Brush-Footed Butterflies)

A majority of the species of butterflies are found in this family. The members of the family are differentiated from all others in that the first pair of legs is greatly reduced in size. The most commonly known groups are the fritillaries, the angle wings, the emperors, and milkweed butterflies.

The fritillaries are butterflies of medium size. The wings are tawny or dull yellow, checkered and bordered with black. Their underside is often marked with rows of silvery spots. The larvae are cylindrical, their bodies are more or less clothed with hairs, and they are sometimes armed with branching spines.

In the angle wing butterflies the outer margins of the front wings are ragged in appearance as if parts were missing. The red admiral (*Vanessa atalanta*) is a common representative of this group. The wings are dark with a bright orange band crossing the front pair from the middle of the costa to near the inner angle. Lying between this band and the apex are several white spots. The larvae feed on elm, nettle, and other plants.

The painted beauty (*Vanessa virginiensis*) is widely distributed, occurring throughout the United States, and in Canada and South America. The wings are marked with brownish-black and golden orange. The apical portions of the front wings are marked with several white spots. The painted lady (*Vanessa cardui*, Fig. 240**B**) is related to the painted beauty in appearance; however, it is not so brightly colored.

FIG. 240. Some common butterflies. **A,** The black swallowtail *(Papilio polyxenes)*. **B,** The painted lady *(Vanessa cardui)*. **C,** The mourning cloak butterfly *(Nymphalis antiopa)*. **D,** The queen *(Danaus berenice)*.

The mourning cloak *(Nymphalis antiopa,* Fig. 240**C**) is one of the better known butterflies. The purplish-brown wings are bordered by a yellow band on the outer margins. The larvae, which are gregarious in habit, feed on the foliage of willow, hackberry, elm, and poplar.

Butterflies of the genus *Polygonia* are marked by a metallic spot on the underside of each hind wing. Some of the more common species are the hop merchant *(Polygonia comma)* and the question-sign *(Polygonia interrogationis)*.

The viceroy *(Limenitis archippus)* is of much interest because of its close resemblance to the monarch butterfly. The mimicry is thought to be for protection, as the bodies of milkweed butterflies contain acrid substances which are distasteful to insectivorous animals (Fig. 241**B**). This is a brownish butterfly and may be readily differentiated from the monarch by its smaller size and by the presence of a black transverse band on the hind wings. The larvae feed on the foliage of willow, cottonwood, aspen, and other trees.

The best known representatives of the hackberry butterflies are the gray emperor *(Asterocampa celtis)* and the tawny emperor

FIG. 241. Protective mimicry. **A,** The monarch butterfly (*Danaus plexippus*) which is distasteful to insectivorous animals. **B,** The viceroy (*Limenitis archippus*), an edible butterfly which mimics the monarch so closely that animals are thought to avoid it.

(*Asterocampa clyton*). These are brown butterflies marked with both darker and lighter spots. The larvae feed on the leaves of hackberry.

The monarch (*Danaus plexippus,* Fig. 241**A**) and the queen (*Danaus berenice,* Fig. 240**D**) are interesting representatives of the milkweed butterflies. The wings of the monarch are light brown with black veins and borders, and with white spots on the costal and outer borders. The wings of the queen are light chocolate brown with the front wings spotted white, and the costal and outer margins bordered with black. The outer margins of the hind wings are also black-bordered. Milkweed butterflies are provided with acrid secretions which are distasteful to birds and other insectivorous animals. Larvae of both species feed only on milkweeds (*Asclepias*).

The monarch butterfly has migratory habits. There is a migration of the adults southward in the fall and again northward in the spring. It is thought all stages of the insect die in the northern part of the United States each winter. There are several life cycles each season.

Family *Lycaenidae* (Blues, Coppers, and Hairstreaks)

The butterflies of this family are small and quite delicate. Their larvae are rather slug-like in form with short broad bodies. Some species have osmeteria which are protruded between the seventh and eighth abdominal segments. These osmeteria excrete honeydew, which is fed upon by ants.

Probably the best known group of this family is the hairstreaks. They are so named because of their delicate striped markings. The cotton square borer (*Strymon melinus*) is the only member of the family that is economically injurious. The velvety, green, slug-like caterpillars eat holes in pods of lima beans and cowpeas, and in cotton squares. The fully grown larvae attain a length of slightly more than ½ inch. The posterior margin of each hind wing of the adults bears a tail-like prolongation which is marked with an orange-red spot near the base. There are three generations of this insect annually in the South, and two are produced in the North. Winter is normally passed in the pupal stage.

19

ORDER DIPTERA[1]

FLIES

All types of small insects with membranous wings are called flies, and the term fly has been used to form compound names for insects of other orders, such as butterfly, dragonfly, and mayfly. However, from an entomological viewpoint, a fly is a two-winged insect belonging to the order *Diptera.*

The general characteristics of the order are:

1. **Winged members with only one pair of wings borne on the meso-thorax; the second pair of wings represented by a pair of thread-like, knobbed structures, known as halteres.**
2. **Mouthparts adapted for piercing and sucking, or for lapping or sponging.**
3. **Complete metamorphosis.**
4. **Larvae of the more common forms known as maggots.**

The Diptera (Fig. 242) are one of the largest orders of insects, consisting of more than 80,000 species of worldwide distribution. In many respects, this is the most important group of insects with which man has to contend. Many species, such as mosquitoes, gnats, and flies, suck the blood of man and other animals. These insects are also vectors of a number of important diseases such as malaria, yellow fever, filariasis, and encephalitis. House flies and other flies associated with filth are distributors of such diseases as typhoid fever and dysentery. Larvae of screw-worm flies, bot flies, and other forms attack animals. Some, e.g., the Hessian fly, fruit flies, and cabbage maggot, are crop pests.

However, all flies are not harmful. Larvae of some species aid in

---

[1] *Dis,* two; *pteron,* wing.

the decomposition of organic matter. Many are parasitic on other insects, e.g., the *Tachinidae* and a number of the *Sarcophagidae*. Some are predators on insects, such as the robber flies (*Asilidae*) and

the larvae of a number of *Syrphidae*. Also, other dipterous insects are beneficial as pollinators of useful plants.

A majority of the members of the order are rather small, soft-bodied insects. Most of them are readily distinguished from other insects by the possession of only one pair of wings, the front pair, and a pair of small, knobbed structures, the halteres, which function as balancing organs and represent the reduced hind wings. The wings of flies are relatively small, transparent, and have rather simple venation (Fig. 243). Some Diptera are wingless but the halteres are usually present.

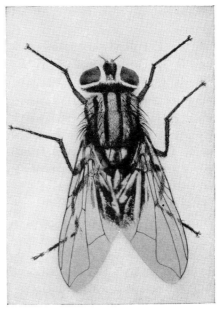

FIG. 242. The house fly (*Musca domestica*), typical of Diptera. (From Agricultural Research Service, U.S.D.A.)

The head is large, attached to the thorax by a slender neck and is quite mobile. The compound eyes are usually large and often occupy much of the surface of the head. Usually, three ocelli are present. Antennae of the more generalized families consist of many segments, but in the specialized groups there is a reduction in number of segments. Mouthparts of the adults are formed for piercing and sucking, sponging or lapping.

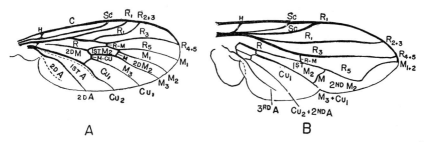

A					B

FIG. 243. Wings of Diptera with veins and cells labeled. **A**, Wing of *Anisopus*. (Based on Comstock, *An Introduction to Entomology*, Comstock Publishing Associates, 1940. By permission of the publisher.) **B**, Wing of house fly (*Musca domestica*).

There are several subtypes of the former. They are usually quite complicated. Most adult Diptera feed upon nectar, sap, honeydew, and liquid materials from decaying organic matter. However, a number feed on the blood of man and other animals. Some Diptera partake of no food in the adult stage and their mouthparts are non-functional.

Metamorphosis of Diptera is complete. The larvae are more highly specialized than this stage of other orders. They are distinctly separated from the adults in both habit and morphology. Seldom are larvae and adults found in the same environment partaking of the same food, as so often is the case in the Coleoptera (beetles). All larvae are legless, and most of them have no distinct head. In those generalized families with a distinct head, the mouthparts are of the chewing type. In the other forms, the bodies taper from the rear forward and terminate in a small conical segment which can be retracted. This segment bears no true mouthparts but is provided with a pair of mouth hooks which move vertically, tearing the food or tunneling into tissues. These larvae are known as maggots.

Pupae of Diptera are usually either naked or encompassed by the last larval skin; only rarely are cocoons spun. When the larval skin serves as a covering for the pupa it is called a *puparium*. It often has the appearance of a large seed and is a water-tight case.

The order is divided into two suborders, the *Orthorrhapha* and the *Cyclorrhapha*. Adults of the *Orthorrhapha* have antennae which are usually longer than the head and consist of six or more segments. If the antennae are not distinctly six-segmented, the last segment is annulate. Larvae often have a distinct head. When the head is not well developed, it is retractile. The pupae are not enclosed in a puparium. Pupae escape from the larval skin through a T-shaped or straight slit down the dorsal surface, or a transverse slit between the seventh and eighth segments of the abdomen. The adult *Cyclorrhapha* have three or fewer segments in the antennae. The third segment bears a dorsal or terminal arista. The larvae have no distinct head. Pupation is within a puparium from which the adults emerge by pushing off the anterior end.

KEY TO SOME COMMON FAMILIES OF DIPTERA

1. Abdomen indistinctly segmented; body leathery or horny in texture; wings present or absent; parasitic on birds and mammals (Louse Flies)   **Hippoboscidae**, p. 430

Abdomen distinctly segmented; wings always present; body
    not leathery or horny   2
2. Antenna with 6 or more freely articulated segments   3
    Antenna with 5 or fewer (usually 3) freely articulated seg-
    ments; the last segment may be annulated and may bear
    an arista   8
3. Mesonotum with a distinct V-shaped suture; legs long
    (Crane Flies)   **Tipulidae,** p. 388
    Mesonotum without a V-shaped suture   4
4. Margin and veins of wing fringed with scales (Mosquitoes)
    Culicidae, p. 389
    Margin and veins of wings not fringed with scales   5
5. Anal veins absent (see Fig. 243); media indicated by an un-
    branched fold or absent (Gall Midges)
    Itonididae (Cecidomyiidae), p. 396
    Anal veins present; media present or indicated by a
    branched fold   6
6. Ocelli present (March Flies)   **Bibionidae.**
    Ocelli absent   7
7. Antenna longer than the thorax; joints plumose or hairy;
    small delicate insects (Midges)
    Tendipedidae (Chironomidae), p. 395
    Antenna shorter than thorax; joints not provided with
    whorls of hair; small, stout-bodied insects (Black Flies)
    Simuliidae, p. 400
8. Antenna with 4 or 5 segments; the terminal segment may
    be annulated   9
    Antenna with 3 distinct segments; terminal segment never
    annulated but may bear an arista   12
9. Tarsus with 3 pads   10
    Tarsus with 2 pads   11
10. Calypters large, conspicuous (Horse Flies, Deer Flies)
    Tabanidae, p. 401
    Calypters small or vestigial (Soldier Flies)   **Stratiomyidae,** p. 403
11. Vertex sunken; eye bulging (Robber Flies)   **Asilidae,** p. 404
    Vertex only slightly, if any, sunken; eyes not bulging (Bee
    Flies)   **Bombyliidae,** p. 403
12. Wing with a false or spurious vein lying between R_{4+5}
    and M_1 (Syrphid Flies or Flower Flies)   **Syrphidae,** p. 405
    Wing with no false or spurious vein   13
13. Radius 4-branched   14
    Radius with 3 or fewer branches   15
14. Vertex distinctly sunken between eyes (Robber Flies)
    Asilidae, p. 404
    Vertex not distinctly sunken between eyes (Bee Flies)
    Bombyliidae, p. 403
15. Second joint of antenna with a longitudinal suture or seam
    along the upper outer side; calypters large   16

Second joint of antenna without a longitudinal suture or
    seam; calypters small   23

16. Mouthparts much reduced; mouth opening small; body
    hairy but not bristly   17

Mouthparts functional; mouth opening normal; body not
    hairy; bristles present or not   19

17. Scutellum long; postscutellum not developed; palpi short
    (Rodent Bot Flies)   **Cuterebridae**, p. 417

Scutellum short; postscutellum developed   18

18. Cell R_5 closed (Bot Flies)   **Oestridae**, p. 414

Cell R_5 open (Warble Flies)   **Hypodermatidae**, p. 415

19. Bristles on both hypopleura and pteropleura (see Fig. 244);
    postscutellum developed; ventral abdominal sclerites
    overlapped by dorsal sclerites; arista usually bare
    (Tachina Flies)   **Tachinidae**, p. 417

Hypopleura, abdominal sclerites and cell R_5 variable; post-
    scutellum absent; arista generally plumose   20

20. Bristles on both hypopleura and pteropleura; cell R_5 api-
    cally closed or narrowed   21

Bristles usually absent on hypopleura; pteropleural bristles
    absent if hypopleural bristles present, or cell R_5 not nar-
    rowed apically, or mouthparts fitted for piercing-sucking   22

21. Body usually metallic in color, particularly on abdomen;
    usually 2 notopleural bristles present; arista plumose
    (Blow Flies)   **Calliphoridae**, p. 419

Body not metallic in color; usually 4 notopleural bristles
    present; arista of antenna plumose on basal half (Flesh
    Flies)   **Sarcophagidae**, p. 422

22. Cell R_5 open, only slightly or not at all narrowed apically;
    anal vein extending to margin of wing (Anthomyiids)
                                  Anthomyiidae, p. 428

Cell R_5 narrowed or closed; anal vein only seldom reaching
    margin of wing (Typical Muscids)   **Muscidae**, p. 423

23. Mouthparts vestigial; opening of mouth small (Horse Bot
    Flies)   **Gasterophilidae**, p. 412

Mouthparts normally developed; opening of mouth normal   24

24. Subcosta apically bent forward at almost right angle and
    tending to fade out beyond bend; wings patterned or pic-
    tured (Fruit Flies)   **Tephritidae (Trypetidae)**, p. 406

Subcosta curved gently toward costa; wings not pictured   25

25. Costa broken twice, once beyond the humeral cross vein
    and again just before the end of R_1; anal cell absent
    (Vinegar Flies)   **Drosophilidae**, p. 410

Costa broken only once and this at end of subcosta; anal
    cell present, but often small (Leaf Miners)   **Agromyzidae**, p. 410

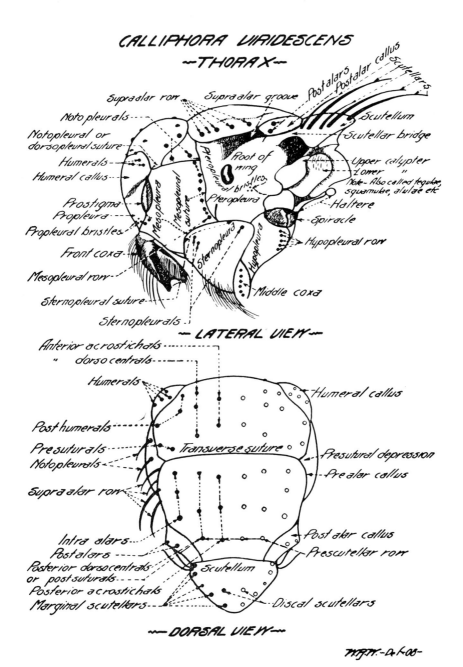

FIG. 244. Bristles and regions of the thorax of a blowfly (*Calliphora viridescens*).
(After Walton, from *Entomological News*, 1909, *20*.)

Suborder ORTHORRHAPHA

Straight-Seamed Flies

More than 30 of the families of Diptera are included in the *Orthorrhapha*. Only the more common families can be mentioned here.

Family *Tipulidae* (Crane Flies)

Most of the common species of crane flies (Fig. 245) resemble overgrown mosquitoes with slender bodies and long legs. They are sometimes referred to as the daddy long-legs of the air. Some species

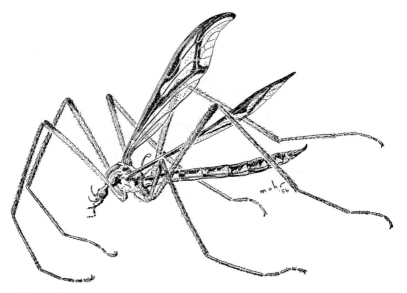

FIG. 245.   A crane fly *(Pedecia albidivittata)*. (Courtesy of C. O. Mohr.)

attain a length of more than an inch while others are quite small in size. The most distinctive characteristic of these insects is the V-shaped transverse suture on the dorsal surface of the thorax.

Crane flies are found chiefly in damp environments, especially where a heavy growth of vegetation occurs. However, they are some-times seen in numbers in pastures and fields. Most species are slug-gish in flight, although the power of flight seems to be quite well developed in certain of the smaller species. These often collect in swarms and dance up and down in the air as do some of the midges.

Habits of the larvae of crane flies vary, both as to food and the environment in which they are found. Some are aquatic, a number of species are found in the moist soil of marshes, along margins of bodies of water, or in woods; while others live in the soil of grasslands. Most larvae feed on decaying vegetable matter, but some attack tissues of living plants, and others are carnivorous in habit. A few species occasionally are destructive to grain, grasses, and alfalfa in the West. The best known of these species is the range crane fly (*Tipula simplex*). These larvae and related forms are frequently called "leatherjackets." Some crane flies complete one generation annually while others have two life cycles.

Family *Culicidae* (Mosquitoes)

Mosquitoes are familiar to everyone. They are small insects and are readily identified by the presence of scales on the body, and along the fringes and veins of the wings. They possess long antennae, most joints of which bear whorls of hairs. In the males the whorls of hairs are so dense that they produce a bushy appearance. Females of most species feed upon blood. Mouthparts of the males are not developed for piercing and they do not suck blood. Their food consists of plant juices, nectar, and other liquids. The larvae and pupae of all species are found in water. (See Fig. 246.) More than 100 species are native to North America.

Biology of mosquitoes varies considerably. Many species overwinter in the egg stage, some as adults, and others as larvae in the water. Eggs are laid in water, or in those places where water will collect later. The larvae are commonly known as "wrigglers." They have large heads and chewing mouthparts and feed on microscopic plant and animal material in the water. The thorax is large but does not bear legs. The abdomen is slender, and on the eighth, or next-to-the-last abdominal segment, is located a respiratory tube which is known as a siphon. The larvae thrust this tube above the water at intervals to breathe. Oxygen is also supplied in part by four tracheal gills located on the last segment of the abdomen. The larvae pass through four instars or growing stages. Then, they change into pupae which are commonly known as "tumblers," and unlike most insect pupae, are quite active. Respiration in the pupal stage is through two trumpet-like tubes located on the thorax. Following a pupal period of short duration, usually two or three days, the insect's skin splits down the back, the adult emerges and after a few

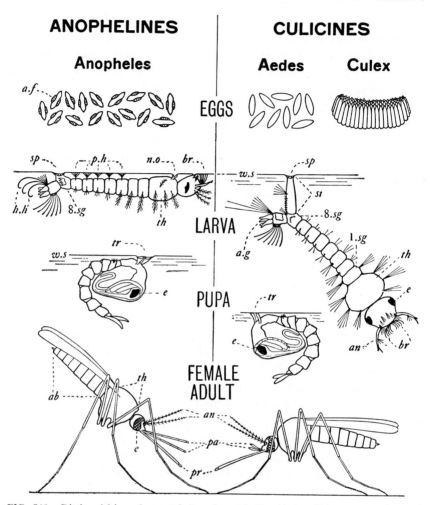

FIG. 246. Distinguishing characteristics of anopheline and culicine mosquitoes. *a.f.*, air floats; *a.g.*, anal gills; *ab.*, abdomen; *an.*, antenna; *br.*, mouth brush; *e.*, eye; *h.h.*, hooked hairs; *n.o.*, notched organ; *pa.*, maxillary palpus; *p.h.*, palmate (or float hairs); *pr.*, proboscis; *1 sg.*, first abdominal segment; *8 sg.*, eighth abdominal segment; *si.*, siphon; *sp.*, spiracle; *th.*, thorax; *tr.*, respiratory trumpets; *w.s.*, water surface. (From Smart after Marshall. Courtesy of British Museum of Natural History.)

moments flies away. The length of the life cycle of mosquitoes from egg to adult varies from ten days to several weeks. Most mosquitoes have a number of generations each year. The females live from one to several months, but the length of life of male mosquitoes is usually much shorter.

Anopheles. Members of this genus are known as malaria mosquitoes. *Anopheles* mosquitoes are recognized by their spotted wings, maxillary palpi as long as the proboscis, cresent-shaped scutellum, and characteristic resting position. They rest with the proboscis, head and abdomen in nearly a straight line, with the body lifted at an angle from the surface. (See Fig. 246.) Other species rest with the body almost parallel to the surface.

Eggs of anophelines are laid singly upon the surface of the water. The *Anopheles* larvae are readily recognized by their resting position which is parallel to the surface. Larvae of other species rest with the head downward and the body at an angle of 45° with the surface. The adults of the most common species are weak fliers. The length of a life cycle is dependent on temperature, and may vary from 18 days to several weeks in duration. Usually only adult females overwinter. Several generations are produced during the year.

Anopheles quadrimaculatus (Fig. 247A) is the most common vector of malaria in the United States but *Anopheles freeborni* is more important in the western part of the country.

Culex.   *Culex* mosquitoes develop in standing water, such as polluted ponds, marshes, tanks, street gutters, and water barrels. Eggs

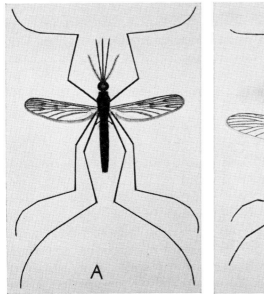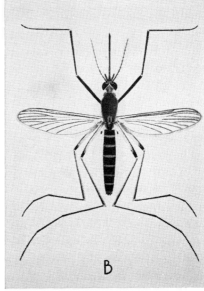

FIG. 247.   Two common mosquitoes. **A,** *Anopheles quadrimaculatus.* **B,** *Culex quinquefasciatus.* (From Carpenter and La Casse, *Mosquitoes of North America,* University of California Press, 1955. By permission of the publisher.)

are laid in rafts (Fig. 246); these masses may contain 100 or more eggs each. Breeding may continue through the winter months in the warmer parts of the Gulf coast region. In colder climates, the adult females hibernate in hollow trees, buildings, or other protected places. The males die with the arrival of cold weather.

The southern house mosquito, *Culex quinquefasciatus (fatigans)* (Fig. 247**B**), is probably the most abundant house mosquito in towns and cities of the South. *Culex pipiens,* a closely related species, is the common house mosquito in the North. The life cycles of the two species are similar. In warm weather, the life cycle from egg to adult may be completed in ten to 14 days, but it is prolonged by cool weather. There are several generations each year. *Culex tarsalis,* a common species west of the Mississippi River, breeds in a variety of places and large populations often build up.

Culiseta inornata is related to the *Culex* mosquitoes and is found throughout the United States and southern Canada. It breeds throughout the winter where weather permits, and is usually present only during the winter months in southern climates.

Aedes. With the exception of the yellow fever mosquito (*Aedes aegypti*) and a few other species, *Aedes* mosquitoes usually breed in flood waters, rain pools, and salt marshes. Eggs are deposited singly, usually in depressions and on edges of pools, where they may survive long periods of desiccation. When these places are filled with water and the weather is favorable, some of the eggs hatch while others do not hatch until subsequent flooding. Although some species may lay eggs on the surface of the water, most of them will not hatch until the water is evaporated and the pool refilled. Some species are single brooded; others produce a generation following each wet season.

The yellow fever mosquito (*Aedes aegypti,* Fig. 248A) is the most important transmitter of this dreaded disease. Adults are characterized by the presence of white rings on the tarsi and white spots on the abdomen and thorax. There is also a lyre-shaped figure on the mesonotum. This mosquito is domestic in its habits and is found breeding almost entirely in the vicinity of dwellings, sometimes even breeding within homes. Eggs are deposited on the surface of the water or slightly above the water line on the sides of various receptacles where it is possible for them to survive desiccation for several months. Clean water is preferred for egg deposition to water

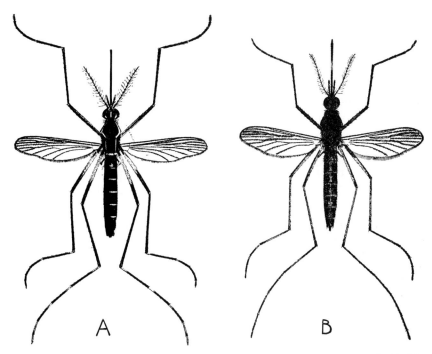

FIG. 248. Aedes mosquitoes. **A,** The yellow fever mosquito (*Aedes aegypti*). **B,** The salt-marsh mosquito (*Aedes sollicitans*). (From Carpenter and La Casse, *Mosquitoes of North America*, University of California Press, 1955. By permission of the publisher.)

polluted with sewage. Breeding may occur in vases, tin cans, old automobile tires, flower pots, and almost any other type of container. The females bite chiefly during the day and are troublesome during the summer months throughout the South. Although adults may live for several months, they are quite susceptible to cold and succumb to temperatures below 40° F. The species probably does not survive the winter in the United States except in the extreme southern portion of the country. The length of a life cycle may be as short as ten days under optimum conditions. If the temperature and food supply are not favorable, a much longer period of time is required for its completion.

Aedes sollicitans, Aedes taeniorhynchus, and *Aedes dorsalis* are the most important salt-marsh mosquitoes. *Aedes sollicitans* (Fig. 248B) is commonly known as the salt-marsh mosquito or the New Jersey mosquito. It is found breeding along the Atlantic and Gulf coasts. *Aedes taeniorhynchus* may be found breeding along the Atlantic, Gulf, and Pacific coasts. *Aedes dorsalis* is the most common salt-marsh mosquito on the Pacific coast. All are strong fliers and may migrate many miles from their breeding places. They are prolific and may increase to huge numbers at which times they make life miserable for both man and beast.

Mosquito control generally should be conducted on a large area basis. As larvae must develop in water, elimination of breeding places by drainage, filling, and other means is of primary importance. Those domestic species, such as the yellow fever mosquito, may be largely controlled by eliminating receptacles that hold water such as tin cans, buckets, barrels, cisterns, and old automobile tires. Water should also be prevented from standing in gutters, drains, and depressions. Keeping the surface of water in lakes, reservoirs, and streams free of vegetation and floating materials aids materially in preventing larval development. This practice eliminates part of the source of food and places of protection, and provides the top-feeding minnows better opportunities to search out and feed upon the larvae and pupae. Adjusting the water level of lakes and reservoirs to prevent water from standing in marginal vegetation serves the same purpose. Fish, such as the top-feeding minnow (*Gambusia affinis*), are frequently used to prevent mosquito breeding in small ponds and pools. However, they usually cannot be relied upon for complete control.

Elimination of breeding places, the proper care of lakes and other bodies of water, and the use of natural agencies, although important, usually are not sufficient for satisfactory mosquito control. Other measures such as insecticides, screens, and repellents must be employed. Oil (usually #2 fuel oil) applied to the surfaces of pools, ponds, streams, and other breeding places is most frequently used. Oil solutions of DDT, DDD, and benzene hexachloride are very effective larvicides as are emulsions of these compounds. Dusts containing Paris green, DDT, or BHC are effective in the control of the surface-feeding *Anopheles* larvae.

Adult mosquitoes are most effectively combated in dwellings. Sixteen mesh screen will prevent the entrance of all but possibly a few of the smallest individuals. The use of space sprays containing pyrethrins, or pyrethrins combined with DDT, will result in quick knock-down and relief from attacks. Residual sprays of DDT may remain effective for several months. When persons are exposed to mosquito bites, protection for a few hours from their attacks may be obtained by the use of repellents, such as dimethyl phthalate and diethyl-meta-toluamide.

Family *Tendipedidae (Chironomidae)* (Midges)

Members of this large family of insects are small, delicate, and mosquito-like in appearance. They may be distinguished from mosquitoes by the absence of scales on the body and wings. Antennae of the males are very plumose. The adults frequently collect in huge swarms in the late afternoon or evening near streams, ponds, and lakes. They produce a weak, rather high pitched humming sound entirely unlike that of mosquitoes.

Midges (Fig. 249) breed chiefly in water, but some develop in decaying vegetable matter, manure, or under bark of trees. Because the larvae occur in huge numbers in water, they are an important source of food for many species of fish. Many of the larvae are known as blood-worms because of their red color. Common species of

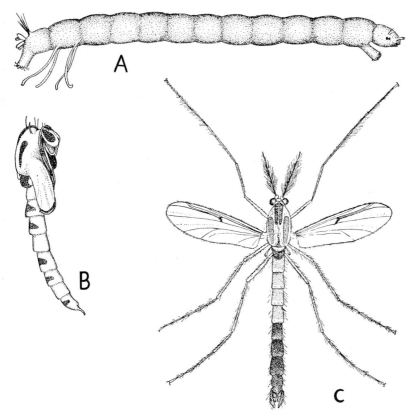

FIG. 249. Developmental stages of midges. **A,** Larva of *Chironomus tetans.* **B,** Pupa of *Cricotopus trifasciatus.* **C,** Adult of *Chironomus ferrugineovittatus.* (From Illinois Natural History Survey.)

midges have a rather short life cycle, producing a number of generations annually.

Most midges do not bite; however there are some, chiefly in the genus *Culicoides,* that are blood-suckers. They are commonly known as "punkies," or "no-see-ums," because they are very small and are somewhat difficult to see. Because of their blood-sucking habits, they may become serious pests along seashores, and near rivers and lakes. The larvae are aquatic or semiaquatic and are probably scavengers. Satisfactory control has been obtained by treating breeding places with DDT dusts and emulsions. An application of DDT in kerosene to doors and window screens usually prevents entrance of the adults into dwellings for a period of several weeks. When persons are exposed to attacks of these insects, applications of approved repellents afford fair protection against their bites.

Family *Itonididae (Cecidomyiidae)* (Gall Midges or Gall Gnats)

This is a family of very small midge-like flies. The insects are delicate with long legs and antennae, and reduced wing venation. The larvae are small maggots that feed only on liquid foods; many of them are brightly colored. The mode of pupation differs; some species form a puparium while others spin cocoons or provide no protection at all for the naked pupae.

Food habits of the larvae are quite varied. Most species feed on plants where galls, which are typical of the species of midge, are frequently formed. Some forms feed on fungi or excrement, and others are parasitic or predaceous on such insects as aphids. Winter is usually passed in the larval stage. The number of generations produced annually varies from one to several.

An unusual type of reproduction has been observed in *Miastor americana,* the larval stage of which is found in decaying bark. Paedogenesis, that is, reproduction in the larval stage, occurs in this species. The daughter larvae feed within the mother larva which is eventually consumed, after which they escape and may reproduce likewise for several generations before pupation occurs.

The Hessian Fly (*Phytophaga destructor*). The Hessian fly (Fig. 250) is an important pest of wheat; barley and rye are also common hosts. A few specimens have been taken on wild grasses. The insect was probably brought to this country during the Revolutionary War in the straw bedding of Hessian soldiers. It has spread to all of the wheat-growing areas of the country with the exception of some of the arid and semiarid sections of the West and Southwest where climatic conditions are unfavorable for its development.

The small sooty-black flies normally emerge from their puparia in late summer or early fall and lay their minute reddish eggs on the upper surface of the leaves of volunteer or early-sown wheat. In a few days they hatch into small reddish maggots that soon turn white. The young larvae work their way behind the leaf sheaths where they rasp the stems and suck the sap. Infested wheat in the fall is stunted and the leaves are dark bluish-green. The central shoot is frequently absent. Severely injured plants usually die during the winter.

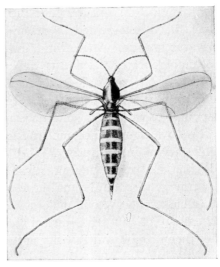

FIG. 250. The Hessian fly (*Phytophaga destructor*). (From Agricultural Research Service, U.S.D.A.)

When the heads fill the next June, the infested straws often break over. Heavily infested wheat may have a large percentage of fallen straws, which considerably reduces yields.

The Hessian fly usually overwinters as a mature larva within a brown puparium called the "flaxseed." Partly grown larvae occasionally are able to survive the winter. The overwintering forms are found between the leaf sheaths and the stems above the surface of the ground. In the spring the larvae pupate and the adults appear a week or two later. They are not strong fliers and are never found far from their food plants. The adults are not known to feed and they usually die in three days or less after emergence. During this time each female lays 250 to 300 eggs.

Usually there is only one spring generation. The flaxseed stage is reached before the heads of grain are formed. This stage remains in the stubble during the summer. Pupation occurs and adults emerge in late summer or fall following rains and after the appearance of volunteer wheat. Generally, there are two complete generations each year, but when weather conditions are exceptionally favorable there may be a maximum of five.

No insecticidal control has been developed; only cultural practices are employed in combating this pest. The most valuable preventive measure is planting the wheat sufficiently late in the fall so that the plants will not be up and growing until after the emergence, egg deposition, and death of the adults. Satisfactory planting dates have been determined by research workers in the principal wheat production areas where the Hessian fly is found. Naturally the time of emergence of the adults varies from year to year. However, the planting dates are sufficiently reliable to usually prevent all but light infestations, and still provide time for the plants to grow large enough to withstand winter weather. The destruction of volunteer wheat which may become infested in the fall helps prevent heavy infestations in the spring. Wheat stubble should be plowed under soon after harvest when practicable, since the adult flies are not able to emerge through the soil. However, the practice of planting grasses and clovers in the wheat fields prior to harvest frequently prevents the use of this effective control measure. Crop rotation and the maintenance of high soil fertility are of considerable value, inasmuch as lightly infested plants in fertile soil will overcome the injury and still produce fair yields. Certain varieties of wheat have been found to have a measure of resistance to the Hessian fly, and some are of commercial value at this time.

The Sorghum Midge (*Contarinia sorghicola*).   This is an important pest of sorghums in the South. Most injury is produced in the more humid areas of the Gulf states, where almost entire crops of grain may be lost when conditions are most favorable for the insect. Losses of 20 percent of the crop occur frequently.

Injury is produced by the small larvae or maggots rasping the developing seed and feeding on the exuding sap. The seed fail to develop and the heads of grain appear blasted or blighted and produce practically no grain. It is said that one larva may destroy all the grain in a spikelet. The insect attacks all varieties of sorghums, Sudan grass, and Johnson grass.

The sorghum midge is a small, orange-colored, gnat-like fly. Each female in her short life span lays 30 to 100 small, white eggs in the spikelets or seed husks. The maggots or larvae are orange-colored. Under average summer conditions a complete life cycle may be completed in only 14 to 16 days. The life cycle is somewhat longer in cooler parts of the season. As many as 13 overlapping generations have been observed. The insects overwinter as larvae within cocoons in the heads of the host plants, and transform to pupae the next spring, from which adults soon emerge. However, some do not transform or complete their development until the second or even the third spring.

Several practices may be employed which will reduce losses from the sorghum midge. Plowing under crop residues, and burning fields early in the spring to destroy hibernating larvae are recommended. Johnson grass near fields of sorghum should be cut to prevent the formation of heads before the plants bloom. It is advisable to plant uniformly blooming varieties of sorghum. Heads blooming prior to the main crop should be cut. With the recommended restrictions endrin, toxaphene, Dibrom, and sevin may be used as sprays against the pest.

The Clover Seed Midge (*Dasyneura leguminicola*).   The clover seed midge is an important pest in the production of red clover seed. Other clovers are attacked but the insect is of little importance on these plants. The seeds are destroyed by the maggots or larvae feeding on the ovules. Winter is passed as larvae within flimsy silken cocoons which are found on or slightly below the surface of the soil. The larvae pupate and the tiny mosquito-like adults emerge in the spring and deposit eggs in the young clover heads. The young larvae find their way inside the flowers and attack the ovules. About a month later the mature larvae drop to the ground in which they pupate within cocoons. There are usually two generations each season, but in the southern part of the country there may be three.

When this insect occurs in damaging numbers it is advisable to cut the clover and remove the hay just before the uninjured heads are in full bloom. This is an effective control measure, as it eliminates all young midge larvae within the heads. Also, a measure of control may be obtained by clipping the clover about two weeks prior to blooming and again a month later. This practice brings the clover into bloom before the second generation of midges has emerged. This preventive measure does not always result in the greatest production of seed, however, when other clover insects are involved.

As the name gall midge suggests, a large number of species cause the formation of galls on a variety of plants such as willow, oak, hickory, and chrysanthemum. Each causes the formation of a gall which is characteristic for the species, and common species may be readily identified by the type of gall formed.

Family *Simuliidae* (Black Flies and Buffalo Gnats)

Adults of this family are small, short, stout, and appear to be humpbacked. The antennae are slightly longer than the head and consist of 11 joints. The mouthparts are for piercing and sucking and are similar to those of the horse fly. Only females bite and many species are fierce blood-suckers, and are important pests of man and animals. They are strong fliers; and with the aid of favorable winds, they may drift considerable distance from their breeding places.

With rare exceptions the insects develop in running water. Rapidly flowing streams are preferred breeding places. The masses of eggs are laid on rocks, logs, and other objects at or slightly below the surface of the water. The larvae have a disc-like sucker provided with hooks on the end of the abdomen with which they cling to submerged objects. The head is provided with two fan-like organs which are used to collect algae, protozoa, and diatoms for food. Respiration is by blood gills which are located on the dorsal surface of the last abdominal segment. Mature larvae pupate in cocoons which are attached to rocks or other objects where the larvae live. When the adults emerge, they escape from the pupal cases, float to the surface, and fly away immediately, before they are swept away by the current. Soon after emergence the females lay their eggs. Most species pass the winter as larvae. Some produce several generations each season, while others have one sudden emergence of adults early in the spring with only stragglers appearing later.

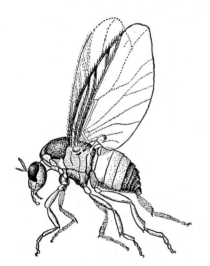

FIG. 251. The southern buffalo gnat (*Cnephia pecuarum*). (From Herms, *Medical Entomology*, 4th ed., The Macmillan Company, 1950. By permission of the publisher.)

Common Species. The southern buffalo gnat (*Cnephia pecuarum*, Fig. 251) is frequently a serious pest in the southern states, particularly along the lower Mississippi River and its watershed. The adults appear in early spring; and, when outbreaks occur, they make life miserable for livestock. In fact, there are many records of horses and mules having been killed by their vicious attacks. Indications are that, in addition to the bites and exsanguination, the animals are sometimes smothered by huge numbers of the gnats packing in the nostrils and blocking the air passages.

The turkey gnat (*Simulium meridionale*) is often a pest of poultry as well as other animals in the South. This species appears later in the spring than the southern buffalo gnat. It attacks the combs and wattles of the birds.

Simulium pictipes is a common black fly in the East. This species does not attack man and is rarely found on animals. Its feeding habits are not known. The Adirondack black fly (*Simulium hirtipes*) is a widely distributed form but is best known in the northeastern states. It is a vicious biting species and is feared by fishermen and hunters.

Prevention and control of black flies and buffalo gnats is a difficult problem. The removal of logs, roots, dipping branches, and other debris from streams will aid in preventing breeding, but this is often not practicable. Treating streams with DDT emulsion will kill the larvae. However, fish and other forms of aquatic life may be destroyed also. Smudges are commonly used for the protection of livestock. Protective smears of oil and grease of various concoctions are employed by most farmers to protect their animals. One of the most commonly used is crankcase oil mixed with a small amount of pine tar. DDT aerosols have been found effective in control of the adults when applied over large areas. DDT livestock sprays may kill the flies but not before they have engorged themselves with blood.

When man is exposed to attacks of the insects, protective clothing and even head veils may be worn. Repellents, such as dimethyl phthalate, will protect against attacks for several hours.

Family *Tabanidae* (Horse Flies and Deer Flies)

This is a large family containing more than 2,500 species, of which nearly 300 are found in North America. They are medium to large, stout-bodied insects with large heads. (See Fig. 252.) Their size ranges from that of a house fly to a bumble bee. The adults are most common in the warmer months of the year and are encountered in greatest numbers along marshes and streams, and in wooded areas. The females of practically all species suck the blood of both wild and domestic animals such as horses, cattle, hogs, dogs, and deer. Man is also attacked. When animal hosts are not available, the females will feed on plant juices. The males do not suck blood but subsist on nectar, honeydew, and plant sap. Horse flies are strong fliers and are said to outstrip the fastest horse. They transmit various diseases such as anthrax, tularaemia, and trypanosomiasis of animals. However, most injury is caused by their bites and the blood that they take from the animals. It has been estimated that when horse flies are abundant, an animal may lose more than three ounces of blood daily. Wounds caused in feeding may also be predisposing causes of screw-worm infestations.

FIG. 252. The life cycle of a horse fly (*Tabanus punctifer*). **A,** Adult male. **B,** Adult female. **C,** Egg masses. **D,** Mature larva. **E,** Pupa. (From Agricultural Research Service, U.S.D.A.)

Eggs of horse flies are deposited in masses on grasses, foliage of other plants, and rocks at the water's edge or in swampy places. The larvae drop to the surface of the water, mud, or damp earth and quickly go to the bottom of the water or burrow into the wet soil. Here they feed on small animal life, including each other. When the larvae complete their development they move into drier earth for pupation.

Most common species belong to the genera *Tabanus* and *Chrysops*. The species of *Tabanus* are the larger and the more common forms. Members of the genus *Chrysops* are called deer flies. They may be recognized by their smaller size, black or brown color, and dark markings on the wings. These forms are particularly troublesome around swamps in woodlands.

The striped horse fly or green head (*Tabanus lineola*) is one of the most common species. This insect has at least two generations annually in the south central states. The black horse fly (*Tabanus atratus*) is a vicious biter. It measures about one inch in length and is black. This species generally has one generation each year.

No very satisfactory control measures for horse flies have been developed. The drainage of breeding places is of value, but this practice is usually considered impracticable in most instances. The oiling of stagnant pools has been found to be of value in some cases. Covering horses with fly nets or blankets and stabling during the day help protect the animals. Sprays are generally unsuccessful. A spray containing pyrethrins and piperonyl butoxide has been found to be fairly satisfactory.

Family *Stratiomyidae* (Soldier Flies)

Most soldier flies (Fig. 253**A**) are of medium size, brightly colored, and wasp-like in appearance. The abdomen is generally broad and flat. They are usually sluggish and are found around flowers.

A   **B**

FIG. 253. **A,** A soldier fly (*Hoplitimyia constans*). **B,** A bee fly (*Villa lucifer*).

The larvae are flattened, elliptical or spindle-shaped, and appear somewhat leathery-like. Some are found in privies, manure, and other decaying organic matter. Others are aquatic, or are found under loosened bark of trees, or in the nests of rodents and Hymenoptera. Several hundred species have been recorded from North America.

Family *Bombyliidae* (Bee Flies)

Bee flies (Fig. 253**B**) are usually short, broad, and densely clothed with fine hairs. Their most common colors are black, brown, or yellow with somewhat clouded wings. This is a large family; about

500 species are known in North America. The adults are most frequently observed hovering over flowers or resting in the sun on flowers, sticks, stones, or the bare earth. Food consists of nectar and pollen.

The larvae are parasitic or predaceous. The predators are the more common forms. Some species feed on pods of grasshopper eggs. Perhaps the best known of these species is *Aphoebantus mus,* the adults of which are often observed hovering over the oviposition grounds of grasshoppers. It is believed that the eggs are laid in crevices in the ground near egg pods of grasshoppers, upon which the larvae feed. There is one generation annually; the winter is passed in the larval stage.

The parasitic species infest larvae and pupae of a wide variety of insects. Perhaps the most important forms are found in the genus *Anthrax.* Several species of this genus are known to parasitize cutworms. Another species, *Anthrax anale,* is a parasite of tiger beetle larvae.

Family *Asilidae* (Robber Flies)

More than 500 species of this large family are found in North America. The adults (Fig. 254) are usually large with an elongate body and tapering abdomen. But, some are quite stout and resemble bumble bees, not only in form, but also in the dense clothing of black and yellow hairs.

The adults are predaceous on other insects. They are frequently observed during the summer months in flight over pastures, along roadsides, in open woodlands, or perched on limbs, dead weed stems, fence posts, or other places of vantage. The various species prey upon

FIG. 254. Some common robber flies. (From Texas Agricultural Experiment Station.)

a wide variety of insects which they capture, pierce with the mouth-parts and suck the body juices. Certain species of *Erax* and *Procta-canthus* appear to prey chiefly on grasshoppers. Others, such as *Sparopogon dispar,* collect in numbers around apiaries where they prey upon honey bees. They may cause considerable loss in young queen bees which are captured on their mating flights.

The larvae are reported as living in the ground or in decaying wood where they prey on larvae of beetles, pods of grasshopper eggs, and possibly other insects; although some are thought to feed on the roots of plants.

Suborder CYCLORRHAPHA

Circular-seamed Flies

This is the larger of the two suborders of Diptera. Here are found more than 40 families, some of which are quite large. The suborder is so-called because the pupa is always found in a puparium from which the adult escapes through a circular opening made by push-ing off the anterior end of this pupal case. The adults are rather stout and short. The antennae are usually composed of three seg-ments, the third bearing a style or arista.

Family *Syrphidae* (Syrphid Flies or Flower Flies)

The adults are also known as hover flies and sweat flies. The fam-ily is large and has more than 2,500 species. Its members may be recognized by the presence of a longitudinal spurious or false vein in the wings between the radius and the media. Many are brightly colored and a number of them mimic bees, bumble bees, wasps, and other hymenopterous insects (Fig. 255). They feed upon nectar and pollen of flowers and are of value as pollinators of many plants. Many hover motionless in the air except for the beating of the wings; others fly with a buzzing sound like that produced by bees.

The larvae vary much in appearance and habits. Several are pre-daceous on small insects, many feed upon decaying organic matter, a few attack living plants, and some have taken up their abode in the nests of wasps, bumble bees, and ants. *Syrphus americanus* and *Allographa obliqua* (Fig. 256) are common examples of those spe-cies that prey upon aphids. They are valuable as natural enemies of these insects.

The adult of *Eristalis tenax* so closely resembles the drone of the honey bee that it is known as the drone fly. The larvae of this spe-

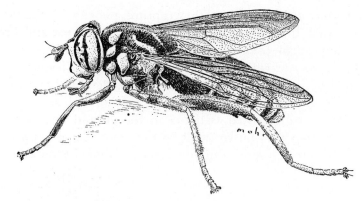

FIG. 255. A syrphid fly (*Spilomyia fusca*), mimic of the bald-faced hornet (*Vespula maculata*). (Courtesy of C. O. Mohr.)

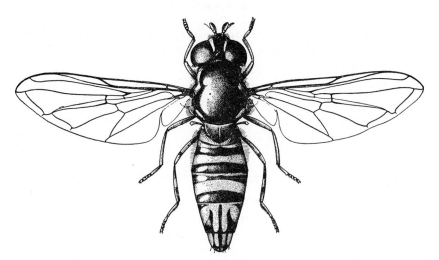

FIG. 256. A syrphid fly (*Allographa obliqua*). (From Agricultural Research Service, U.S.D.A.)

cies and others of the genus live in highly polluted water. They are known as "rat-tailed" maggots because of the presence of a long anal appendage. This is a breathing tube which can be lengthened or shortened at will and permits respiration even when the insect is submerged for as much as several inches in the water.

Family *Tephritidae* (*Trypetidae*) (Fruit Flies)

The fruit flies constitute a large family of small to medium sized flies. The wings are usually banded or spotted and the bodies of many species are brightly colored. Adults of this family are identified by the apical part of the subcosta which abruptly bends forward and then becomes weak. The flies are frequently found on flowers and fruit. Many of them have the peculiar habit of raising and lowering the wings when at rest. Most larvae feed on living plants. Some are leaf miners, others tunnel in stems or form galls, but the most important injury is produced by those species that infest fruit.

FIG. 257. The Mediterranean fruit fly (*Ceratitis capitata*). (From Agricultural Research Service, U.S.D.A.)

The Mediterranean Fruit Fly (*Ceratitis capitata*). This insect (Fig. 257) is the most important of the fruit flies. It is widely distributed in the tropical and subtropical regions of the world where it attacks a wide variety of fruits. The peach is probably the favorite host. All citrus fruits are attacked with the exception of lemons and sour limes. The larvae feed and develop in the pulp of the fruit.

The adults, which are slightly smaller than the house fly, are rather strikingly colored with black, brown, yellow, and white. Females may oviposit as many as 500 eggs each within the rind of the fruit. Under favorable conditions a generation may be completed in less than three weeks; however, the average period is considerably longer. The number of generations produced annually varies in different parts of the world under various weather conditions from one to probably as many as 16.

Infestations of the Mediterranean fruit fly have been discovered in Florida on three separate occasions. The third has just recently been reported. The basic procedure in the 1929-30 eradication program was the destruction of host fruits and the use of sugar bait sprays. The 1956-57 infestation was eliminated chiefly through the use of protein hydrolysate bait sprays and use of insecticides in soil-surface treatments under the infested hosts. The flies have sponging mouthparts and feed on liquid foods. Bait sprays are attractive to them and are effective in their control. The protein hydrolysate bait spray contains malathion as the effective killing agent. This spray is also effective against the Mexican fruit fly. In soil-surface treatment to destroy larvae entering the ground for pupation, dieldrin in granular form is very satisfactory. Strict quarantine measures are enforced in an effort to prevent re-entry of the pest. Larvae in infested fruit may be destroyed by means of heat or cold treatment, or by fumigation with methyl bromide or ethylene dibromide.

The Mexican Fruit Fly (*Anastrepha ludens*). This is the principal fruit fly (Fig. 258) found in Mexico. During the fall and winter, numbers of these flies may drift across the Mexican border into the

FIG. 258. The Mexican fruit fly (*Anastrepha ludens*). **A,** Larva. **B,** Adult. (From Texas Agricultural Experiment Station.)

Lower Rio Grande Valley of Texas and infest citrus groves there. Infestations disappear the next spring and summer following the harvesting of the fruit. Habits and hosts of this pest are similar to those of the Mediterranean fruit fly. However, it has a longer life cycle and the females do not deposit as many eggs; consequently its capacity for injury is not so great. The adults are larger than house flies and are of a yellowish-brown color. The females have a very long ovipositor sheath which is nearly as long as the combined length of the thorax and abdomen.

Quarantine measures are enforced to prevent the spread of the insect. Fumigation with ethylene dichloride or sterilization by means of either heat or cold treatment may be required before regulated citrus fruit may be shipped to nonregulated areas.

The Oriental fruit fly (*Dacus dorsalis*) had been known as a pest in the Pacific Islands for a long time. It was introduced into Hawaii during World War II. This is a serious pest of many tropical and subtropical fruits and it is considered by some to be more injurious than the Mediterranean fruit fly because it has a wider range of host plants.

The Apple Maggot (*Rhagoletis pomonella*). The apple maggot or railroad worm (Fig. 259) is a pest of apples chiefly in the colder sections of the United States. In addition to apples; haws, wild crabapples, plums, blueberries, and other fruits are attacked. Injury is caused by the larvae burrowing through the pulp of the fruit. The medium sized adults are black, yellow, and white with banded wings.

FIG. 259. Adults of apple maggot (*Rhagoletis pomonella*) on fruit. (From Agricultural Research Service, U.S.D.A.)

Hibernation is as pupae in brown puparia within the soil. Eggs are deposited singly in the skin of the fruit. Infested fruits usually drop. When growth is completed the larvae enter the ground and the puparia are formed. One generation develops annually except in the southern range where there may be a partial second brood. Some individuals have a prolonged life cycle and remain in the puparia for an additional year before the adults emerge.

Sprays of lead arsenate or DDT applied to the trees when the adults are active are effective in the control of the pest. As the flies feed on moisture they will be killed by the poisoned spray. Gathering and disposing of the fruit drops will prevent many larvae from completing their development and entering the ground.

The fruits of the cherry are infested by two related species (*Rhagoletis cingulata* and *Rhagoletis fausta*). Their biologies are similar to that of the apple maggot. They also may be controlled by poisoned sprays.

The larvae of *Eurosta solidaginis* (Fig. 260) produce the round goldenrod gall. This insect overwinters as larvae. Pupation occurs

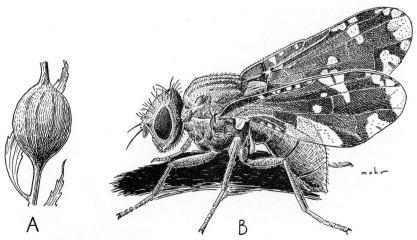

FIG. 260. The goldenrod stem-gall fly (*Eurosta solidaginis*). **A,** Gall. (From Chicago Museum of Natural History.) **B,** Adult. (From Illinois Natural History Survey. Drawn by C. O. Mohr.)

in the spring and the adults emerge to lay eggs in the apical portions of the young plants. Only one generation develops each season.

Family *Drosophilidae* (Vinegar Flies)

The adults are small yellowish flies, usually not more than three or four millimeters in length. They are most common around decaying or fermenting fruit. The small white larvae of the common members of the family burrow in the decaying fruit and feed on yeasts growing there.

Drosophila melanogaster has been employed extensively in the study of animal genetics. This insect has a short life cycle, is easily reared, and produces a number of mutant forms, so it has proved to be an ideal insect for the study of heredity. More is known about the heredity of this small fly than that of any other animal.

Family *Agromyzidae* (Leaf Miner Flies)

Members of this family are small flies and are usually colored yellowish or blackish. Most of the larvae are leaf miners and feed between the upper and lower epidermis of leaves; nearly all plants are attacked. The larvae of one genus (*Cryptochaetum*) are parasites of scale insects.

It is said of the leaf-mining forms that most species may be more readily recognized by the type of mines produced than by an examination of the insects themselves. Most larvae make narrow tortuous mines which become larger as the insect grows. The serpentine leaf miner (*Liriomyza brassicae*), together with several related species, attacks a number of field and vegetable crops (Fig. 261). Their

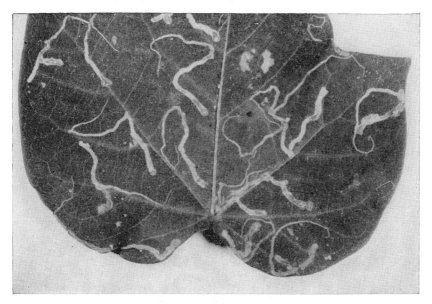

FIG. 261. Injury to foliage by a leaf miner (*Liriomyza*).

serpentine mines are often quite noticeable in leaves of cotton; however, actual damage to this crop is probably of little economic importance. But, serious injury may be produced on peppers and tomatoes. Leafy vegetables, following attacks of this pest, are rendered less attractive to the buyers. Biology of these insects is imperfectly known but they are known to have a rather short life cycle and a number of generations may be completed in a season. They are frequently highly parasitized. The corn leaf blotch miner is a common species and feeds on corn and various grasses. Control of leaf miners is difficult. Most insecticides are usually ineffective in combating these insects. Applications of parathion and diazinon have provided the most satisfactory control measures.

Cryptochaetum iceryae is an important parasite of the cottony cushion scale. It was introduced from Australia to aid in the control of this pest. It is now thought that much of the credit given *Rodolia cardinalis* in the control of the cottony cushion scale is due this tiny parasite.

Family *Gasterophilidae* (Horse Bots)

The horse bot flies have a superficial resemblance to honey bees. They are commonly seen buzzing around horses and mules which greatly fear them. They do not bite or sting and their only purpose is to glue their eggs (usually known as nits) to the hairs of the animals.

FIG. 262. The horse bot fly (*Gasterophilus intestinalis*). (From Castellani and Chalmers, *Manual of Tropical Medicine*, Bailliere, Tindall & Cox, 1919. By permission of the publisher.)

Three species of bots commonly occur in the United States. They are the common horse bot or nit fly (*Gasterophilus intestinalis*, Fig. 262), the throat bot or chin fly (*G. nasalis*), and the nose bot or nose fly (*G. haemorrhoidalis*). The larvae of all three species develop in the digestive tract where they attach themselves to its walls (Fig. 263) and remain for eight to 11 months. The fully grown larvae or maggots are robust and tough-skinned. Each body segment is provided with a circle of spines. The fully grown bots are pinkish or dirty white and about ¾ inch long. When development is completed the larvae release their hold and pass out with the excrement. Pupation takes place in the soil. Winter is passed as larvae within the digestive tract of the animal. There is one generation annually. The adults are usually most abundant during the summer months.

The common bot fly lays eggs on the legs, shoulders, belly, and

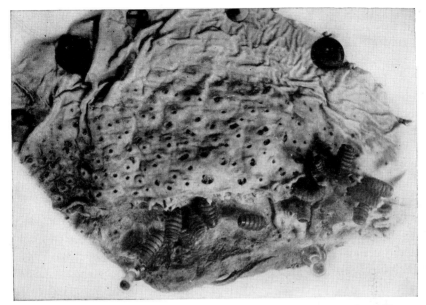

FIG. 263. Section of stomach of a horse showing lesions and attached bots (*Gastero-philus* sp.). (From Agricultural Research Service, U.S.D.A.)

mane, but chiefly on the front legs. The eggs are incubated in about seven days, but the larvae do not emerge until the animal licks or bites itself where the eggs are located. When this stimulus of moisture and friction is provided the larvae emerge and attach themselves to the animal's tongue and lips. The larvae may remain alive in the eggs for as long as three months waiting for this stimulus. The larvae enter the mucous membrane of the lips and tongue where they burrow for about a month before they pass to the stomach and attach to its walls.

Eggs of the throat bot fly are laid on the hairs beneath the jaws. Upon hatching the larvae crawl into the animal's mouth. It is said they attach themselves between the molar teeth where they remain during the first larval instar. Then they pass to the stomach and small intestine where they are found in the pyloric end of the stomach and the duodenum.

Eggs of the nose bot fly are attached to the hairs of the lips. Upon hatching the young larvae enter the mucous lining where they burrow for more than a month before they pass to the stomach for attachment.

On rare occasions a young horse bot is found in the skin of humans. The behavior of the bots in this accidental and unfavorable host is quite unlike that in horses; they have never been known to grow to any size or to reach the digestive tract. They rapidly burrow in the skin where they cause severe itching and irritation.

The use of repellents and nets is of some value in protecting animals. Annoyance by the nose bot fly and the throat bot fly and their infestations may be partly prevented by covering those areas where the eggs are deposited. It is difficult, however, to provide such protection for animals in pastures. A high percentage of the young larvae of the common horse bot may be destroyed by applying warm water to the areas of the body where the eggs are deposited and rubbing vigorously with a sponge or swab. This stimulus causes the eggs to hatch and the larvae perish. The carbon disulphide treatment given by veterinarians is a satisfactory remedy for removal of bots. This treatment should not be administered until about a month after the first killing frost. At this time all the eggs for that season will have been laid and most larvae will have reached the digestive tract. Dipteryx given in food or capsule is proving satisfactory for control of the parasites.

Family *Oestridae* (Bot Flies)

These are large, robust flies somewhat similar to bees in appearance. The larvae are parasites of various animals. The best known species is the sheep bot or nose fly (*Oestrus ovis*, Fig. 264). The adults are hairy, brownish or yellowish flies and are as large as the common horse flies. They deposit living young, not eggs, around

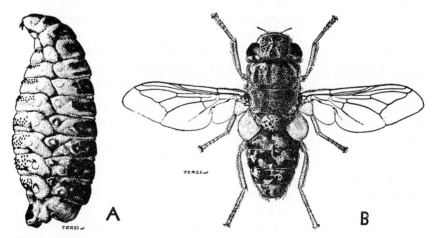

FIG. 264. The sheep bot fly (*Oestrus ovis*). **A,** Larva. **B,** Adult. (From Castellani and Chalmers, *Manual of Tropical Medicine*, Bailliere, Tindall & Cox, 1919. By permission of the publisher.)

the nostrils of sheep. The small larvae crawl into the nasal passages. Here they remain for a varying period of time before migrating to the frontal sinuses where they complete their larval development. The mature larvae find their way to the ground into which they burrow and pupate. The life history of the insect varies considerably since individuals may complete a life cycle in three to 5½ months, and others do not complete their development until the next season. In the Southwest adults may be found throughout the year. A number of remedies for the prevention or treatment of sheep bots have been suggested, but most of them are of little or no value. In recent research very promising results have been obtained by use of several of the animal systemic insecticides.

Larvae of the bot flies of the genus *Cephenomyia* infest the sinuses of deer. The adults are large, grayish-brown flies which are reported to fly more rapidly than any other insects. They deposit living young in the nostrils of the hosts. The young larvae migrate to the sinuses where they develop.

Family *Hypodermatidae* (Warble Flies)

Warble flies are similar in appearance to the bot flies and many authorities consider them in that family. The most important species of this family are the ox warbles (*Hypoderma lineatum* and *H. bovis*). The former is known as the cattle grub or heel fly and

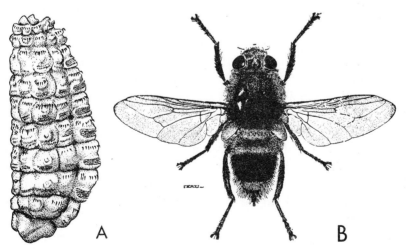

FIG. 265. **A,** The cattle grub (*Hypoderma lineatum*). (From Agricultural Research Service, U.S.D.A.). **B,** The bomb fly (*Hypoderma bovis*). (From Castellani and Chalmers, *Manual of Tropical Medicine,* Bailliere, Tindall & Cox, 1919. By permission of the publisher.)

the latter is the northern cattle grub or bomb fly. (See Fig. 265.) The bomb fly is not found in the southern states but is the more prevalent species in the Northeast. Although cattle are the principal hosts of the warble flies, buffaloes and rarely, horses, goats, and man are attacked.

Heavy losses are attributed to cattle grubs annually. In the latter stages of development the larvae migrate to the backs of the animals and encyst underneath the skin in which holes are made. Occasionally as many as one hundred grub holes may be found in a hide. Hides with a number of grub holes are worthless for making leather. There are also losses in meat and milk. Activities of the flies cause apprehension and fear among the cattle. Stampedes may occur. Cattle frequently seek protection in water to escape them. Feeding of the animals may be curtailed at this time which results in failure to gain weight and reduction in milk production.

Heel flies first appear in late winter or early spring in the South. The period of their activity is about six weeks. The females glue the eggs to hairs usually just above the hoof. Eggs may be deposited also on hairs of the belly, udder, or escutcheon when the animals are lying down. The northern heel flies appear later in the season and are active for a longer period of time. Their grubs also remain in the backs of cattle for a longer period.

The female warble fly rarely lays more than 800 eggs. The eggs hatch in three to seven days, the larvae tunnel in the skin, and then bore into deeper tissues. Although they migrate slowly through the connective tissues of the body of the host animals, they are forever on the move, which prevents attacks of the white corpuscles. About nine months after entering the skin they appear in the backs of the animals. The routes followed by the two species differ somewhat. The larvae of the heel fly are usually first discovered after tunneling into the skin in the walls of the gullet and esophagus in late spring or summer. The larvae then travel up the diaphragm, along the ribs, and through connective tissues to the back. Some may enter the neural canal in their passage to the back. When the skin is reached holes are cut to obtain air. Around the grubs cysts or warbles are produced. In the South the grubs begin to appear in the backs of the animals in the middle of the fall. The northern cattle grubs appear to take a more direct route to the back of the animal. They are rarely found in the walls of the gullet and are more frequently observed in the neural canal. Growth of the grubs is more rapid after the backs of the animals are reached. Development is completed here in five weeks to almost three months. The mature larvae work their way out of the cysts, drop to the ground, and pupate under trash or within the soil. The adult flies usually emerge from the puparia about six weeks later. Only one generation is produced annually.

Cattle grubs in beef animals are most effectively controlled by use of certain organic phosphorus compounds acting as systemic insecticides. Those which have been approved for use are Co-Ral, trolene, and Ruelene. Co-Ral is applied as a spray. Sick animals and calves less than three months of age should not be treated, and animals three to six months old should be sprayed only lightly. Trolene, a drug grade of ronnel, may be administered in a bolus or by mixing it in the feed of the animal. Sick animals should not be fed the compound. Ruelene may be applied either by spraying or by pouring on the animals' backs. The above materials are recommended for use at the end of the heel fly season. In grub control on dairy cattle rotenone is the only insecticide permitted for use. It is applied as a wash, dust or spray after the grubs appear in the backs of the animals during fall and winter.

A warble fly (*Oedemagena tarandi*) is a pest of reindeer in northern Europe and Alaska. Holes in the hides result in a large loss in leather. There is also a loss in meat and its quality.

Family *Cuterebridae* (Rodent Bots)

The adults are large, stout, hairy flies resembling bumble bees. Most of the larvae of this family are parasites of rodents such as rabbits, mice, and squirrels. *Cuterebra cuniculi* is a common species infesting rabbits. *Cuterebra emasculator* attacks the scrotum of squirrels which may result in their emasculation.

The human bot fly (*Dermatobia hominis*) is the most interesting member of this family. This insect is found in South America, Central America, and parts of Mexico. It is a pest of importance to man, cattle, and other animals. The female flies do not lay the eggs on the larval hosts, but deposit them on flies, mosquitoes, and ticks. When these parasites feed, the larvae hatch and bore into the skin of the animal where they encyst. Infestations on cattle can be reduced by systematic use of a livestock spray as toxaphene and lindane. Systemic insecticides are also effective.

Family *Tachinidae* (*Larvaevoridae*) (Tachina Flies)

This is the most beneficial family of Diptera. The group is very large and all its members are parasites of other insects. The flies have the general appearance of flesh flies and house flies. Many are rather large, bristly, and somewhat resemble bees or wasps. Members of the family have bristles on both the hypopleura and pteropleura; the postscutellum is prominent, and the ventral abdominal sclerites are overlapped by the dorsal sclerites.

Tachina flies parasitize a wide variety of insects. Most of them attack the larvae of Lepidoptera, larvae of sawflies, and adult Coleoptera; some parasitize Orthoptera, Hemiptera, and insects of other orders. Their life histories and host relationships are often quite intriguing.

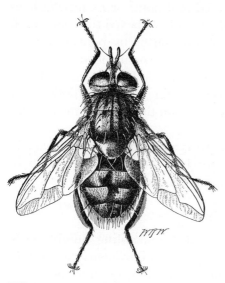

FIG. 266. An important tachina parasite (*Winthemia quadripustulata*). (From Agricultural Research Service, U.S.D.A.)

Reproductive habits are diverse. Eggs are usually deposited directly on the hosts. Eggs glued to the body of a caterpillar are commonly observed. Some lay their eggs on the food and hatch after they are ingested by the feeding caterpillars. The maggots then attack the internal organs of the host. Others produce living larvae which are deposited upon the host or inserted into the body by means of the ovipositor. Other types of reproductive habits are known.

Winthemia quadripustulata (Fig. 266) is one of the most important native parasites. It is widely distributed, multiplies quite rapidly, and attacks a large number of caterpillars. Most of the eggs are placed on the thorax where the caterpillars cannot reach them with their mandibles. Upon hatching, the larvae bore into the host and feed upon the tissues. Pupation occurs in the soil. A generation may be completed in less than three weeks in warm weather.

Compsilura concinnata (Fig. 267) was imported from Europe. It is an important parasite of larvae of the gypsy moth and browntail moth, and it also attacks a number of other caterpillars. The female inserts living larvae within the body of the host by means of its ovipositor. Three or four generations are produced annually. Hibernation is as small larvae within the body of the host.

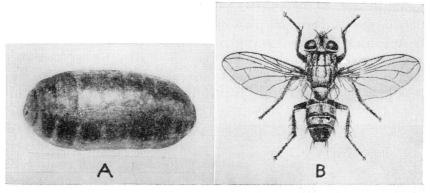

FIG. 267. *Compsilura concinnata.* An important parasite of the larvae of the gypsy moth and the brown-tail moth. **A,** Puparium. **B,** Adult. (From Agricultural Research Service, U.S.D.A.)

Adult females of *Sturmia scutellata* deposit their eggs on the foliage to be ingested by the feeding caterpillars. This introduced European parasite is an important natural enemy of the larvae of the gypsy moth, its only host. Only one generation is produced annually by this parasite. Hibernation is within a puparium in the soil.

Archytas analis, which is a native parasite, preys upon the variegated cutworm (*Peridroma saucia*) and other caterpillars. The females deposit small larvae on the foliage of plants to which they are attached by means of minute membranous cups. The larvae patiently await the passing of a host. When the leaf is disturbed a larva rears upward like a snake, and swings the head in a wide circle. If a host comes near enough it quickly attaches itself. Development is completed within the pupa of the host where it also pupates. Several generations are produced each season.

Family *Calliphoridae* (Blow Flies)

Many blow flies are brightly colored. Here are found the greenbottle flies and the bluebottle flies that are so familiar to almost everyone. These flies have the arista of the antennae plumose to the tip, the postscutellum is absent; both hypopleura and pteropleura bear bristles, and two notopleural bristles are present. Most blow fly larvae are scavengers, developing in decaying matter. Some are parasites of vertebrates and others feed on invertebrates.

The Screw-Worm (*Cochliomyia hominivorax*). This insect (Fig. 268) is a parasite of livestock, various wild animals, and man. It is found in both North America and South America, but overwinters only in the southernmost parts of the United States and southward to Argentina. It spreads northward each season in infested livestock and through flight of the adults.

The screw-worm is a livestock pest of considerable importance, especially in the Southwest. It does not breed in carcasses, but infests wounds of living animals. In fact, larvae have been known to enter the unbroken skin of experimental animals. Eggs are occasionally deposited in the nostrils of man.

The females deposit 250 to 300 eggs each in shingle-like masses on dry tissues near the wound. These hatch in 11 to 21 hours. The larvae tunnel into the live tissues with the head downward. After feeding for four to eight days the larvae drop from the wound to the ground in which they pupate in brown puparia. The fully grown larvae are about ⅔ inch long, of the typical muscoid type, and with elevated, spine-like circlets around each body segment which produce a screw-like appearance. The pupal period varies in length from seven to 54 days. During warm summer weather in the Southwest the average length of a life cycle is about 24 days. The adults (Fig. 269) are larger than house flies, blue-green with three dark stripes on the thorax and a reddish-orange to brown head. It is possible for this insect to produce a number of generations in a season.

FIG. 268. Screw-worms (*Cochliomyia hominovorax*). (From Agricultural Research Service, U.S.D.A.

Preventive measures are important in combating the screw-worm. Castration, dehorning, docking, and branding should be done, if possible, during the cold months when the flies are not present, or at least not abundant. Cuts while shearing sheep and goats should be treated until they are healed. It is desirable for animals to be born in late winter or early spring in most areas when there is least likelihood of infestations. Care should be taken to prevent unnecessary injury to livestock. In preventing or eliminating infestations in both dairy and beef animals, wounds may be treated with either Smear 62 which contains diphenylamine, or E.Q. 335 with lindane as the active ingredient. For beef cattle only, Co-Ral and Korlan are

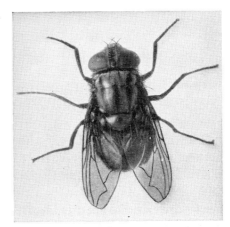

FIG. 269.   The screw-worm fly (*Cochliomyia hominovorax*). (From Agricultural Research Service, U.S.D.A.)

recommended. The spectacular use of male-sterile flies eliminated this pest in the southeastern states.

The secondary screw-worm (*Callitroga macellaria*) closely resembles the primary screw-worm. It is primarily a scavenger and breeds abundantly in dead animals. The larvae are found also in old infected wounds of living animals where they feed on dead tissues, and in urine-soaked wool; live tissues are not attacked.

The black blow fly (*Phormia regina*) is a common insect which usually breeds in animal wastes and carcasses. The larvae may infest sores, old wounds, and urine-soaked wool of sheep. It is the most prevalent of the wool-maggots. Wool-maggots may be controlled by use of several insecticides. A locally applied lindane or Co-Ral spray; dips or sprays of either Delnav or Korlan; or the latter compound prepared as a smear, are used. Sick animals should not be treated.

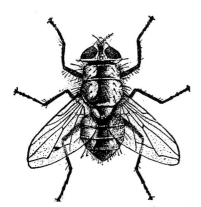

FIG. 270. A greenbottle fly (*Lucilia caesar*). (From Agricultural Research Service, U.S.D.A.

The bluebottle flies (*Calliphora erythrocephala, C. vicina, C. vomitoria,* and others) are readily recognized by their large size and buzzing noise. They breed in carcasses, excrement, and wastes. Sometimes they enter houses in search of breeding places.

The greenbottle flies (*Lucilia sericata, L. illustris, L. sylvarium,* and related species) breed in wastes of many types as do the bluebottle flies (Fig. 270). The larvae of *L. sericata* may also be found in old wounds and sores of animals, feeding as scavengers; they are also wool-maggots.

The cluster fly (*Pollenia rudis*) is common in the colder climates. The adults frequently collect in attics and other protected places in late summer and fall to hibernate. The flies are larger and darker colored than house flies, and sluggish in habit. The larvae are parasites of earthworms.

Family *Sarcophagidae* (Flesh Flies)

Flies of this group are medium in size, usually grayish in color, and often with checkerboard-like patterns on the abdomen. The

postscutellum is undeveloped. Both hypopleural and pteropleural bristles are present, and there are four notopleural bristles.

The adults (Fig. 271) are commonly associated with decaying organic matter and dead animals in which a number of species breed. But, some members of the family parasitize invertebrates, such as insects and snails; mammals are hosts of others. The adult females usually do not lay eggs, but deposit small larvae. This is a large family of flies with about 1,000 known species which are worldwide in distribution.

FIG. 271. A flesh fly (*Sarcophaga plinthopyga*). (From Agricultural Research Service, U.S.D.A.)

Sarcophaga kellyi is one of the best known members of this family. It parasitizes grasshoppers chiefly, but a few other insects are attacked also. The flies usually deposit their larvae on the grasshoppers in flight. The females dart at flying grasshoppers and deposit their small larvae usually on the underside of the wings. When the flies are numerous they may dart at stones or other small objects thrown into the air. The female flies also deposit their larvae on grasshopper nymphs as they hop about, and on newly molted individuals which are resting while the body wall hardens. The small maggots tunnel into the hosts and feed upon the internal organs. From one to several larvae are often observed in dissected grasshoppers. When the larvae are mature they leave the dead or dying hosts and enter the soil for pupation. Several generations may be completed in one season. Hibernation takes place as mature larvae in puparia within the soil. A number of other related species are also parasites of insects.

Several species of *Sarcophaga* develop in the pitcher plant (*Sarracenia*) in which they feed on trapped insects. They are cannibalistic, and it is said only one larva ever develops in a pitcher.

Wohlfahrtia vigil is a large gray fly found in the cooler parts of North America. It is a parasite of a number of animals such as rabbits, minks, dogs, and foxes. Occasionally small children are attacked. The larvae produce superficial lesions.

The red-tailed flesh fly (*Sarcophaga haemorrhoidalis*) is a widely distributed well known species. The larvae normally feed as scavengers but may occasionally be found in wounds and the digestive tracts of mammals.

Family *Muscidae* (House Flies, Stable Flies)

This large group of flies is often referred to as the house fly family because of this well known insect. Other common species of the family are the stable fly, horn fly, and the tsetse fly.

The House Fly (*Musca domestica*). This insect (Fig. 272) is of world-wide distribution and the most common fly observed around human habitations. If the flies around a home were collected, probably more than 90 percent of them would prove to be the house fly. This dark gray fly is marked by four longitudinal lines on the thorax and is about $\frac{1}{4}$ inch in length. The arista of the antenna is plumose. Vein M_1 of the wing bends sharply forward and almost meets R_{4+5} at the margin, nearly closing cell R_5. Mouthparts are of the sponging type; house flies cannot bite.

House flies are associated with filth. The larvae develop in the manure of horses, pigs, chickens, and cows; human excrement; garbage; and decomposing vegetable matter. The adults may feed on human excrement, sputum, exudates of sores, and other filth, and then feed upon the foods of man. Since their bodies and feeding habits are well adapted to transmit disease organisms, they may transmit a number of diseases such as typhoid fever, dysentery, cholera, and yaws. Eggs of several parasitic worms may also be transmitted by house flies. Their sponging mouthparts are well adapted

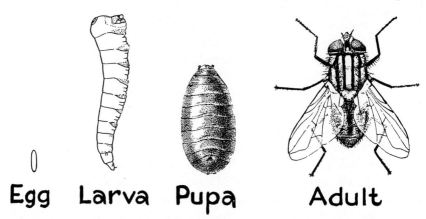

Egg   Larva   Pupa   Adult

FIG. 272. Life history of the house fly (*Musca domestica*). (From Agricultural Research Service, U.S.D.A.)

for feeding on liquid materials. Solids may be dissolved by means of saliva or regurgitated contents of the crop.

The distance flies may fly from their breeding places is important in the problem of control. It has been shown experimentally they can travel more than ten miles. However, flies usually go no farther than is necessary to procure food and places for egg laying. When flies are quite abundant it is reasonably certain they are breeding in the immediate neighborhood.

House flies usually overwinter as larvae or pupae in colder climates, but in the South some breeding may continue throughout the winter months. This insect may reproduce with great rapidity; the females lay a large number of eggs, and the life cycle is short. The small, white, elongate eggs are laid in batches in manure or other breeding media. Each female lays about 500 eggs. Eggs hatch in 12 to 24 hours. The larval stage is about seven days in duration. The mature larvae are 1/3 to 1/2 inch in length and are white. Before transforming to the pupal stage the larvae seek a drier area of the breeding material. A brown puparium is then formed in which the larva pupates. The pupal stage requires four or five days.

Under favorable conditions a generation may be completed in about 12 or 14 days, but the length of a generation is prolonged in cool weather. Therefore, with proper temperature and moisture conditions enormous populations of house flies may develop in relatively short periods of time.

Elimination of breeding media is the first and most important step in fly control. The proper disposal of garbage, sewage, and other organic materials in which flies breed is mandatory. Outdoor toilets should be eliminated or made as flyproof as possible. The excreta should be covered daily with borax, waste oil, or heavy applications of lime. Manure should be removed and spread thinly over fields and pastures every two or three days. Treatment of manure with borax and other chemicals to prevent fly breeding is recommended and used, but as a whole the practice is not too satisfactory.

Regardless of measures employed there will be some breeding of flies and supplementary control measures will be needed. Electric fly screens and fly traps aid in the reduction of populations. Space sprays and aerosols containing pyrethrums give a quick knockdown of the flies and provide temporary relief. DDT residual sprays produced most excellent control until the development of resistant flies. When the use of DDT became less effective other chlorinated hydrocarbon insecticides, such as chlordane, lindane, toxaphene, and methoxychlor were employed, but these compounds also were not very satisfactory in the control of DDT-resistant flies. Because of milk contamination the only chlorinated hydrocarbon insecticides that may be employed in fly control in dairy barns are lindane and methoxychlor.

Certain organic phosphorous compounds of sufficiently low mammalian toxicity have been found to be efficient in house fly control. Malathion is currently recommended for use under some conditions. Baits containing malathion or related compounds as the toxic principle are reasonably satisfactory.

The Stable Fly (*Stomoxys calcitrans*). The stable fly (Fig. 273) rather closely resembles the house fly with which it is often confused. Its mouthparts are of the piercing-sucking type and are held bayonet-like in front of the head. The abdomen is broad and spotted. Cell R_5 is not closed nearly so much as in the house fly. The insect prefers to live in the open and is commonly seen in the sunshine on fences, posts, and boards. During stormy weather stable flies frequently enter houses and bite people, who think they are house

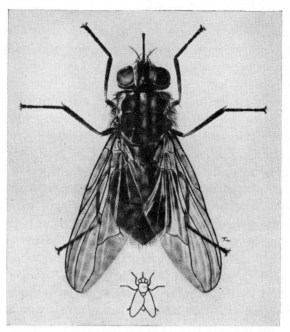

FIG. 273. The stable fly (*Stomoxys calcitrans*). (After Austen, from British Museum of Natural History.)

flies that have assumed biting habits. Both males and females are vicious blood-suckers. Horses, mules, cows, and other animals are attacked. Such animal diseases as anthrax may be transmitted by these insects.

In cold climates the insect overwinters as larvae and pupae. Under southern conditions some breeding may continue throughout the winter months. Eggs are laid in rotting and fermenting straw. Larvae are not found in pure manure, but a mixture of manure and straw affords an ideal breeding medium. The bases of old straw stacks and piles of decomposing vegetable matter of all types are favorite breeding places. The larvae resemble those of the house fly. The length of a life cycle is about three weeks. As the female flies must feed on blood before eggs can be produced, they are one to two weeks old before the first eggs are deposited for the next generation. Eggs are laid in batches and the total number deposited by each female is about 500.

In the control of stable flies elimination of breeding places is of prime importance. Straw should be baled and stored in a dry place or scattered thinly over the ground. Mixtures of manure and straw or wet, sodden feed around feed troughs should be spread on the land so it will dry, as neither stable flies nor house flies breed in dry matter. Decaying vegetable matter such as lawn clippings and vegetable trimmings afford breeding quarters and should be properly disposed of. Marine plants washed in heaps along certain Gulf coast beaches afford breeding quarters. Spraying this material with a mixture of creosote and fuel oil will eliminate breeding.

Several compounds may be used in spraying the resting surfaces of the flies. Those more commonly employed inside barns are malathion, lindane, and methoxychlor. DDT, toxaphene, and chlordane are recommended for use outside of barns only. Treatment of animals with approved sprays will afford relief from attacks for a while.

The Horn Fly (*Haematobia irritans*). Injury by horn flies to cattle is similar to that of stable flies. Occasionally they attack sheep, horses, goats, dogs, and other animals. Warm, moist weather is most favorable for horn fly development, and under such conditions they may increase to huge numbers and cause irritation and much loss of blood and vitality of cattle.

FIG. 274. A tsetse fly (*Glossina palpalis*). (After Austen, from British Museum of Natural History.)

The horn fly is about one-half the size of the house fly and the stable fly. Unlike these flies, it remains on the animal all the time. Throughout the warm season it may be seen on the shoulders, backs, and bellies of animals, or resting on the horns.

Horn flies breed only in fresh cow manure. Each female lays 375 to 400 eggs. A life cycle may be completed in ten to 12 days. Winter is passed as larvae or pupae. Several compounds such as methoxychlor, toxaphene, and Co-Ral are used as sprays for control on beef cattle. On milk animals methoxychlor and malathion are used with restrictions. Pyrethrum sprays are also applied.

Tsetse flies (*Glossina* spp., Fig. 274) are important pests in Africa as they transmit sleeping sickness of man and nagana of cattle. The causative organisms are trypanosomes. The female flies do not lay eggs but deposit mature larvae.

Family *Anthomyiidae* (Anthomyiids)

The anthomyiids are common flies and are quite similar in appearance to the *Muscidae*. Members of this family have cell R_5 of the wing only slightly, if at all, narrowed. Feeding habits of the larvae are diverse. Most of them develop in decaying plant material. Some feed on growing plants and others are parasites of insects.

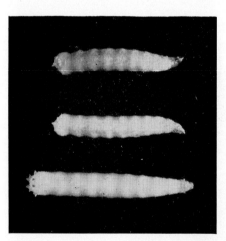

FIG. 275. Seed-corn maggots (*Hylemya cilicrura*). (From Agricultural Research Service, U.S.D.A.)

The Seed-Corn Maggot (*Hylemya cilicrura*). The maggots (Fig. 275) feed in seeds which, as a result, either fail to sprout or produce weak plants. The seeds of corn, peas, beans, and other plants are attacked. The adult flies are grayish and about ⅕ inch in length. The insects hibernate in puparia and the adults emerge in early spring in the South. Eggs are deposited in soil in which there is an abundance of organic matter. Pupation is in the soil. The life cycle is relatively short and three to five generations develop annually.

Planting sufficiently late to insure rapid germination in well prepared seed beds is probably the best preventive measure. Satisfactory control has been obtained by use of dieldrin, lindane, or heptachlor in seed treatment. Commercial seed are often treated previously to control this and other soil insects.

The Onion Maggot (*Hylemya antiqua*).   The maggots tunnel and feed in the bulbs and underground stems of onions, causing serious damage. Most injury occurs when the spring seasons are wet. The onion is the only crop that suffers injury by this pest. It is found chiefly in the northern part of the United States and Canada. Damage occurs only rarely in southern climates.

Winter is passed chiefly as larvae or pupae in puparia which are found in the soil or in piles of cull onions. Some adults may survive the winter. They are grayish, bristly flies with large wings (Fig. 276) and are about ¼ inch long. Eggs are deposited around the bases of the plants. Upon hatching, the young larvae migrate down the plants and tunnel into the bulbs where they feed for two weeks or

FIG. 276.   Adult of the onion maggot (*Hylemya antiqua*).   (From Agricultural Research Service, U.S.D.A.)

longer. The mature larvae are yellowish-white and about ⅓ inch long. Pupation is in the soil, and two or three weeks later the adults emerge. A third generation may attack onions just prior to harvest and cause them to rot in storage.

Effective control has been provided by applications of ethion or trithion to the soil prior to planting. Malathion dusts or sprays, or diazinon sprays are satisfactory for use on rows of growing plants. Cull onions, which are a source of infestation, should be destroyed or removed immediately after harvest.

The Cabbage Maggot (*Hylemya brassicae*).   The biology of the cabbage maggot is similar to the two preceding insects. The maggots attack the underground parts of cabbage, cauliflower, broccoli, radishes, and turnips. When infestations are heavy the roots of the plants may be honeycombed. The insect is an important pest only in Canada and the northern United States.

Soil treatments with either aldrin or chlordane are recommended for control of the pest. The insecticides should be applied to the soil around the base of the plants when the leaves appear and with a second treatment made shortly following thinning or transplanting. In treatment of transplants the soil around each should be drenched with a water dilution of the poison.

The spinach leaf miner (*Pegomyia hyoscyami*) is a common example of a leaf miner of this family. The adult is similar in appearance to the house fly. The larvae feed between the upper and lower surfaces of the leaf, producing both linear and blotch-like mines. The use of parathion would probably provide the most satisfactory control. Lindane, chlordane, and toxaphene are also suggested for use in the control of the pest.

FIG. 277. The lesser house fly (*Fannia canicularis*). (After Austen and Thompsen, from British Museum of Natural History.)

Several members of this family are often observed in homes. The two species most commonly seen are the lesser house fly (*Fannia canicularis*, Fig. 277) and the latrine fly (*Fannia scalaris*). These insects breed in filth and they could be of some importance as disseminators of disease.

The Pupipara. This section is comprised of several families of rather aberrant forms of Diptera. The adults are louse-like in form, flattened and leathery in appearance, and most members are wingless. All but a few species are external parasites of birds and mammals which suck the blood of their hosts. These insects do not lay eggs but give birth to mature larvae that are ready to form their puparia—thus, the name *pupipara*.

Family *Hippoboscidae* (Louse Flies)

This is the only family of the group that needs to be discussed here. The most common representative is the sheep ked (*Melo-*

phagus ovinus, Fig. 278). The adults are wingless, about 1/5 inch long, brownish, and covered with short spine-like hairs. The sac-like abdomen is somewhat flattened, broad, and unsegmented.

Sheep, and occasionally goats, are attacked. The presence of a few keds on animals does no material harm, but a heavy infestation produces emaciation and unthriftiness. Only two stages may be found on the animals. They are the brown seed-like puparia enmeshed in the wool, and the adults. Each female produces a total of ten to 20

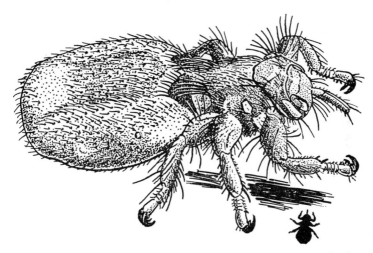

FIG. 278. The sheep ked (*Melophagus ovinus*). (From Illinois Natural History Survey. Drawn by C. O. Mohr.)

mature larvae with an interval of about one week between each. Several overlapping generations may be completed within a year. Sheep keds are obligatory parasites and die if separated from the hosts for more than a few days. A number of insecticides are effective in control of sheep keds. Pyrethrins with a synergist and rotenone may be used without restrictions. Chlorinated hydrocarbons, such as lindane, toxaphene, dieldrin and DDT, and such organic phosphorous compounds as Co-Ral, Delnav, and malathion are also recommended. These compounds, however, must be used with the suggested precautions.

Two louse flies are found on deer (*Lipoptena depressa* and *Neolipoptena ferrisi*). The adults have wings when they emerge from the pupal stage but these are shed a few days later. Several of the parasites have been observed attached to each other in chains. The first fly takes blood from the host. The second draws blood from the abdomen of the first, and so on down the chain to the last member.

Several louse flies are common parasites of birds. The pigeon fly (*Pseudolynchia canariensis*) is a common parasite of pigeons in warm climates. The adults are winged and are able to fly. *Lynchia americana* is fairly common on owls, hawks, and grouse. Other species infest quail and doves.

20

ORDER SIPHONAPTERA[1]

FLEAS

Fleas are small, wingless, laterally compressed parasites (Fig. 279) that feed on the blood of mammals and birds. This is a small order of insects with only about 1,100 known species in the world. However, the group is important as some are transmitters of disease, others are intermediate hosts of tapeworms and most annoy man and animals by their feeding.

General characteristics of the order are:

1. **Wings absent.**
2. **Piercing-sucking mouthparts.**
3. **Complete metamorphosis.**
4. **Body compressed laterally; legs modified for jumping.**

The bodies of fleas are greatly modified for their parasitic way of life. They are oval and compressed in form which, combined with a hard, smooth body with backward projecting bristles and spines, permits them to slip easily through the hairs and feathers of the hosts and makes capture difficult. The legs are long and are modified for jumping which aid further in escaping their enemies and in finding their hosts.

Mouthparts are for piercing and sucking. Both males and females pierce the skin and suck the blood of the hosts. Their antennae are three-jointed, small, and are found in grooves on the sides of the head. Eyes are simple; they are sometimes absent. There are ten segments in the abdomen, the last three of which are greatly modified. Bristles on the body and the short, stout, comb-like spines,

[1] *Siphon,* tube; *apteros,* wingless.

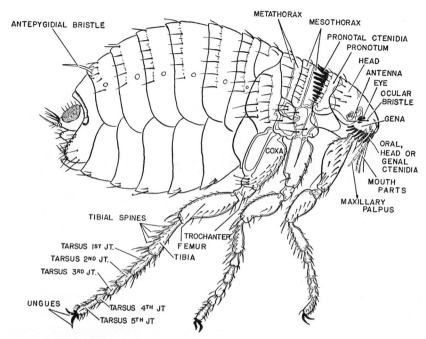

FIG. 279. A female flea (*Siphonaptera*) showing characters used in identification. (Redrawn from Herms, *Medical Entomology,* 3rd ed., The Macmillan Company, 1939. By permission of the publisher.)

ctenidia, which are often present on the head and pronotum, are of value in the taxonomy of the group.

Most species of fleas are quite active on the host and they frequently transfer from one animal to another. Considerable time may be spent off the hosts. They do not exhibit a marked degree of host specificity; the cat flea, for example, also attacks dogs, man, rabbits, squirrels, rats, poultry, and other animals.

Adult fleas are relatively long-lived. Some may live for more than a year. They usually feed at least daily, but they may exist without food for long periods of time. The human flea has been observed to live for four months without food. It is believed that females must have blood before the development of eggs.

The eggs, which are white, rounded at the ends, and relatively large may be laid on the hosts, the ground, or in the nests of animals. Most flea eggs are dry, and even though they may be laid among the feathers or hair of the host, they readily roll off the animal. The eggs hatch into elongate legless larvae. Their mouthparts are for chewing and their eyes are absent. The larval food consists of organic matter including feces of the adult fleas and their own cast skins. When the larvae are mature they spin silken cocoons in which they pupate. As with most parasites of warm-blooded animals, some reproduction may continue throughout the year. The largest flea populations are usually developed in localities where sandy soils prevail since moisture conditions are more uniform and, consequently, are more satisfactory for the development of the larvae.

Fleas are transmitters of the bubonic form of plague (black death). Plague, which is one of the dreaded diseases of mankind, is caused by the bacillus (*Pasteurella pestis*). Plague is essentially a disease of rodents, among which it is transmitted by fleas. Man becomes infected when bitten by an infected flea. The disease among wild rodents is referred to as the sylvatic plague.

The endemic or murine type of typhus fever is a flea-borne disease and is also essentially a disease of rodents. This is a mild form of typhus which must not be confused with epidemic typhus which is transmitted by body lice.

Fleas are intermediate hosts of the double-pored dog tapeworm (*Dipylidium caninum*). The fleas become infected in the larval stage when the tapeworm eggs are ingested in feeding. The primary hosts are infected by the ingestion of a flea or parts of its crushed body. Usually only dogs, cats, and certain wild animals are infected, but occasionally is man, especially children. A common tapeworm of rats and mice (*Hymenolepis diminuta*) has a number of arthropods as intermediate hosts. Among these are several species of fleas such as the rat fleas. This parasite is rarely found in man.

KEY TO FAMILIES OF SIPHONAPTERA

1. The combined thoracic tergites shorter than the first abdominal tergite   **Hectopsyllidae**, p. 438
   The combined thoracic tergites longer than the first abdominal tergite   2
2. Abdominal tergites with only 1 row of bristles   **Pulicidae**, p. 436
   Abdominal tergites with 2 or more rows of bristles   3
3. Genal comb consists of 2 broad, tooth-like lobes in front of maxillary palpi; parasites of bats   **Ischnopsyllidae.**
   Genal comb, if present, not as above; not parasites of bats   4
4. Genal comb present   **Hystrichopsyllidae**, p. 437
   Genal comb absent   **Dolichopsyllidae**, p. 437

Family *Pulicidae*

This is a large family and contains some of the most common species as the cat flea (*Ctenocephalides felis*, Fig. 280) and the dog flea (*C. canis*). These are pests of cats, dogs, and man, but other

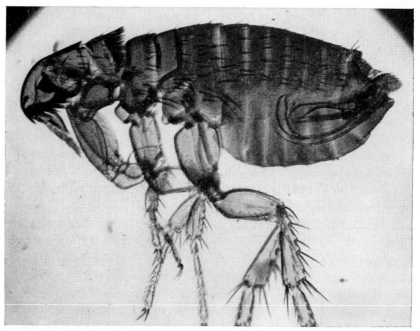

FIG. 280. The cat flea (*Ctenocephalides felis*). (From Department of Entomology, A & M College of Texas.)

animals such as rats, rabbits, and poultry are also attacked. They breed where cats and dogs and other hosts frequent, as in sheds, homes, cellars, and lawns. Both species possess genal and pronotal combs. The length of the developmental stages from egg to adult may be as short as two weeks but frequently the time is much longer, dependent upon weather conditions. The cat flea is much more common than the dog flea. Both species are intermediate hosts of the double-pored tapeworm (*Dipylidium caninum*).

The human flea (*Pulex irritans*) (Fig. 281) attacks man, cats, dogs, rats, rabbits, horses, and a number of other animals. Breeding places are the habitats of its hosts. When conditions are favorable, a life cycle may be completed in three weeks. Pronotal and genal combs are absent. The maximum length of life of the adult human flea is said to be more than two years.

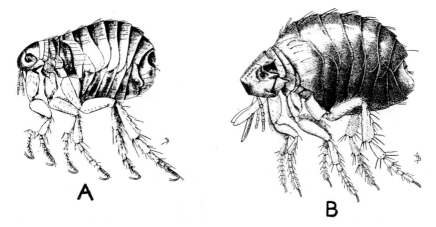

FIG. 281. **A,** The human flea (*Pulex irritans*). **B,** The sticktight flea (*Echidnophaga gallinacea*). (From Agricultural Research Service, U.S.D.A.)

The oriental rat flea (*Xenopsylla cheopsis*) resembles the human flea as both pronotal and genal combs are absent. It is generally found in buildings and frequently bites man. This species is very important as it is the chief transmitter of bubonic plague. Rodents, chiefly rats, are its principal hosts. The life cycle of this flea is given as five weeks or longer. Adults have been reported as living for as long as a year.

Family *Dolichopsyllidae*

This is the largest family of fleas. Rodents and birds are the normal hosts. The fleas are characterized by bearing two or more rows of bristles on the abdominal tergites and by the absence of the genal comb. The northern rat flea (*Nosopsyllus fasciatus*) is the most important species. It is widely distributed in both Europe and America. Common hosts are rats, mice, skunks, and man. This species is capable of transmitting bubonic plague but it is a weak vector.

Family *Hystrichopsyllidae*

The fleas of this small family are parasites mostly of rats and mice. The cosmopolitan mouse flea (*Leptopsylla segnis*) is one of the best known members. It is worldwide in distribution. Man is rarely attacked by it.

Family *Hectopsyllidae*

Fleas of this family remain attached on the hosts more or less permanently. The best known members are the sticktight flea and the chigoe flea.

The sticktight flea (*Echidnophaga gallinacea,* Fig. 281) is a common pest of poultry, dogs, cats, and other animals. The adults often collect in masses, mostly on the head of the host, and remain attached even for weeks. A life cycle is completed in 30 to 60 days.

The chigoe flea (*Tunga penetrans*) is a native of tropical regions; it does not occur in the United States. The female burrows into the skin of man and animals, chiefly in the feet, and an ulcer (Fig. 282) is produced. These ulcers may become infected with serious results to the host.

Control of fleas consists essentially in ridding the animals of the parasites and their eradication in breeding places. Powders containing rotenone, pyrethrum, malathion, or methoxychlor may be used to control fleas on both cats and dogs. Dusts of DDT, lindane, and chlordane are also effective on dogs, but these compounds should not be applied to pups under two months old, or to cats. Because cats may ingest poisons in cleaning themselves, care must be exercised in selecting insecticides for use on them. Fleas on rodents may be eliminated by dusting their runways and between the walls of buildings with DDT, and then poisoning the rodents. Sprays or dusts of DDT, lin-

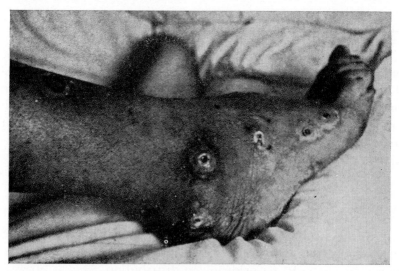

FIG. 282. Ulcers produced on foot of man by chigoe fleas (*Tunga penetrans*). (After Manson-Bahr, from British Museum of Natural History.)

dane, chlordane, malathion, or methoxychlor will control fleas on lawns, in barns or other animal quarters, and under houses. In the home, the pests may be controlled by sprays of DDT or methoxychlor. Before spraying, thoroughly clean the rooms, rugs, and upholstered furniture with a vacuum cleaner. Such repellents as diethyl-meta-toluamide and dimethyl phthalate will give protection against fleas. Some species have developed resistance to DDT and to certain other chlorinated hydrocarbon compounds. When resistance is encountered, malathion or methoxychlor should be used.

21

ORDER HYMENOPTERA[1]

SAWFLIES, ANTS, WASPS, BEES, AND OTHERS

The Hymenoptera are a large order of insects with more than 90,000 known species. This is thought to be the most beneficial order, inasmuch as it contains many parasites and predators of injurious insects, as well as the most important insect pollinators of plants —the bees. However, some destructive forms are found here, e.g., certain species of ants, sawflies, and the wheat strawworm. Within the order is exhibited a great diversity in size, form, and development.

Its members may be recognized by the following general characteristics:

1. **Wings, usually present, two pairs, membranous; hind pair smaller; venation specialized and more or less reduced.**
2. **Mouthparts for chewing, or for chewing and sucking.**
3. **Metamorphosis complete.**
4. **Abdomen of female usually provided with a saw, piercing organ, or sting.**

The ants, bees, and wasps are the best known members of the order. However, there is another group, composed of parasites, predators, sawflies, and others which, although less commonly known, is much larger. Instinctive behavior in its highest form is exhibited in members of this order, particularly among the social insects. These insects have been studied by naturalists since early times, and many books have been written about them, but still much about their way of life remains to be known.

[1] *Hymen,* membrane (or marriage); *pteron,* wing.

FIG. 283. The yellow bumble bee (*Bombus fervidus*). (Courtesy of C. O. Mohr.)

The Hymenoptera are placed at the top of the list of the orders of insects by most authorities. The unusually highly developed instinctive behavior of the higher forms of the order is the chief reason for placing them in this position. In morphological aspects the order cannot be so rated. Mouthparts of Lepidoptera, Diptera, and Siphonaptera are more diverse in form. Wing venation of Diptera, Coleoptera, and other orders exhibits greater modifications. In both morphology and habits dipterous larvae are more specialized. These and other reasons may justify placing the Hymenoptera in a lower position among the orders with a complete metamorphosis.

The meaning of the word Hymenoptera is generally accepted as "membrane wings" because of the nature of the wings. But the characteristic of membranous wings is not distinctive as it is shared by a number of other orders. Perhaps the interpretation "marriage on the wing" is more appropriate because certain common forms, such as honey bees and ants, have mating flights. Normally two pairs of wings are present, but some adults are wingless. The hind wings are smaller than the front wings. The front and hind wings are held together by small hooks, hamuli, on the front margin of the hind wings which fasten into a fold on the hind margin of the front wings. The front and hind wings are thus fitted together so securely on each side that they may be mistaken for a single wing by the novice. Wing venation is specialized and complicated. (See Fig. 284.)

All hymenopteron insects are provided with chewing mouthparts, but in the more specialized groups they are modified also for suck-

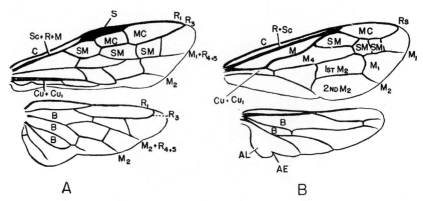

FIG. 284. Diagrammatic sketches of hymenopteron wings showing principal veins and cells. **A,** Front and hind wings of *Symphyta*. **B,** Front and hind wings of *Apocrita*. AE, axillary excision; AL, anal lobe; B, basal cell; C, costa; Cu, cubitus; M, media; MC, marginal cell; R, radius; S, stigma; Sc, subcosta; SM, submarginal cell.

ing or lapping. In the more generalized forms (e.g., sawflies) the mouthparts are quite similar to those of the Orthoptera, but the mouthparts of bees exhibit marked modifications. The honey bee, for example, has retained the labrum and mandibles as structures typical of chewing mouthparts while the maxillae and labium are modified into a suctorial or lapping organ. Between these extremes of mouthpart types intermediate forms are found.

The female adults of the order usually have a well developed ovipositor. This organ is variously modified for egg deposition or into a sting in the more highly developed forms. As the sting is a modified ovipositor it is quite obvious that the drone bee and other males of the Hymenoptera are harmless.

The Hymenoptera have a complete metamorphosis. The larvae have a distinct head, chewing mouthparts, and spiracles along the sides of the abdomen. In the suborder *Symphyta* the larvae are caterpillar-like in form and bear thoracic legs and also usually abdominal prolegs. In some forms, especially internal feeders, prolegs are absent. Larvae of the suborder *Apocrita* are grub-like or maggotlike and legless. Pupae are of the exarate type. Larvae of many species spin cocoons in which to pupate. Cocoons of some forms are composed of rather loose silk, somewhat like the cocoons of moths, and in others they are parchment-like in texture.

The order Hymenoptera is divided into two suborders, the *Symphyta* (*Chalastogastra*), sawflies and horntails; and the *Apocrita* (*Clistogastra*), wasps, bees, ichneumon flies, and others. In the suborder *Symphyta* the abdomen is broadly joined to the thorax, the trochanter has two segments, and there are at least three basal cells in the hind wing. Most members of the Symphyta are plant feeders. In the suborder *Apocrita* the first segment of the abdomen known as the propodeum is fused with the thorax and the second segment is conspicuously constricted into a slender petiole, producing the characteristic "wasp-waisted" appearance. The Apocrita are further characterized by having not more than two basal cells in the hind wing and with a one- or two-segmented trochanter.

KEY TO COMMON FAMILIES OF THE SUBORDER SYMPHYTA (CHALASTOGASTRA)

SAWFLIES AND HORNTAILS

1. Front tibia armed with only 1 apical spur   2
   Front tibia with 2 apical spurs   3
2. Last abdominal segment bears a dorsally located spear-like
      plate or spine; stout forms (Horntails)   **Siricidae**, p. 449
   Last abdominal segment bears no dorsally located spear-like
      plate or spine; slender forms (Stem Sawflies)   **Cephidae**, p. 449
3. Antenna clubbed; large and robust species (Cimbicid Saw-
      flies)   **Cimbicidae**, p. 447
   Antenna filiform, or of other types, not clubbed   4
4. Antenna with 13 or more segments; subcosta distinct (Web-
      spinning Sawflies)   **Pamphiliidae**, p. 448
   Antenna with 7 to 12 segments; subcosta absent or not well
      developed (Sawflies)   **Tenthredinidae**, p. 446

KEY TO COMMON FAMILIES OF THE SUBORDER APOCRITA (CLISTOGASTRA)

ICHNEUMON FLIES, BEES, WASPS

1. Petiole composed of 1 segment bearing a dorsal node, or 2
      segments with usually 1 or both with dorsal nodes or pro-
      jections, both winged and wingless forms present (Ants)
                                                    Formicidae, p. 465
   No nodes borne on petiole   2
2. Wings present   3
   Wings wanting   16
3. Either hind wing without closed cells or antenna with more
      than 13 joints; legs usually with 2 joints in trochanter;
      parasites   4
   Hind wing with closed cells; antenna with not more than 13
      joints, legs with 1 joint in trochanter   8

4. Body more or less compressed; flea-like; costal vein not de-
      veloped (Gall Wasps)   **Cynipidae,** p. 460
   Body not compressed flea-like   5
5. Front wing without costal cell (Fig. 284); antenna with 17
      or more joints, rarely with fewer joints; closed cells nearly
      always present in hind wing   6
   Front wing with costal cell; antenna with not more than 13
      segments   7
6. Front wing with vein M_2 wanting, causing confluence of
      cells M_1 and M_2; usually small insects (Braconids)
                                                             Braconidae, p. 452
   Front wing with vein M_2 present, separating cells M_1 and
      M_2; larger insects (Ichneumon Flies)   **Ichneumonidae,** p. 451
7. Abdomen with 3 visible segments, concave ventrally; me-
      dium in size (Cuckoo Wasps)   **Chrysididae,** p. 463
   Abdomen with more than 3 visible segments, cylindrical;
      small, usually less than 1/8 inch in length (Chalcids)
                                                             Chalcididae, p. 455

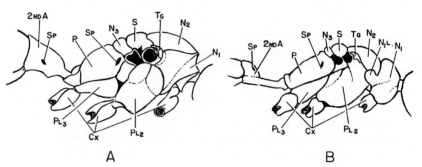

FIG. 285. Thorax with abdominal attachment of typical Hymenoptera, lateral view.
A, A paper wasp (*Vespidae*). **B,** A digger wasp (*Sphecidae*). 2nd A, second abdominal
segment; Cx, coxa; N_1, pronotum; N_2, mesonotum; N_3, metanotum; N_1L, pronotal lobe;
P, propodeum (first abdominal segment); PL, pleuron; S, scutellum; SP, spiracle;
TG, tegula.

8. Pronotum with each posterolateral corner not lobed (Fig.
      285) and touching the tegula   9
   Pronotum with each posterolateral corner in form of a
      rounded lobe and not touching the tegula   11
9. Front wing with cell M_4 longer than cell $Cu + Cu_1$; wings
      fold lengthwise (Typical Wasps)   **Vespidae,** p. 474
   Front wing with cell M_4 not as long as cell $Cu + Cu_1$; wings
      cannot fold lengthwise   10
10. Mesothoracic coxae not contiguous; hind wing always with
      anal lobe (Tiphids)   **Tiphiidae,** p. 464
    Mesothoracic coxae contiguous; hind wing with anal lobe
      often wanting; very hairy insects (Velvet Ants)   **Mutillidae,** p. 464

11. Hairs on dorsum of thorax simple; corbicula (pollen basket)
    absent on hind tibia (Mud Daubers)   **Sphecidae,** p. 478
    Hairs on dorsum of thorax branched or plumose; corbicula
    usually present on hind tibia of females   12
12. Hind tibia with apical spurs absent (Honey Bee)   **Apidae,** p. 487
    Hind tibia with apical spurs present   13
13. Front wing with the first submarginal cell (cell below the
    stigma) divided by a transverse line extending downward
    from the base of the stigma; hind wing with anal lobe ab-
    sent (Bumble Bees)   **Bombidae,** p. 486
    Front wing with the first marginal cell not divided by hair-
    like line or, if divided, hind wing with anal lobe   14
14. Front wing with 3 submarginal cells below the stigma
    (Andrenids)   **Andrenidae,** p. 482
    Front wing with 2 submarginal cells below the stigma   15
15. Female with no pollen-collecting brush on ventral side of
    abdomen; labrum large, free, and uncovered (Andrenids)
                                       Andrenidae, p. 482
    Female usually with a pollen-collecting brush on ventral
    side of abdomen; labrum not large and free, usually cov-
    ered by the clypeus (Leafcutting Bees)   **Megachilidae,** p. 484
16. Abdomen compressed flea-like (Gall Wasps)   **Cynipidae,** p. 460
    Abdomen not compressed flea-like, cylindrical or depressed   17
17. Pronotum not movable; very hairy insects (Velvet Ants)
                                       Mutillidae, p. 464
    Pronotum movable; less hairy insects   18
18. Antenna elbowed; posterolateral lobe of pronotum not
    touching the tegula (Chalcids)   **Chalcididae,** p. 455
    Antenna not elbowed; posterolateral lobe of pronotum
    touching tegula   19
19. Ovipositor exposed; sternites of second and third abdomi-
    nal segments membranous (Ichneumon Flies)
                                       Ichneumonidae, p. 451
    Ovipositor usually retracted; sternites of second and third
    abdominal segments sclerotized (Tiphids)   **Tiphiidae,** p. 464

Suborder SYMPHYTA (CHALASTOGASTRA)

Sawflies and Horntails

The more generalized members of the Hymenoptera belong in this suborder. The body build of the adults is less modified and the wing venation less reduced than with other members of the order. The mouthparts are for chewing. Antennae and eyes are well developed. The ovipositor of the females is well developed and more or less saw-like in form for the insertion of eggs in the tissues of the host plants. The larvae are phytophagous, with rare exceptions, and the majority are external feeders. Most of them are caterpillar-like and differ from lepidopterous larvae in having more than five pairs of prolegs, which do not bear crochets. Also, they usually have only one pair of ocelli while caterpillars have several pairs.

Most members of the suborder have only one generation each season and winter is passed either as larvae or pupae in protected places. Those forms that are external feeders usually hibernate in cocoons or within cells in the soil, while the internal feeders generally pass the winter in the feeding tunnels of the host plants.

Family *Tenthredinidae* (Sawflies)

This is a large family and most members of the *Symphyta* belong here. Adults are small to medium in size; the largest individuals are seldom more than 4/5 inch in length. Some are brightly colored and the sexes of the same species may be dimorphic in color. The larvae are mostly external feeders; a few are leaf miners or form galls. Space will permit only a brief discussion of a few of the most common species.

The Pear-Slug (*Caliroa cerasi*). The larvae feed on the leaves of pear, plum, and cherry, and occasionally other plants. Feeding is chiefly on the upper surface of the leaves and only the parenchymatous tissue is used as food. This produces a scorched appearance to the foliage, which drops prematurely. The larvae are slimy and slug-like in appearance and are about 1/2 inch long when fully grown. When mature they leave the trees and form cells in the ground for pupation. Probably two generations occur each season throughout most of the insect's range in the United States. The insect hibernates as prepupae in the soil. Sprays of lead arsenate readily control the pest.

The Imported Currantworm (*Nematus ribesii*). The larvae of this insect are pests of the currant and gooseberry. They are found wherever the currant grows and first appear on the plants early in the spring. The greenish, black-spotted larvae feed on the leaves, and heavily infested bushes may be stripped of their foliage. When mature, cocoons are formed by the larvae either beneath rubbish or slightly underneath the surface of the soil. The adults are about 1/3 inch long and black with yellow markings on the abdomen. There are two generations each season with a partial third in the South. The pest is easily controlled with insecticides. Before the formation of fruit, lead arsenate sprays may be employed. When fruit is present on the plants, applications of rotenone or malathion are recommended for use.

The Green Leaf Worm (*Isodyctium spp.*). These small green larvae are commonly observed during the spring on foliage of the pecan in Texas and Louisiana. The larvae are found chiefly on the underside of the leaves which they riddle with holes. When mature they enter the soil for pupation. There appears to be only one generation each season. The adults emerge in April, and eggs are inserted in tissues of the new growth. The adults are about ⅕ inch long and bee-like in appearance. Lead arsenate or DDT sprays provide effective control should control measures be justified.

The Larch Sawfly (*Pristiphora erichsonii*). This is an important pest of the larch in the northern part of the United States and Canada. The larvae often defoliate trees over large areas. The pest overwinters as larvae in brown cocoons found among fallen leaves and debris. Following pupation, adults emerge in late spring or summer. Eggs are deposited in slits made in the young shoots of the plant. The larvae feed first on the edges but later devour the entire leaves. There is one full generation with possibly a partial second each season. Timely applications of stomach poisons control the pest.

Other common species of sawflies are several species of rose slugs, the birch leaf miner (*Fenusca pusilla*), and the willow sawfly (*Pteronidea ventralis*).

Family *Cimbicidae* (Cimbicid Sawflies)

Adults of the Cimbicidae are large, stout, and bear clubbed antennae. The group is small in number of species. The most common member is the elm sawfly (*Cimbex americana*, Fig. 286). The adults are bluish-black and nearly one inch in length. The fully grown larvae are about 1½ inches long, yellowish-white or greenish-white with a black stripe down the back and with black spiracles. The larvae assume a spiral position when at rest. If disturbed a fluid may be ejected from glands located slightly above the spiracles. This insect has only one generation annually. Winter is passed

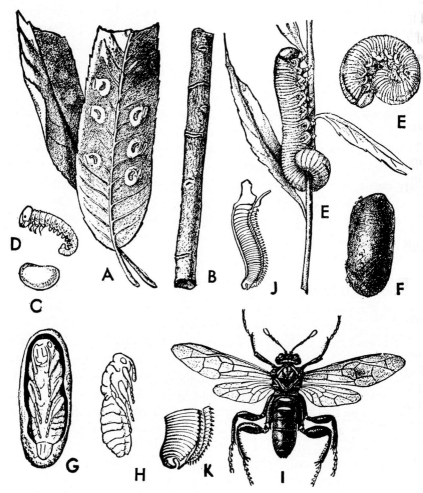

FIG. 286. The elm sawfly (*Cimbex americana*). **A,** Leaf with egg blisters. **B,** Twig with incisions made by adult. **C,** Egg. **D,** Young larva. **E,** Mature larvae. **F,** Cocoon. **G,** Cocoon cut open to show pupa. **H,** Side view of pupa. **I,** Adult. **J-K,** Saw of ovipositor. (From Agricultural Research Service, U.S.D.A.)

as mature larvae in cocoons found in the ground. The larvae feed on the foliage of elm, willow, and occasionally other trees.

Family *Pamphiliidae* (Web-Spinning Sawflies)

The adults are rather stout-bodied in appearance and about ½ inch in length. The family is small in species and the biologies of only a few are known. The plum web-spinning sawfly (*Neurotoma inconspicua*) appears to be the best known member of the group.

The larvae feed on the leaves of plums and cherries. They are gregarious and web the leaves together, among which they live. The mature larvae enter the soil in which cells are formed. Here they remain in the larval stage until the next spring when they pupate. Adults emerge the latter part of spring or early summer. Eggs are inserted in slits made in the leaf petioles or midribs of the leaves. Only one generation occurs each season. *Pamphilius persicum,* a leaf-rolling member of the family, feeds on the foliage of the peach.

Family *Siricidae* (Horntails)

This family of rather large insects is known to have only about fifteen species in North America. All the larvae are wood borers. Adults of both males and females are characterized by a horny spear-like plate borne on the dorsum of the last abdominal segment, and the females bear a long ovipositor.

The best known species is the pigeon tremex (*Tremex columba*). The adults (Fig. 287) are black and brown, and about 1½ inches in length. Elm, maple, apple, beech, and other trees are hosts. Eggs are laid in the wood and frequently the ovipositor becomes fastened and cannot be removed, and the trapped female dies. The larvae tunnel through the wood and as they grow, the tunnels become progressively larger. The fully grown larvae attain a length of about 1¼ inches. Pupation is in thin silken cocoons within

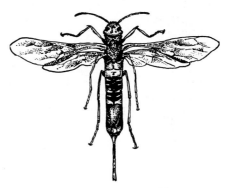

FIG. 287. Pigeon tremex (*Tremex columba*).

the tunnels. The insect seldom occurs in numbers large enough to cause appreciable damage.

Family *Cephidae* (Stem Sawflies)

The adults are slender and elongate with compressed bodies. The larvae are borers in the stems of grasses, shrubs, and other plants.

The Wheat-Stem Sawfly (*Cephus cinctus*). This is an insect (Fig. 288) of importance to wheat in the Plains states. A related species, the European wheat sawfly (*Cephus pygmaeus*), occurs in New York and Pennsylvania. Infested wheat fields will have fallen straws suggestive of injury by Hessian flies or joint worms. The adults are

black with yellow rings on the abdomen. The larvae are found in the frass-filled burrows within the straws. They are wrinkled, pale yellow, and about ⅓ to ½ inch in length. Native grasses, wheat, rye, barley, timothy, and other plants are attacked.

Mature larvae overwinter in the straws near the surface of the ground. Pupation occurs in the spring and adults emerge in early summer. Eggs are deposited within the stems. The larvae tunnel downward in the stems and reach the basal parts of the plants near the ground by late summer. A groove is then cut completely around the inside of the stem which causes breaking of the straws. A larval chamber is formed for hibernation in the base of the stem.

FIG. 288. The wheat-stem sawfly (*Cephus cinctus*). (From Agricultural Research Service, U.S.D.A.)

The most effective control measure is plowing infested stubble under deeply in the fall. Harvesting as early as possible reduces losses. Rotation with immune crops such as corn, alfalfa, and oats is helpful in reducing infestations.

The larvae of the currant-stem girdler (*Janus integer*) tunnel out the canes of the currant in feeding, and reach maturity in the fall. They hibernate within the burrows, enclosed in silken cocoons. The adults are shining black and about ½ inch in length. They emerge in the spring and the females lay their eggs in the canes. Following deposition of the egg, the female girdles the cane with the ovipositor above the puncture. This injury kills the tip of the cane, which checks growth and provides conditions more conducive for development of the larva.

Suborder APOCRITA (CLISTOGASTRA)

Ichneumon Flies and Wasps

Most members of the order Hymenoptera belong to this suborder. Its chief morphological characteristic is the constricted base of the abdomen. The thorax appears to consist of four segments. However, the fourth segment, known as the propodeum, is the first abdominal segment. So, the constricted abdominal segment, which would seem to be the first is really the second. The hind wings do not have more than two basal cells. Most of the larvae are grub-like or maggot-like in form, and legless. The form of the ovipositor varies, dependent upon the function. In some members, it is used for boring; in others, it is employed to place eggs within the bodies of other insects; and in some, as bees and wasps, it is modified into a stinging organ and connected with poison glands.

The Apocrita have a wide range of feeding habits. Many larvae are parasites of other insects and so they are extremely important in helping keep in check other harmful insects. Some larvae feed on plant materials. Food of the adults consists chiefly of nectar, pollen, sap, other plant materials, and, in case of certain parasites, body fluids of the hosts. The most important pollinators, the bees, are found in this suborder.

The taxonomy of the group is quite difficult. It is divided into a number of superfamilies, many families, and subfamilies. Only some of the more important families and their members can be discussed briefly here.

Family *Ichneumonidae* (Ichneumon Flies)

This is one of the largest families of insects and its members are very widely distributed. There are probably more than 6,000 species in North America. Much variation is found in size, form, and markings of the adults. Most are somewhat wasp-like in appearance and many of the females have a very long ovipositor, often longer than the body. The adults are commonly observed around flowers of the composite group.

All species are parasites in the larval stage. Most groups of insects are parasitized by some member of this family, and spiders are attacked by certain forms.

FIG. 289. *Megarhyssa macrurus*, the long-tailed thalessa, a parasite of horntail larvae. (From Agricultural Research Service, U.S.D.A.)

Megarhyssa macrurus (Fig. 289) is the largest and probably most interesting of the ichneumons. The larvae are parasites of the larvae of horntails. The female locates in some way a tree infested with horntails and then selects a spot which is judged to be over a tunnel of a horntail larva. She then makes a derrick of her body and drills a hole into the tree with her long ovipositor. When the tunnel is reached, an egg is deposited and the ovipositor is withdrawn. Sometimes the ovipositor becomes wedged and cannot be withdrawn and the trapped insect dies. Upon hatching from the egg, the larva apparently searches out the borer and then feeds upon it. The mature larva pupates within the burrow of the horntail and the adult emerges the next season.

Pimpla conquisitor is an important parasite of a number of lepidopterous pupae. Eggs are deposited on the larvae in the prepupal stage and the small larvae feed on the pupae. This insect is one of the most important parasites of the cotton leafworm (*Alabama argillacea*), and it is also an important natural enemy of the eastern tent caterpillar (*Malacosoma americanum*) as well as a number of other Lepidoptera. The larvae hibernate within the cocoons of some of the hosts. Several generations are thought to be completed each season. The genera *Glypta, Campoplex, Phobocampe,* and others too numerous to mention contain important parasites.

Family *Braconidae* (Braconids)

The Braconidae are another large family of parasitic insects. More than two thousand species are known from North America alone. They parasitize a wide range of insects, but chiefly aphids, and the larvae of Lepidoptera, Coleoptera, and some Diptera. The adults resemble the Ichneumonidae. The species tend to be somewhat smaller and stouter-bodied than the ichneumon flies and the wing venation of many is reduced.

Members of this family have much in common with the ichneumons in their habits; however the mode of pupation often differs. Many pupate in cocoons on the outside of the body of the host and others apart from the host with the small cocoons frequently in a mass. Polyembryony (the production of several embryos from one egg) is known to occur in several species.

The genus *Apanteles* is perhaps the most beneficial of the braconids. There are probably 200 species in North America and all are parasites of caterpillars, some of which are of much economic importance.

Apanteles glomeratus (Fig. 290) is one of the best known and most important members of the genus. It is a parasite of the imported cabbageworm (*Pieris rapae*), the cabbage looper (*Trichoplusia ni*) and caterpillars of other butterflies and moths. Thirty to 40 eggs are deposited within the body of each caterpillar. The eggs hatch in three or four days and the larvae feed on the fat and lymph of the host until mature, some 8 to 12 days later. Then the larvae

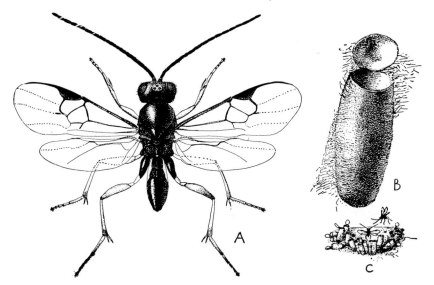

FIG. 290. A braconid parasite (*Apanteles glomeratus*) of the imported cabbageworm and other caterpillars. **A,** Adult. **B,** Empty cocoon. **C,** Adults emerging from cocoons (natural size). **A** and **B** greatly enlarged. (From Agricultural Research Service, U.S.D.A.)

leave the body of the host and spin their small, white silken cocoons near the host. The adults emerge five to ten days following pupation. This insect is of European origin and was introduced into the United States in 1883.

Apanteles congregatus is a common parasite of the larvae of sphinx moths. The presence of the small white cocoons (often mistaken for eggs) on the backs of tobacco and tomato hornworms is frequently observed.

Macrocentrus ancylivorus is an important parasite of the oriental fruit moth (*Grapholitha molesta*) and the strawberry leaf roller (*Ancylis comptana*). This parasite has provided effective control of the oriental fruit moth in some sections. Eggs are laid within the host caterpillar. The length of a life cycle is 25 to 30 days. Three generations develop annually on the East Coast. Winter is passed as larvae within the bodies of the hibernating hosts.

Microbracon mellitor parasitizes the pink bollworm (*Pectinophora gossypiella*) and other caterpillars. Before eggs are deposited, the host larva is stung and paralyzed. Eggs are deposited either on or near the host. The parasitic larva feeds only on the surface of the body of the caterpillar, sucking the body fluids from lacerations made by the mandibles. A generation of this parasite may be completed in 15 to 20 days with favorable conditions.

Meteorus laphygma is quite important as a parasite of the fall armyworm (*Laphygma frugiperda*) and other cutworms in the Southwest. The eggs are inserted in the bodies of second and third instar caterpillars. Each female parasite produces about 100 eggs. Upon reaching maturity, the larvae leave the host and pupate in brown cocoons attached to the host plant of the caterpillar or some nearby object. When conditions are most favorable, a generation may be completed in 12 days. There may be as many as 18 generations annually in warm climates.

Members of the subfamily *Aphidiinae* parasitize only aphids. These tiny and delicate parasites are among their most important natural enemies. The most important genera of the group are *Aphidius, Lysiphlebus,* and *Praon.* Eggs are deposited within the bodies of the aphids, and the developing parasites devour the internal organs of the hosts. Prior to pupation, a hole is cut through the ventral side of the host, which is then glued to the plant so it will not drop to the ground. A cocoon is then spun in the abdomen of the aphids with the exception of members of the genus *Praon* which spin their cocoons underneath the body of the dead hosts.

FIG. 291. An important aphid parasite (*Lysiphlebus testaceipes*) depositing an egg in its host. (From Agricultural Research Service, U.S.D.A.)

The adults cut circular holes through which they emerge. The dead parasitized aphids are brownish and inflated in appearance. *Lysiphlebus testaceipes* (Fig. 291) is the most common of this group of parasites. Its life cycle is short, varying from one to three weeks, dependent upon temperature.

Family *Chalcididae* (Chalcid Flies)

This extremely large family of insects is generally considered a superfamily and subdivided into a number of families. Most of its members are small; however some are as large as bees. The general color is metallic blue or green. Only one vein is usually present in the wings. The antennae are elbowed and contain not more than 13 segments.

Nearly all of the chalcid flies are parasites and attack mostly the egg and the larval stages of their hosts. They parasitize chiefly members of the Homoptera, Coleoptera, Lepidoptera, and Diptera. A number of species has been introduced into this country to aid in the control of certain pests. A few species of the family are phytophagous and are pests, e.g., the wheat strawworm (*Harmolita grandis*) and the wheat joint-worm (*Harmolita tritici*). However, some forms, such as the fig wasps (*Blastophaga*), although phytophagous, are beneficial as pollinators. Space will permit the brief discussion of only a few members of this large and important family of insects.

Trichogramma evanescens is a common egg parasite (Fig. 292) which has been used quite extensively in this country in biological control. The insect parasitizes the eggs of Lepidoptera chiefly, and those of Hymenoptera, Neuroptera, Diptera, and Coleoptera to a lesser extent. The eggs of the parasite are inserted through the chorion of the host eggs. Each female deposits 35 to 40 eggs. The length of a life cycle of the insect is dependent chiefly on temperature. In summer weather, a life cycle may be completed in nine to 16 days. Hibernation is as immature larvae within the host eggs. These tiny and frail insects are greatly influenced by weather conditions which determine their abundance. Some beneficial results have been reported in their use, but as a whole, their use in biological control has not been too encouraging.

FIG. 292. An egg parasite (*Trichogramma evanescens*) depositing its egg within the egg of a moth. Greatly magnified. (From Agricultural Research Service, U.S.D.A.)

Species of the genus *Euplectrus* are gregarious and feed as ectoparasites on caterpillars. *E. platyphenae* feeds on larvae of cutworms. The females deposit their eggs on the bodies of the hosts, usually in clusters of 20 to 30. Upon hatching, the larvae attach themselves in a cluster to the body of the host. Here they remain until they are ready to pupate. Pupation is within cocoons underneath the dead caterpillar. The life cycle is short. It is said a life cycle of this insect may be completed in as little as seven days during warm weather. As many as 18 to 20 generations may be completed during one season in warm climates. *E. comstocki* (Fig. 293) is a related species which feeds in clusters on the cotton leafworm (*Alabama argillacea*), the brown cotton leafworm (*Acontia dacia*), the fall armyworm (*Laphygma frugiperda*), and other caterpillars.

Coccophagus gurneyi is a native of Australia which was introduced into this country to aid in the control of the citrophilus mealy bug (*Pseudococcus gahani*), a citrus pest of California. Each female lays 125 or more eggs. A life cycle is completed in about four weeks during warm weather.

Aphelinus mali is a parasite of the woolly apple aphid (*Erisoma lanigerum*). Eggs are deposited within the abdomen of the host. One or more eggs may be deposited in the abdomen of each aphid, but only one parasite ever develops. Each female parasite lays about

FIG. 293. *Euplectrus comstocki,* an ectoparasite, feeding on the brown cotton leafworm (*Acontia dacia*). (From Department of Entomology, A & M College of Texas.)

100 eggs. The dead aphids appear black and swollen, and the body wall hardens. Pupation is within the abdomen of the host. The adult parasite emerges through an opening it makes in the body wall, usually in the dorso-caudal region of the abdomen. A generation is normally completed in about one month.

Eretmocerus serius is an important parasite of the citrus blackfly (*Aleurocanthus woglumi*). It has proved to be very effective in controlling this important pest in those regions where climatic conditions are favorable for its development. Each female lays about 200 eggs and a generation is completed in about four weeks. The parasite produces two generations while its host is producing one.

Metaphycus lounsburyi was introduced from Africa to aid in the control of the black scale (*Saissetia oleae*). The parasite reproduces both sexually and asexually. The parthenogenetic offspring are females, and approximately ⅕ of the progeny of fertilized females are males. The length of a life cycle depends upon weather conditions and may vary from one to three months.

The Fig Wasp (*Blastophaga psenes*). The production of the Smyrna fig is dependent upon the tiny fig wasp (Fig. 294). Without the pollination services of this insect no fruit would be matured. The common fig plants are dioecious. The male plant is known as the caprifig and produces inedible fruit. The female plant is represented by many commercial varieties including the Smyrna fig. Only this variety requires pollination to mature its fruit. The fruit of the fig plant is a hollow receptacle and flowers are borne on its

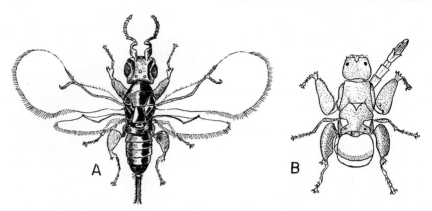

FIG. 294. The fig wasp (*Blastophaga psenes*). **A,** Female. **B,** Male. (From Agricultural Research Service, U.S.D.A.)

inner surface. On the free end of the fruit is a tiny entrance to the receptacle, known as the eye.

The fig wasp develops in galls within the receptacle of the caprifig fruit which produces an abundance of pollen. The bodies of the winged females become covered with this pollen as they crawl over the stamens in leaving the fruit by way of the eye. They enter other fruit in seeking places for oviposition, including the fruit of the Smyrna fig plant. The walls of the receptacle of the latter are not suitable for oviposition, but pollination is effected as the insects crawl over the pistillate flowers. The Smyrna fig develops only the pistillate flowers.

For centuries it has been known by natives of Asia Minor that the suspension of caprifig fruit in the Smyrna fig trees in the spring was essential in the production of a crop, although they did not understand the reasons why. The practice of distribution of caprifigs among the branches of the Smyrna fig trees is known as caprification. The establishment of this insect in the United States was essential for the production of this fruit here. The growing of the caprifig trees is necessary to maintain a supply of the tiny wasps. In commercial production, the caprifig fruit containing mature fig wasps is removed at the proper time and suspended by various methods among the branches of the Smyrna fig plants.

The Wheat Straw-Worm (*Harmolita grandis*).   There are two generations annually of this wheat pest, and each generation produces a different type of injury. Larvae of the first generation cause a stunted appearance of the plants in early spring and usually the crown is destroyed. The infested plants later die or are so injured that they produce no grain. The second generation causes stunting and weakening of the straw which reduces the yield of wheat.

This widely distributed insect is chiefly a pest in the wheat-growing sections west of the Mississippi River. Winter is passed in the straw or stubble as pupae. The adults emerge in the early spring. They are about $1/6$ inch in length, wingless, brownish, and ant-like in appearance. Eggs are deposited within the stems near the base of the small wheat plants. The larvae tunnel into the stems and eat out the developing heads. Pupation is within the plants and the adults of this generation emerge in late spring. These adults are larger, and most of them have wings. At the time of their emergence the wheat is usually heading.

Eggs for this generation are inserted in the higher joints near the wheat head. The larvae remain in the straw or stubble through the summer and they pupate in midautumn.

As the adults either are wingless or not strong fliers, crop rotation is the most satisfactory method of control. Destruction of volunteer wheat is advised. Disposal of straw aids in reducing the population of the pest.

The Wheat Jointworm (*Harmolita tritici*). This insect (Fig. 295) is probably second in importance to the Hessian fly as a wheat pest in wheat-growing sections east of the Mississippi River. Infested fields show broken or bent straws, suggestive of the injury caused by the Hessian fly. The straws exhibit gall-like swellings in which are found the small yellowish larvae.

Winter is passed as larvae or pupae in the galls within the straws. The small, black adults emerge in the spring, and the females deposit their eggs within the straws above the joints. Irritation produced by the larvae causes the straws to thicken and produces the swellings. Larval development is completed as the wheat is maturing; however, the insect remains in this stage until fall when most of the individuals transform into pupae. Only one generation is produced annually.

Plowing under the wheat stubble deeply or burning it is recommended. Rotation of crops also is of some aid in reducing infestations.

The Clover Seed Chalcid (*Bruchophagus gibbus*). This pest is of importance in the production of alfalfa and clover seeds. The small

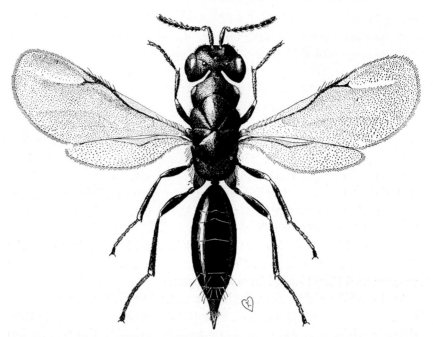

FIG. 295. Adult of the wheat jointworm (*Harmolita tritici*). (From Agricultural Research Service, U.S.D.A.)

larvae feed within the individual seeds, destroying their contents. Winter is passed, usually as larvae, within the seeds which are scattered on the ground. The tiny adults emerge in early summer and eggs are inserted within the soft immature seeds. The larval period is fairly short, being about two weeks in duration. Two or three overlapping generations may develop each season.

This is a difficult insect to control. At the present time, chief dependence for control is on natural enemies. Destruction of chaff and screenings eliminates many immature forms. In some years it is advisable to use the first crop of clover instead of the second for seed as the yield will be greater. When there are evidences of a heavy infestation, cutting and removing the hay before the seed mature is advised.

Family *Cynipidae* (Gall Wasps)

Insects of this family are small, dark colored, and the abdomen is compressed. Most members are gall-makers, but some are parasites or inquilines. The inquilines live within the galls made by other species and the parasites feed on both gall makers and inquilines. Although most species of this family are always associated with galls, it must be remembered that other arthropods produce galls also, e.g., plant lice, mites, gall midges, flies, moths, and beetles. Each species of gall wasps infests a special part of its host and produces a characteristic gall (Fig. 296). The galls are so definite in form that the species may be identified by them.

Eggs are inserted within the tissues of the growing plants where the maggot-like larvae develop. Pupation occurs within the larval cells. Scientists have long speculated on the phenomenon of gall formation and it is still far from being fully understood. The galls appear to be produced in some way by the reactions of the plant tissues to the stimulus caused by the larvae.

The biologies of gall wasps are often quite involved. Alternation of physiologically and morphologically different generations is found in many species. When alternation of generations occurs, the first generation consists of agamic females which produce a gall of one type, and the second is a sexual generation which makes another type of gall. Furthermore, the individuals

FIG. 296. A wool-bearing gall on leaves of live oak produced by a gall wasp (*Andricus lanigerus*). (From Texas Agricultural Experiment Station.)

of the two generations have been found to be so unlike morphologically that they were thought to be different species until life history studies showed them to be the same. Both sexual and asexual reproduction in the same species may occur at the same time. In many species males are not known to occur, and all generations are similar.

Gall wasps are of little economic importance. A few of the galls have a slight commercial value in the manufacture of permanent inks, and as a source of dye and tannic acid. Only a small number of species inflict appreciable damage to plants. Most galls are found on oaks (*Quercus*); however, many other kinds of plants also serve as hosts.

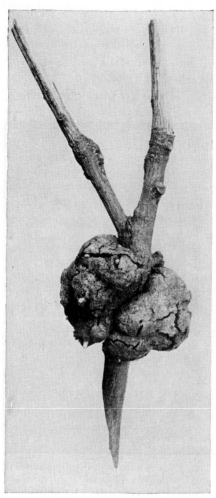

FIG. 297. A stem gall (related to the gouty oak gall) on oak caused by a gall wasp (From Texas Agricultural Experiment Station.)

A huge number of galls of varied forms and sizes are known, but none are more interesting than the "oak apples." They are formed by the deformation of the leaves caused by the developing larvae. The large oak apple formed by *Amphibolips confluens* is one of the most common forms. It ranges in size from one to two inches in diameter, and its interior consists of a spongy mass which contains a larval cell. The galls appear on leaves of red, scarlet and black oaks in early spring. Some of the galls produce both males and females which emerge in early summer; others produce females in the fall.

The empty oak gall is produced by *Amphibolips inanis*. This gall is about one inch in diameter, and it is empty except for filaments which hold the larval cell in position.

The gouty oak gall is one of the better known of the stem galls. It is produced by *Callirhytis punctata*. Twigs and small limbs of red oak, water oak, and black oak are infested. The gall consists of rough woody swellings ½ to 1½ inches in diameter (Fig. 297). The adult gall wasps emerge in the spring and eggs are laid in young buds. Alternation of generations is said to occur in this species. The galls cause some damage to shade trees. Cutting out the newly formed galls is the only practical control measure that can be suggested.

Space does not permit the mention of more members of this large family of insects. It is hoped that the brief discussion of the few forms given here will provide some concept of the way of life of this remarkable family of insects.

Family *Chrysididae* (Cuckoo Wasps)

The cuckoo wasps can be distinguished from other hymenopterous insects by the three- or four-segmented abdomen which is strongly concave below so that it can be folded underneath the thorax. This characteristic enables the insect to roll into a ball for protection when attacked by its enemies. Members of the family are seldom more than ½ inch in length and their color is usually metallic green or blue.

These insects are so named because they are parasitic in the nests of solitary bees and wasps. The female finds a solitary bee or wasp in the process of building its nest. While the owner is away she slips in and deposits an egg. Later the egg hatches and the larva either devours the rightful occupant of the nest or starves it by eating the stored food. A number of species belong in this family; however, their biologies are little understood.

Family *Pompilidae* (Spider Wasps)

These insects provision their nests with spiders and this practice has suggested the common name. As other wasps have the same habits the name is not quite distinctive. Members of this family have slender bodies and long spiny legs. Most are medium in size; however some are quite large. In fact, the largest members of the order belong here.

Most representatives of the family nest in the ground. The wasp seeks out a spider, paralyzes it with the sting, and then digs a burrow. The paralyzed spider is then dragged into the cell prepared at the end of the burrow. Following the laying of an egg on the spider, the passageway is filled with soil. The egg hatches and the larva feeds upon its helpless host. As biologies of the native species have not been carefully studied, they are not very well known.

Perhaps the best known and most interesting members of the family are the tarantula hawks (*Pepsis* spp., Fig. 298) which are found in the Southwest. They provision their nests with tarantulas and trap-door spiders. These giants of the family have steel-blue bodies, orange colored wings, and bear a vicious appearing sting. They are commonly observed in flight, slowly circling near the

FIG. 298. A tarantula hawk (*Pepsis*). (From Department of Entomology, A & M College of Texas.)

ground in search of their prey. Many pitched battles have been fought between these insects and tarantulas, and the aggressors have not always been the victors.

Family *Tiphiidae* (Tiphiids)

This family is closely related to the velvet ants, *Mutillidae*. Most species are average in size, black, somewhat hairy, and have short legs. All known members are parasites of bees; wasps; tiger beetles; and, particularly, larvae of white grubs (*Scarabaeidae*). Those that are parasites of the latter group are very beneficial. One species of this group, *Tiphia popilliavora* (Fig. 299), was imported to this country to help control the Japanese beetle (*Popillia japonica*). The female locates the grub in the soil and burrows to its cell. She paralyzes the prey with her sting and then places an egg on the side of the abdomen between the fifth and sixth segments. The larva which hatches from the egg first feeds as an ectoparasite by puncturing the body wall and sucking out the body fluids. In the last larval stage the entire body contents of the host are devoured and pupation is within the cell of the host. In the North only one generation is completed each year and hibernation is within the cocoon. There may be a succession of generations in warmer climates except when development is halted by dry weather.

Family *Mutillidae* (Velvet Ants)

This common name has been applied to these insects because of their velvety appearance and their resemblance to ants (Fig. 300).

FIG. 299. Larva of *Tiphia popilliavora* feeding on grub of Japanese beetle. (From Agricultural Research Service, U.S.D.A.)

Most species are black and strikingly ringed or marked with red, yellow, or orange. The females are wingless; they are capable of inflicting painful stings. The males usually possess wings and are generally larger than the females. This family consists of many species, most of which are found in the South and West.

Information on the biology of these insects is rather meager. So far as is known, all are ectoparasites in the larval stage of prepupae and pupae of wasps and bees mostly, and

FIG. 300. A velvet ant (*Dasymutilla klugii*).

flies and beetles to some extent. It is said the eggs are laid on the hosts. The eggs hatch and the larvae soon devour the host insect and then spin cocoons, at least in some species, within those of the hosts.

Family *Formicidae* (Ants)

Because of their wide distribution and common occurrence, ants are the most familiar of all insects with the possible exception of the ubiquitous house fly. Ants are recognized by the presence of one or two nodes between the propodeum and the gaster (swollen part of the abdomen), elbowed antennae, and the absence of wings except in the sexually mature forms.

Ants have been observed since ancient times, and many references

FIG. 301. Winged female of the black carpenter ant (*Camponotus herculeanus pennsylvanicus*). (From Agricultural Research Service, U.S.D.A.)

to them are found in literature. They have been seriously studied by biologists, who have written a number of books about them. Still, our information is quite incomplete, and myrmecology remains a most fertile field of investigation.

No solitary species of ants are known; all are social insects. A colony consists of three castes; workers, males, and females (queens). The workers are modified females. Following the mating flight, the males die and the wings of the young queens are shed. The worker caste is wanting only in certain species that are parasites in the nests of other ants.

Polymorphic forms may exist in each of the three castes. Some males are much larger than others, and some have worker-like characteristics. A somewhat similar series of forms may be found among the queens. Still more variations occur among the workers. Two distinct sizes of workers are commonly found in the colonies of many species, the larger forms designated as majors and the smaller individuals known as minors. A so-called soldier caste with very large heads and mandibles is frequently observed.

Great differences occur in the size of colonies of ants. In some of the more primitive species the number of individuals is quite small, while in the more specialized species there may be tens of thousands of individuals with a marked division of labor among them. Considerable differences are found in nesting habits. The more common species make their nests in the ground. The number of nests of all species that may be found in the ground within a designated area is astonishingly large, and ants have some value in the improvement of the texture of the soil, as do earthworms. Colonies of other species are located in such places as under stones, in stumps, timbers of buildings, and stems of plants. A typical nest consists of a series of chambers of various forms connected by tunnels. Special cells, such as those of the wasps and bees, are not provided for the brood. The brood is kept in the chambers and may be moved from one to the other to obtain more favorable temperature and humidity conditions.

Food habits of ants differ very much. Some are carnivorous and feed on both dead and live insects, as well as other small animal life. Some species are important as predators of a number of insect pests. Others feed on plant products—seeds, bark, and bulbs. Many members of the family prefer as food sweet fluids—sap; nectar; and honeydew excreted chiefly by certain homopterous insects, mostly aphids. In some cases ants protect aphids for the honeydew they excrete. Species of the tribe Attii grow fungi on chewed-up leaves, which is their only food. Workers feed the larvae, and they also lick them to obtain excreted exudates for themselves. This exchange of food materials between adults and immature insects is known as trophallaxis.

Swarms of ants are commonly observed at certain seasons. The individuals in the swarms are recently matured winged males and females. They emerge as if by signal from a number of colonies— probably from all colonies of that particular species in the immediate locality in which the males and females developed. A probable benefit in mass flights is an increase in the chances of the females mating with males of other colonies, and thus prevent too much inbreeding. The factors determining the mass flights are not known.

Mating occurs in the air. After the mating flight the males soon die and the females proceed to establish new colonies. Some may be captured by workers of their kind and taken into established colonies; others may find their way into colonies without aid. In the usual procedure the wings of the young queen are broken off, and she makes a small cavity in the soil, underneath a stone or bark. The cavity is closed and she remains isolated here for a long period of time, probably months in some cases, while the eggs in her ovaries mature. Eggs are laid and the larvae hatching from them are fed by the young queen with food material secreted in the saliva until they are mature. The queen gathers no food, and the material which sustains her and the larvae is derived from body fat and dissolved wing muscles. The adults of the first brood are workers; they are quite small because of the limited food supply during their developmental period. They open the chamber and go forth in search of food. The care of the colony is then completely taken over by them. The adults subsequently produced are larger than those of the first brood, for they were more adequately fed in the larval stage. As the colony grows, the nest is enlarged by the addition of more chambers. After the colony becomes well established and populous, probably several years later, winged males and females are produced which again go forth on mass mating flights and establish new colonies.

Only a few of the thousands of young queens that attempt to establish new colonies succeed. Birds and predaceous insects destroy many. Adverse weather conditions cause many fatalities. Many starve because the individual female does not have sufficient food reserves. Ants are among the most successful of all insects in nature. This rigorous process of natural selection probably has materially aided in maintaining this position.

The establishment of new colonies is usually by the method described above. However, some young queens do not have the ability to establish colonies and must be adopted by workers of their own species; sometimes they are accepted by colonies of a different species. The adoption of a young female by another species helps explain the mixed colonies which at times are observed. In certain slave-making species a young queen secures adoption in a colony of aliens. She then proceeds to kill the queen of the colony and takes over her duties.

Ants are long-lived insects. The queens, in particular, live for a long time. One queen was observed to live to the ripe old age of 15 years. No other insect is known to live nearly so long in the adult stage. Their colonies may exist for many years, even as long as a generation of man.

The Carpenter Ants (*Camponotus* spp.).   These ants have attracted attention particularly because of their large size and their making nesting tunnels in timbers. Occasionally they become pests on lawns and in homes. The common name has been applied to them because of the habit of constructing nests in rotten or decaying wood. They may be predaceous but more often they are found feeding on dead insects. Sweets are also favorite foods, and aphids and related insects are attended for their honeydew.

The black carpenter ant (*Camponotus herculeanus*) and its varieties (Fig. 301) are widely distributed throughout the country. They are brownish and blackish and quite large. Their colonies are most frequently found in stumps, logs, tree trunks, telephone poles, and timbers of buildings. Some damage to telephone poles and timbers of old buildings is attributed to these ants.

Camponotus caryae and its varieties are widely distributed and occasionally become household pests. These ants are blackish and brownish with color variations between the varieties. The *discolor* variety appears to be the most common in the South. Its gaster (abdomen) is black, and the head and thorax a brownish-red.

Thallium sulphate baits, and sprays of chlordane or dieldrin are recommended in the control of carpenter ants. If the nests can be located, the application of chlordane dust in the entrances is suggested. These compounds are dangerous poisons and must be used with caution, especially thallium sulphate.

The Pharaoh Ant (*Monomorium pharaonis*). This species is probably the best known of the house ants. Color of this ant varies from yellow to red and it is $\frac{1}{15}$ to $\frac{1}{12}$ inch in length. The species may be differentiated from the thief ant (*Solenopsis molesta*), a closely related species, by having three segments in the antennal club while the latter species has two. The insect feeds on almost everything in the house, such as sweets, proteins, fats, dead insects, and bath sponges. Fats are apparently preferred as food. The ant is reported to be predaceous, attacking bed bugs, immature stages of the boll weevil, and other insects.

Nests may be found almost everywhere. Favorite nesting places are behind baseboards, between floors, in furniture or small boxes, and outdoors in trash or under stones. Colonies are occasionally found in linen and clothing.

This insect is difficult to control. Baits containing thallium sulphate are recommended. Applications of chlordane and dieldrin afford relief from the ants, but repeated applications will need be made to keep them in check.

The Thief Ant (*Solenopsis molesta*). The thief ant is very small; it is only $\frac{1}{20}$ to $\frac{1}{15}$ inch in length. The insect is so small that its presence may be overlooked by the housewife. The color is yellow and the antennal club bears two segments. This is one of the more important house ants. Greasy materials are preferred as food. It is most frequently found around kitchen sinks and cupboards. Nests may be located in cracks and crevices in the homes, but they are usually found outdoors in soil or rotten wood. They are often made near the nests of larger species which the insects enter through tunnels too small for the larger forms. Here they prey upon the larvae and pupae of the host ants. Seed-corn is frequently damaged by this insect. Its presence is indicated by starch grains scattered through the soil near hollowed-out kernels. The same household control measures are suggested as for the Pharaoh ant; however, control is difficult.

The Argentine Ant (*Iridomyrmex humilis*). Wherever this ant (Fig. 302) is found it is the most annoying household pest. The insect is now found in the southern states and California. It is also known in a number of foreign countries. Whenever the pest becomes established in a neighborhood it drives out other species of ants. It infests homes and business places, and feeds on almost all kinds of food materials. Citrus and other fruits suffer injury through

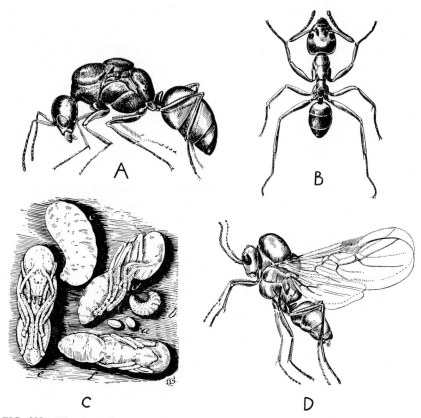

FIG. 302. The Argentine ant (*Iridomyrmex humilis*). **A**, Wingless female. **B**, Worker. **C**, Developmental stages: *a*, eggs; *b*, young larva; *c*, mature larvae; *d*, pupa (lateral view); *e*, pupa (ventral view); *f*, pupa (dorsal view). **D**, Winged male. All considerably magnified. (From Agricultural Research Service, U.S.D.A.)

attacks on the blossoms, and, indirectly, by the ants transporting and protecting aphids, mealybugs, and certain scale insects. Workers are about $\frac{1}{12}$ to $\frac{1}{8}$ inch in length and brown with lighter colored appendages. The petiole has one segment and the inner margins of the mandibles bear about 12 denticles. Nests are established in almost any dark, moist place in lawns, gardens, or orchards. During cold weather the small colonies combine and form large central nests in piles of manure or decaying vegetation.

The best results in control and eradication are obtained through community-wide campaigns. Syrup baits containing either sodium arsenite or thallium sulphate when properly distributed have proved to be efficient in combating the pest. The use of sprays of chlordane and dieldrin within the home are recommended. When nests are located they should be destroyed by treating thoroughly with chlordane sprays prepared with the wettable powders or emulsions. General infestations in gardens, yards, or other outdoor places may be treated with sprays containing suspensions of wettable chlordane powder.

The Southern Fire Ant (*Solenopsis xyloni*). This native species is common in the Gulf states. The workers are larger than those of the Argentine ant, yellowish-red with the smaller individuals much darker colored. This ant is capable of inflicting severe stings. Young animals are often attacked and killed in their nests. The species is omnivorous in its food habits with some preference shown for protein foods. Nests are generally found in open spaces where loose mounds or numbers of craters are formed. A related species (*Solenopsis geminata*) is found chiefly along the coast from Texas to South Carolina. Chlordane and dieldrin sprays and dusts are recommended in the control of these ants.

The Slave-Making Ant (*Formica sanguinea*). This unusual ant is widespread in both Europe and North America. In this country it is found chiefly in Canada and the northern part of the United States. Nests are found in the soil, stumps, or under logs or stones. The workers raid the nests of other species, e.g., *F. fusca;* and carry those pupae that are not devoured to their own colonies. Here the pupae develop into adults and become slaves, so the colony becomes a mixture of the two species.

Formica sanguinea may exist without slaves. However, other species, such as the shining amazon (*Polyergus lucidus*), cannot carry on the normal functions of a colony without slaves to do the work. The mandibles of this species are fitted only for fighting and are not suitable for digging, collecting food, and rearing brood. The amazon queen establishes a new colony by invading a weak colony of *Formica fusca* and killing its queen. In due time, an amazon colony is established. When more slaves are needed, colonies of *F. fusca* are raided, and the pupae are carried off.

The Red Harvester Ant (*Pogonomyrmex barbatus*, Fig. 303). The barren, circular areas marking the locations of colonies of the red harvester ant are familiar sights in pastures, fields, parks, and wastelands of the Southwest. The diameter of the area the ants keep devoid of vegetation may vary from one to several yards. The height of the mound usually is only a few inches but it may be as much as a foot. Trails lead from the nest to the foraging grounds. The nests may persist for a number of years. We once observed a colony which was thought to be more than 40 years of age. Food consists of seeds of many kinds which are stored within chambers of the nests. Sprouted seed are not used as food and are discarded.

The workers (Fig. 303) are reddish-brown and are 1/4 to 1/2 inch in length. They have a vicious sting which is to be feared. The presence of nests near homes and on the grounds of parks, schools,

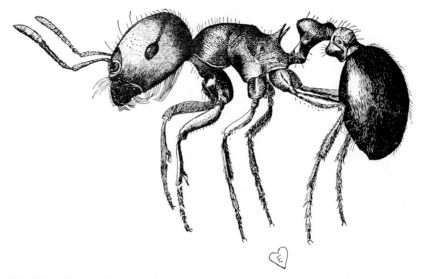

FIG. 303. Worker of the red harvester ant (*Pogonomyrmex barbatus*). (From Agricultural Research Service, U.S.D.A.)

and other public places is a considerable nuisance. Some loss is caused through the collection and storage of seed within the colonies, particularly alfalfa seed. However, the most important loss is the destruction of vegetation around the nests. Frequently a number of colonies may be found in a designated area of pasture and farm land. As each nest represents the destruction of several square yards of grass or field crops, the aggregate loss is appreciable.

The red harvester ant is difficult to control. The use of one of several insecticides provides temporary control; but after a period of time, in some cases months later, ants may reappear in a number of the treated colonies. And, again, new colonies are being established each year. However, annual treatment of all nests in a designated area greatly decreases the number and prevents the establishment of all but small colonies. Early season treatments before much, if any, brood has been raised enhances the chances of destruction of the colony. Dieldrin and chlordane dusts produce the most satisfactory control. The 2 percent dieldrin dust or the 5 percent chlordane dust is applied in a circle as a continuous band about six inches wide two or three feet from the entrance of the nest. A teacupful of water containing 2 percent chlordane as an emulsion or a wettable powder in suspension poured into the entrance of the nest is also an effective treatment.

The Texas Leaf-Cutting Ant (*Atta texana*). This is the most destructive species of the genus in the United States. It is found in Mexico, south and east Texas, Louisiana, Oklahoma, and probably also occurs in Arkansas.

Damage caused by these ants is in stripping plants of their foliage. A number of trees, shrubs, weeds, and cultivated crops serve as hosts; however, only one species of plants is attacked at one time. Large trees may be defoliated in a relatively short time. Small shrubs and other plants may be denuded overnight. The leaf fragments are carried into the nests, cut into small pieces, and stored in special chambers. The leaves are not used as food, but are utilized as a medium upon which the ants cultivate a fungus which constitutes the only food supply.

This insect is reddish-brown and its size is most variable. There are a number of castes within a colony and a marked division of labor. Each caste performs its own special duties. The large, so-called soldiers may be from 1/3 to 1/2 inch in length and the smallest workers, which tend the fungus gardens, are hardly larger than the Pharaoh ant. This species does not sting, but it does bite with the mandibles. A number of queens may be present in a colony.

A colony of leaf-cutting ants (Fig. 304) may consist of a few mounds or it may cover an area of several thousand square feet. The interior consists of a series of connected chambers which are usually about the size of squirrel nests and oboovoid in conformation. These

FIG. 304. A colony of the Texas leaf-cutting ant (*Atta texana*). (From Department of Entomology, A & M College of Texas.)

chambers may extend downward in the soil to a depth of 12 to 15 feet in exceptional cases. Colonies occur most frequently in sandy soils; however, they occasionally may be found in heavy soil.

During the winter months, the worker ants and the queens are concentrated near the center of the colony. With the advent of warm weather, the queens move to more distant parts of the colony and establish individual centers of activity. It is evident that control measures should be applied before the queens disperse if the best results are to be obtained. The most favorable time for applying control measures is during late winter or early spring.

The use of methyl bromide is the most effective measure for control of the leaf-cutting ant. A one-pound can of the fumigant will destroy a colony of ordinary size. The gas is injected through a length of rubber tubing inserted in a large entrance tunnel near the center of the colony.

The Honey Ants (*Myrmecocystus* spp.). Some species of this genus have a most unusual caste known as repletes. They may be considered as living storage tanks or honey jugs. These ants occur in arid sections. In seasons of plenty the workers collect honeydew and give it to the repletes, which hang from the ceilings of the chambers of the nests. The gasters of the repletes may become swollen to the size of a pea. When food becomes scarce the food is regurgitated and fed to the colony as needed.

Family *Vespidae* (Wasps, Hornets, and Yellow Jackets)

All adult vespids are winged, and when at rest the wings of most species fold lengthwise like a fan. The lateral extensions of the pronotum reach the tegulae and do not form rounded lobes as in the *Sphecidae* and the bees. These two characteristics differentiate members of this family from almost all related insects with which they may be confused. All members of the family construct nests of some type; and they may be divided into two separate groups on the basis of their nesting habits, the solitary wasps in which one female makes a nest for her young, and the social wasps in which a number of individuals work together to construct a nest and rear the young.

The Solitary Wasps. Most of the solitary wasps belong to the subfamily *Eumeninae,* and its members are commonly known as eumenids. Nesting habits are varied. Many make burrows in the ground; some in wood; others in stems of pithy plants; and some are mason wasps, constructing nests of earth. A nest may consist of one or a series of cells. Each cell is provisioned with insects, chiefly caterpillars, which have been paralyzed by the sting. Then an egg is laid and the cell is sealed. Most species have the unusual habit of suspending the egg by a slender thread from the cell walls. Adults are carnivorous and also feed on nectar.

A majority of the eumenids belong to the genus *Odynerus*. The body conformation and frequently the color markings resemble the yellow jackets, but the body is usually smaller and more slender. Many species of the genus make their burrows in level ground or on sides of cliffs and ravines. The cells are provisioned with caterpillars. Some forms construct mud turrets over the entrance to the burrows. Members of the genus *Eumenes* construct mud nests (Fig. 305), which resemble tiny water jugs, on twigs of plants.

FIG. 305. Mud nest of a potter wasp (*Eumenes*) on the stem of a plant.

The Social Wasps. Within a colony of social wasps are found three castes, as with the ants, the females or queens, workers, and males. The workers are females which are imperfectly developed sexually. Both workers and queens are capable of inflicting painful stings. In the common paper wasps, *Polistes,* the queens and workers are quite similar in appearance.

In temperate climates colonies of social wasps are not permanent and the nests are abandoned at the close of the season. Males are reared in a colony only during the latter part of the season. When the weather becomes cold in the fall the males and workers die, and the fertilized females seek hibernation quarters in sheltered places. In the spring the females emerge from hibernation, begin the construction of new nests and lay eggs. The first brood consists of only workers, which upon emergence proceed to procure food for the larvae and queens, and expand the nests. After the emergence of the first brood the sole function of the queen is egg-laying.

Social wasps have predatory habits, and the larvae are fed chewed-up insects. The adults also feed on nectar, honeydew, exuding sap, and fruit juices. Another source of food of the adults is a liquid material emitted from the mouth of the larvae.

The common paper wasps belong to the genus *Polistes,* which is represented by a number of species and varieties. Their familiar nests consist of a single horizontal series of cells, not enclosed in an envelope, and supported by a short stout peduncle. They are most commonly found hanging under eaves of buildings, in sheds, barns, and from branches of shrubs and trees. The nests are gray and are composed of a paper-like material made from weathered fibers of wood. This material is collected from dead trees, unpainted boards, fences, and posts, and is chewed by the mandibles into a paste with the addition of a salivary fluid. Most nests are relatively small; however, some nests of *Polistes annularis* (Fig. 306) may be found during the latter part of the season approximately the size

FIG. 306. Paper wasps (*Polistes annularis*) and nest. (From Agricultural Research Service, U.S.D.A.)

of a man's hat. Wasps are beneficial because they destroy the caterpillars of many injurious insects, such as the corn earworm and the cotton leafworm.

Each section of the country has its common species of wasps. *Polistes annularis* is a black form which builds its nests outdoors in shrubs and trees. The individuals fight and sting viciously when the nest is disturbed, to which any country boy can attest. *Polistes rubiginosus* constructs its nests in such dark and protected places as between walls and in hollow logs. *P. pallipes* is a black form with yellow markings, commonly found in the East. Its nests are located in old buildings and other sheltered places. *P. exclamens* and related species are common in the Southwest. These adults are conspicuously marked with yellow and are erroneously called yellow jackets by many. True yellow jackets belong to the genus *Vespula* and make their nests in the ground.

The bald-faced hornet (*Vespula maculata*) is a large black and white insect, which is widely distributed in North America. The oval-shaped nests (Fig. 307) are often quite large and are usually found attached to limbs of trees. The nests are constructed of the same paper-like material as that of common wasps. They differ radically from wasp nests in being enclosed in an envelope and consist of several layers of horizontal cells. There is a single opening at the lower end of the nest; this is always guarded by special workers. As a colony increases in size the nest is enlarged. Nests are abandoned at the end of

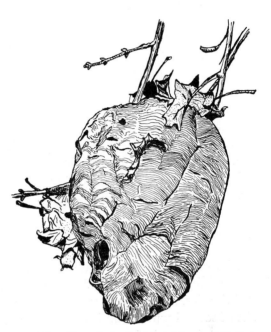

FIG. 307. Nest of the bald-faced hornet (*Vespula maculata*). (Redrawn from *The Hymenoptera of Connecticut*, Bul. 22, Connecticut Geological and Natural History Survey.)

the season. The fertilized females hibernate in barns, attics, and other sheltered places, emerge and begin new nests in the spring. Hornets are beneficial, inasmuch as the workers prey upon such insects as flies and caterpillars. The prey is masticated and fed to the larvae within the cells.

Several species of *Vespula*, e.g., *V. diabolica* and *V. maculifrons*, are known as yellow jackets. They make their nests in cavities within the ground. A favorite nesting site is where a small stump has rotted away. Hollow stumps are also utilized as sites for colonies. These black and yellow-banded insects are much smaller than the hornets and wasps, and their sting, although painful, is not nearly so severe.

Family *Sphecidae* (Mud Daubers, Cicada Killers, and Others)

Members of this large family can usually be distinguished from related insects by the lateral extensions of the pronotum which form rounded lobes and do not reach the tegulae, and by the hairs on the thorax which are simple and not branched or plumose. All adults bear wings which are not longitudinally folded. Nesting habits differ greatly. Some build nests in the ground, others construct nests of mud, and certain species make cells in stems of pithy plants or utilize any other suitable cavity that may be found. All species provision the cells of the nests with spiders or insects which are paralyzed by the sting. When the nests are completed most species quickly store sufficient food for larval development, lay an egg in each cell and seal it. This method of feeding is known as mass provisioning. However, species of *Bembix* and some others feed the larvae from day to day until they are mature. This is termed progressive provisioning. Obviously a female can produce only a few young by this type of feeding. The mature larvae spin cocoons and pupate within the cells. A number of species have been carefully studied because of their intriguing habits. The limited space in a general textbook permits only a few notes on the biologies and habits of some of the most common forms.

The organ-pipe mud daubers belong to the genus *Trypoxylon*. The adults are black, moderate in size, and are rather elongate and slender. Some of the species construct nests of mud which consist of several parallel and contiguous tubes (Fig. 308A) often three or more inches in length. Each tube is divided into cells by transverse partitions. The cells are provisioned with spiders. While the nest is being constructed and provisioned, the male stands guard during the absence of the female. Other members of the genus nest in branches of plants, abandoned tunnels of beetles, and similar cavities.

The thread-waisted wasps are probably the best known members of the family. This name has been given them because of the long petiole of the abdomen. The adults are rather large, measuring an inch or more in length. Most of them make nests in the ground, but the mud daubers that construct the nests of mud found on ceilings and walls of buildings or other protected places are more commonly observed. The adults have the peculiar habit of nervously jerking the wings at frequent intervals. They are commonly seen around damp places collecting mud in small balls and flying

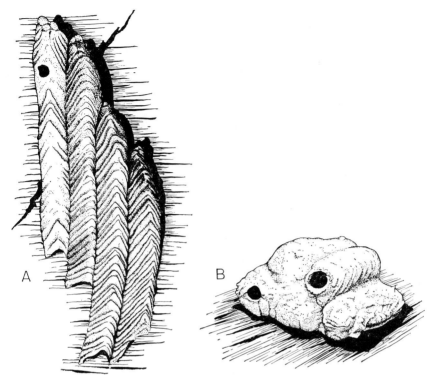

FIG. 308. **A,** Nest of organ-pipe mud dauber (*Trypoxylon*). (Redrawn from Frost, *General Entomology*, 1942. By permission of McGraw-Hill Book Company.) **B,** Nest of yellow mud dauber (*Sceliphron cementarium*).

away to some building or other protected place where the nests are being constructed. The nests usually consist of several rows of cells about one inch long placed side by side. The cells are provisioned with spiders.

The two most common mud daubers are the blue mud dauber, *Chalybion californicum,* and the yellow mud dauber, *Sceliphron cementarium.* The blue mud dauber has a steel-blue body and blue wings. This species does not build its own nest but appropriates the nests of the yellow mud dauber (Fig. 308**B**). It brings water to the nest, softens the mud, and digs open the cells. The cells are carefully cleaned of their contents and restocked with spiders of its own. An egg is then laid in each cell, after which it is resealed. It is said this species uses the black widow spider quite extensively in provisioning its nests. The yellow mud dauber is blackish-brown with yellow markings and yellow legs. At least two generations of this species is completed each season. Hibernation is within cocoons in the cells.

Certain members of the genus *Ammophila* (Fig. 309) are known as the tool-using wasps. They make their nests in the ground and provision the cells with caterpillars. The burrows are closed with earth which is then packed by pounding with a small stone or other object held between the mandibles.

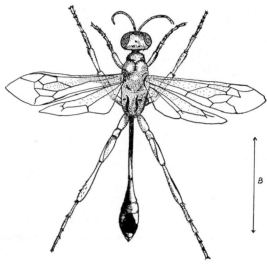

FIG. 309. A digger wasp (*Ammophila*). (From Utah Agricultural Experiment Station.)

The cicada killer (*Sphecius speciosus*) is a large and striking insect one to 1½ inches in length (Fig. 310). It is black or rusty with yellow bands on the abdomen. Adults appear in the summer when cicadas are present and prepare nests in the ground. The cells of the nests are provisioned with cicadas, one or two individuals being placed in each cell, after which an egg is laid and the cell sealed.

The sand wasps are stout-bodied and of moderate size. They are most easily recognized by the elongate and triangular labrum. These wasps nest in sandy soils, and many burrows may be located in a restricted area forming a nesting community. The adults practice progressive feeding; and the larvae are supplied with food consisting chiefly of flies, until they are mature. The best known species of this group in the South is the horse guard (*Bembix carolina*). This common name has been given it because of the habit of hovering around livestock in its search for flies. The adult is about one inch long, black with light yellow or light yellowish-green markings on the abdomen. We once observed a nesting site of this

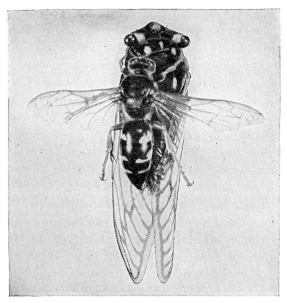

FIG. 310. A female cicada killer (*Sphecius speciosus*) and victim (a cicada) which serves as food for her larvae in the nest. (From Metcalf and Flint, *Fundamentals of Insect Life,* McGraw-Hill Book Company, 1932. By permission of the publisher.)

species in sandy soil about ½ acre in area, in which thousands of nests were located.

BEES

Bumble bees and honey bees are the most familiar members of this group of insects; however, they represent only a few of about 2,500 species which are known to occur in North America. There are not only many species, but the individuals are numerous. Many may be observed visiting flowers on any favorable day during the warm seasons.

Although differing much in habits and size, detailed morphological characteristics of bees are so similar that no satisfactory classification is generally agreed upon. The grouping followed here is that of Comstock. In common with the *Sphecidae,* the lateral extensions of the pronotum of bees terminate in lobes which do not reach the tegulae. A basic difference between bees and most nest-building Hymenoptera is they provision their nests with pollen and honey instead of spiders and insects. Their most distinctive characteristics are morphological modifications which are correlated with the collection of this food material. A characteristic present only in a few other Hymenoptera is branched or plumose hairs on the body, especially the thorax. The branched hairs are concerned with the collection of grains of pollen when flowers are visited. Females are provided with pollen brushes, with the exception of species of *Prosopis* and parasitic bees. Pollen brushes are borne on the hind legs except in the *Megachilidae,* in which family the brush is located on the ventral side of the abdomen. Those bees which carry pollen on the hind legs have the first segment of the tarsus (metatarsus) dilated to form a pollen basket (corbicula) on the outer surface. The maxillae and labium of the mouthparts are greatly modified to form a proboscis for lapping the nectar of flowers. The structure of the proboscis exhibits considerable variation among the groups and provides a useful characteristic in classification.

Nesting habits of bees are similar to those of wasps. Most bees are solitary in habit, and nest in the ground, stems of pithy plants, or tunnel in solid wood. Some, often referred to as cuckoo bees, make no provisions for their young, but oviposit in nests of other bees where they live as parasites or inquilines. The bumble bees and honey bees comprise the social bees which live in colonies consisting of many individuals. Within their colonies are found the three castes; queens, workers, and males (drones).

Honey bees, bumble bees, and also the solitary bees are the most important insect pollinators of plants. These insects are of primary importance in the pollination of many orchard fruits and other economic plants. When the annual value of crops produced on insect-pollinated plants in this country is estimated, the importance of bees to agriculture is quite obvious.

Family *Andrenidae* (Andrenids)

This is a large family of solitary bees. All construct nests, with the exception of parasitic species. The length of the proboscis is quite variable, but it is always pointed at the apex. Females of the nest-building species bear pollen brushes on the hind legs. Only a few genera and species can be discussed here.

Andrena. Some members of this genus (Fig. 311) are about as large as the worker honey bee. Nests are made in ground that is more or less bare of vegetation. The bees dig vertical tunnels from which branching brood chambers are made. Although solitary in habit, the females tend to build their nests close together and form nesting communities.

Halictus. This common group of mining bees includes many species which are small to moderate in size; they are often of a metallic color. Their nests are made in level ground, sides of ditches, or along pathways. Nesting communities containing hundreds of bees

FIG. 311. A mining bee (*Andrena wilkella*). (From Borror and DeLong, *An Introduction to the Study of Insects*, Rinehart & Company, 1954. By permission of the publisher.)

are often observed. A nest consists of a burrow from which short, lateral burrows are excavated. Each lateral burrow terminates in a cell which is lined with clay. A mass of pollen and honey, kneaded into a rounded pellet, is placed in each cell. An egg is then deposited on the food material and the cell is sealed. Information on the biology of the group is rather limited. It appears that only fertile females hibernate. They emerge in the spring and establish nests. Some species produce one generation each season; others may have two. The first offspring reared in the spring are females. The males appear later in the season and die when the weather becomes cold. In some species, at least, several females use the same tunnel to the cells they are preparing and provisioning. The opening to this common tunnel is constricted; a guard is posted there, and only bees that are members of the group are allowed entrance.

Anthophora. This is a widely distributed genus and more than 80 North American species are known. The adults are of average size, robust, and hairy. Nests are usually constructed in steep banks, preferably in clay soils. Walls of adobe houses in the Southwest are favorite nesting sites. While digging the tunnels, the females make frequent trips to bring water for moistening the hard, dry soil. The wet pellets of earth removed from the tunnels are used to construct turrets over the entrances. The turrets are rough on the outside and slope outward and downward. The tunnels terminate in lateral cells. The walls of the cells are water-proofed with a cementing substance. Following the completion of the cells, a mixture of pollen and honey is placed in each, an egg is deposited, and the cell is sealed. Only one generation is completed each season. Winter is passed in the larval stage within the cells. Members of this group also are gregarious in their nesting habits, and numbers of nests may be found in a restricted area.

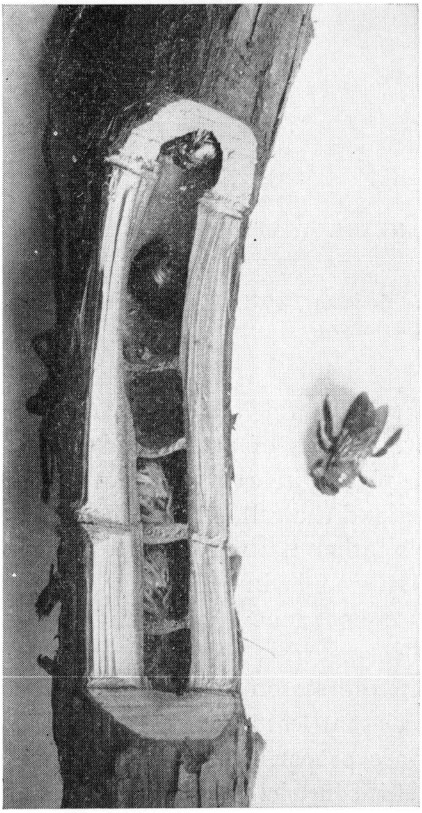

The Carpenter Bees. Two genera comprise this group, the large carpenter bees (*Xylocopa*) and the small carpenter bees (*Ceratina*). (See Fig. 312.) The large carpenter bees are nearly one inch in length and resemble bumble bees in both size and appearance. The dorsum of the abdomen is rather bare, and the females do not have pollen baskets on the hind legs but brushes of hairs instead. Nests are made in solid wood; the tunnels (Fig. 313) may be as much as one foot long. Tunnels are divided into cells with partitions made of bits of wood cemented together. Pollen, honey, and an egg are placed in each cell. Winter is passed as larvae

FIG. 312. Nest of a carpenter bee showing arrangement of the brood cells. (From Texas Agricultural Experiment Station.)

within the cells. Only one generation is thought to be developed each season.

The little carpenter bees are greenish-blue and about $\frac{1}{4}$ inch in length. They make their nests in stems of pithy plants such as sumac. The arrangement of the nest is similar to that of the large carpenter bees. Two generations are developed each year. Winter is passed as females in the old nests.

Family *Megachilidae* (Leaf-Cutter Bees and Related Forms)

Members of the family are fairly large and rather stout-bodied. They may be differentiated from most related bees by the presence of two submarginal cells, subequal in size on the front wings, and by the females of the pollen-collecting species having the pollen brush on the ventral side of the abdomen instead of on the legs.

FIG. 313.   Exit holes of the large carpenter bee (*Xylocopa virginica*) in the end of a log. (From Texas Agricultural Experiment Station.)

Some members of the family are known as leaf-cutters (Fig. 314), because they cut out neat circular pieces of leaves with which they line the cells of their nests. The nests may be difficult to locate, but the work on leaves of plants is quite conspicuous. Nests of *Megachilidae* are made in natural cavities, stems of pithy plants, and the ground. Some species of the family are quite valuable as pollinators of alfalfa and other crops.

The leaf-cutters comprise the genus *Megachile*. The provisions for the brood, consisting of a mixture of honey and pollen, are placed in a leaf-lined cell. Several such cells are usually made end to end in the tunnel. Many species of the genus *Osmia* construct nests of earth which is bound together with a fluid thought to be secreted by the salivary glands. Nesting sites are almost any available cavity in wood, plant galls, stems, snail shells, and between stones. Other common genera are *Anthidium* and *Coelioxys*.

Family *Bombidae* (Bumble Bees)

This family is comprised of the common bumble bees (*Bombus*) and certain parasitic species of the genus *Psithyrus*. Bumble bees are large to medium in size and are rather densely clothed in black and yellow hairs. (See Fig. 283, p. 441.) The common name has been given them because of the noise made in flight.

FIG. 314. *Megachile latimanus,* a leafcutter bee. (From Borror and DeLong, An *Introduction to the Study of Entomology,* Rinehart & Company, 1954. By permission of the publisher.)

The Bumble Bees (*Bombus* spp.). About 50 species of bumble bees are known to occur in North America. All are social insects; a colony consists of three castes— queens, workers, and males. The workers are imperfectly developed females. The males are developed from unfertilized eggs. In temperate climates both males and functional females are produced only the latter part of the season. They mate, the males together with the workers die with the advent of cold weather, and the fertile females (queens) hibernate in protected places.

In the spring the queens emerge from hibernation and proceed to establish new colonies. A nesting site may be a depression in the ground, a deserted mouse's nest, a hollow log, a cavity in a rotted stump, or a place may be made in a pile of grass, weeds, or other rubbish. Having selected a nesting site, the queen prepares the nest. This is made from the finest and softest materials available, e.g., dry grass and moss. Within this heap of material a cavity is formed with an entrance to one side. Pollen and nectar are collected, mixed into a paste, and placed in the center of the floor of the cavity. A small waxen cell is constructed upon this mass of food material. The first batch of eggs is laid in the cell, which is then sealed with wax. The queen carefully guards the cell containing the eggs until they are hatched. A large waxen pot is constructed near the entrance of the nest and filled with honey to provide adequate food for use while she is on guard and during inclement weather. The eggs hatch in about four days, and the larvae first feed upon the mass of pollen and honey which forms their bed. Later, additional food is provided by the queen through a small hole made in the wax covering of the cell. The wax covering is enlarged as the larvae grow. The larval period is about ten days in duration. Then each larva spins a thin but tough cocoon in which to pupate. About two weeks are spent in the pupal stage. The first brood usually consists of only five to 15 individuals. The empty cocoons from which the adults emerged are utilized as receptacles for the storage of pollen and honey. Additional cells of wax are also made for this purpose. All individuals produced in the first part of the season are workers. As soon as the first brood emerges from the pupal stage these workers assume all duties of the colony except egg-laying, to which duty the queen then devotes all her time. If conditions are favorable, the colony increases in strength and when at its peak may contain several hundred individuals.

The proboscis of bumble bees is longer than that of the honey bee and most solitary bees. This longer proboscis enables them to pollinate more efficiently the flowers of certain plants, such as red clover, in which the corrollas are so long that the nectaries cannot be reached very well by bees with shorter proboscides. Since bumble bees are highly beneficial as pollinators their nests should not be destroyed. Moreover, where their services are most needed in the production of seed crops, such as red clover and alfalfa, they should be encouraged in establishment of nests by the creation of more favorable environmental conditions.

Bees of the genus *Psithyrus* are parasites in the nests of bumble bees. The females may be recognized by the absence of pollen baskets on the hind legs. However, the males of the two genera are quite similar in appearance. These parasites have no worker caste. Eggs are laid in the nests of bumble bees, whose workers rear the brood as their own.

Family *Apidae* (Honey Bees)

The family, as considered here, is comprised of only one genus, *Apis* (Fig. 315). Four species are generally recognized; however, one of these may be considered a variety. Only one species, the

FIG. 315. The honey bee (*Apis mellifera*). **A,** Worker. **B,** Queen. **C,** Drone. (From the *American Bee Journal.*)

common honey bee (*Apis mellifera*) which was introduced by the early English and Spanish settlers, is found in North America. Several races of the honey bee are recognized and are used in commercial beekeeping. The remaining species are indigenous to specific regions including the Malay peninsula and India. *Apis dorsata* (the giant bee of India) and *Apis florea* (the dwarf bee of India) build a single comb suspended to a limb or ledge. They are unmanageable and worthless in commercial beekeeping. *Apis indica* is similar in size and habits to the honey bee. Some authorities consider it a variety of the common honey bee.

Unlike the bumble bees, which disband at the close of the season when fertile females hibernate, the honey bees cannot hibernate; and their colonies are established on a permanent basis. Inasmuch as honey bees maintain their colonies throughout the year, which necessitates the storage of food (honey); and whereas they are the only pollinating insects which can be controlled, they are extremely valuable to man.

Man probably began keeping bees before there were any records of the human race; beekeeping, therefore, is one of the oldest agricultural pursuits (Fig. 316). Bees were kept through the centuries for the honey and beeswax they produced. But beekeeping is today a minor branch of agriculture insofar as the monetary return from honey and wax is concerned. However, bees are very important in the pollination of many plants. Their worth to agriculture as pollinators has been conservatively estimated at 15 to 25 times the value of honey and beeswax they produce. Fifty or more crops are dependent upon bees for the maximum production of seed or fruit. Formerly there was more uncultivated land which provided more suitable places for the nesting of the native bees (bumble bees and solitary bees). In most areas there were sufficient numbers of these bees to take care of pollination needs. Since more large areas have been brought under cultivation and the habitats of the native pollinators

FIG. 316. **A,** An old-fashioned bee gum. (From Texas Agricultural Experiment Station.) **B,** Modern bee hives. (From the *American Bee Journal.*)

destroyed, there are not sufficient native insect pollinators, and agriculture must depend more upon honey bees. Probably more than 80 percent of insect pollination of fruit and seed crops today is done by honey bees.

In nature, colonies of bees are found in hollow trees and logs, and in caves. The nests are made up of several vertical waxen combs with cells on both sides. The cells are utilized for the storage of honey and pollen, and the rearing of brood.

A colony of bees is composed of three castes; a queen, workers, and males (drones). (See Fig. 315, p. 488.) It may have a population of 30,000 to 60,000 individuals. The queen resembles a paper wasp with short legs and wings. She is not so robust as the drone but her abdomen is longer and more tapering. She does not rule or direct the activities of the colony in the least. Nevertheless, perfect harmony and unity of action always exist among its individuals. The basic instinct of all is the survival of the colony as a unit.

The only function of the queen is that of egg-laying. During the peak of the brood-rearing season she may lay as many as 1,500 to 2,000 eggs daily for short periods. The queen never mates after she begins to lay eggs. The colony is left only twice in her life; when she takes her mating flight, and again when she emerges with a swarm. Bees mate in the air. Queens are reared in large cells known as queen cells and are fed throughout the larval period on a highly nutritious food, royal jelly, which is a secretion of glandular origin. With rare exceptions queens develop from fertile eggs. The developmental period of the queen brood is 16 days. The life of a queen may be several years in duration.

Drones are reared in drone cells from infertile eggs. The developmental period of a drone brood is 24 days. The individuals are larger and more robust than the queens, but the abdomen is not so long and pointed. They have no sting and are physically disqualified for any work. Their only reason for existence is the fertilization of the young queens. As they consume large quantities of food, the workers will not tolerate their presence any longer when the swarming season is over and the honey flow has drawn to a close. They are starved and driven out of the colonies to die.

Workers are the smallest and most populous members of the colony. They develop in the worker-size cells (Fig. 317) from fertile eggs. As development is in small cells and the larvae are not fed the highly nutritious food, royal jelly, throughout the larval stage, they develop into sexually imperfect females. Three weeks are required for the development of the worker brood.

The length of life of the adult worker depends upon the amount of work it does. It may live throughout the cold winter months, but during the honey-gathering season it expends its energy and dies

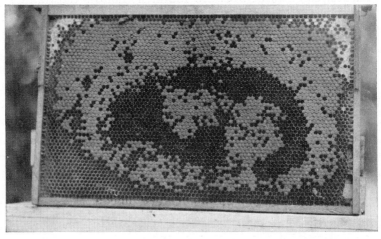

FIG. 317. A comb of brood. (From the *American Bee Journal*.)

in about six weeks. The worker is correctly named for it does all the work both in the colony and in the field, with the exception of egg-laying. The young worker bees feed and care for the queen and brood, polish the cells, secrete wax, build the combs, clean the hives, convert the nectar into honey, ventilate the hives, and act as guards. When they are about three weeks old they become field bees. Their duties as field bees are gathering nectar, pollen ("bee bread"), propolis (a gum from trees for sealing cracks and crevices), and supplying the colony with water.

FIG. 318. A swarm of bees clustered on a limb. (From the *American Bee Journal*.)

Bees collect nectar of flowers when it is available. It then must be converted into honey. The principal sugar found in nectar is sucrose or cane sugar. Enzymes are added to the nectar and most of the sucrose is transformed into dextrose and levulose. The excess water is evaporated to less than 20 percent and the product, which is then honey, is sealed in the cells with waxen caps.

In nature, bees increase the number of colonies by swarming. During late spring or early summer when the colony becomes over-crowded, the weather warm, and some nectar available, the swarm-ing impulse is manifested and the colony prepares for this important event. A number of queen cells are started, work slackens, and scout bees seek a new habitation. As the time approaches for the emergence of the young queens, the swarm, composed chiefly of field bees and the old queen, emerges from the colony and clusters on some convenient object such as the limb of a tree (Fig. 318). Soon afterwards the cluster is broken and the bees fly away to es-tablish a new colony.

Bees have a means of communication by which they can transmit information of new sources of nectar, pollen or water, and also indi-cate directions and distances. This is done by the returning worker bees by means of characteristic dances or movements on the combs. Many other social insects have communication systems also but not much exact information is known about them.

22

COLLECTING, MOUNTING, AND PRESERVING INSECTS

WHAT AND WHERE TO COLLECT

There is no better way to learn about insects than by making a collection. Much information will be acquired which will never be found in textbooks. Observations on habits, host relationships, and life histories of insects will be remembered long after the dull, dry facts of textbooks are forgotten. Working with live specimens, killing and mounting them, creates much more interest than studying museum specimens and looking at pictures. Furthermore, mounting and arranging specimens in a collection increases one's knowledge and understanding of the classification of insects.

Making insect collections is a hobby of many people. It takes one outdoors in the fields and forests, and along streams, which is excellent recreation. It is a stimulating avocation. Incidentally, some very fine collections have been built up in this way, and much information of value has been added to the science. The student should begin by making a general collection. After a knowledge of the most common insects has been acquired he probably will restrict his collecting to insects of certain taxonomic groups.

Insects are to be found almost everywhere and at any time. Hardly a niche in nature exists that does not harbor an insect of some kind. Even though insects may be collected in any season, they are naturally most abundant in warm, moist weather, particularly in the spring and early summer. Also, collecting may be excellent in the fall when conditions are favorable. As many species are present for only a limited period, collecting should be done throughout the year if the greatest variety of insects is desired.

Every insect has its preferred habitat and hosts, and collections should be made in as many places as possible. Flowers afford the best places for collecting nectar and pollen feeders, such as butterflies, bees, many wasps, and certain flies. Collections should be made on all kinds of plants, for all are host to some type of insect which may be found feeding on the leaves, fruit, stems, trunks, or roots. Rotten logs, loose bark, and debris of all types harbor many diverse forms. Many insects are found in aquatic environments. Some live in the water, others on the surface. Certain species are found on aquatic plants or along the shore line. Animals and their refuse attract many species. Homes and other buildings, stored products, such as grain and foods, yield many specimens. Large numbers of different insects are attracted to lights under favorable weather conditions, and they may be collected around street lights, screens of lighted homes, or in light traps installed for the purpose.

Better specimens are frequently obtained by collecting the immature stages and rearing the adults. This practice entails more work and time; but one is compensated, not only in better specimens, but also in learning more about the biology of the insects and marks of recognition of the developmental stages.

COLLECTING EQUIPMENT

Only a few inexpensive pieces of equipment are needed to make an insect collection. The most important items are an insect net, killing bottle, insect pins, and storage boxes. Other equipment and supplies are desirable, and these will be mentioned later in the discussion. All items may be purchased from entomological supply houses, but most of the equipment may be made.

Nets

An insect net (Fig. 319) consists of a handle fitted with a wire hoop to which a cloth bag is attached. Two general types of nets are used, the heavier sweeping net and the lighter aerial or butterfly net. The sweeping net needs to be of sturdier construction and the bag of more substantial material (muslin or light canvas). The aerial net is used in collecting such wary insects as butterflies, dragonflies, and wasps. It should be of light weight and provided with a porous bag of some material such as fine netting or marquisette.

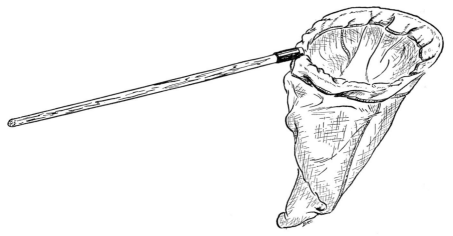

FIG. 319.   An insect net.

The length of a bag should be about twice the diameter of the hoop.

If the net is to be homemade, a handle should be selected that is light in weight, strong, and about three or four feet in length. On one end of the handle grooves are cut on opposite sides to receive the bent wire of the hoop. (See Fig. 320.) One groove should be made about 3½ inches long and the other 2½ inches with a small hole drilled through the handle at the end of each. If it is not

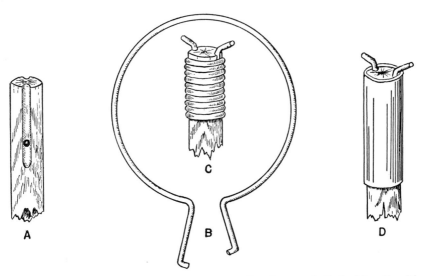

FIG. 320.   Details of a homemade hoop and handle of a net. **A**, End of handle with grooves terminating in small holes in which ends of wire hoop fit. **B**, Hoop of stiff wire. **C**, Wire-wrapped joint. **D**, Joint fitted with ferrule to hold net in place.

planned to change bags, the joint may be securely wrapped with small wire. If bags are to be changed occasionally, the handle should be provided with a metal ferrule which can be pushed up to secure the joint. If one is not at hand, a ferrule may be obtained from a tinsmith. The hoop should be made from a 4-foot length of stiff wire (20 gauge). When the ends are bent for attachment to the handle the diameter of the hoop will be slightly more than twelve inches.

Killing Bottles

When an insect is collected, it should be killed as quickly as possible in a killing bottle to avoid damaging the specimen. Any wide-mouthed glass jar or vial is satisfactory for use in making a killing bottle. It will need to be provided with a tightly fitting cork or screw cap. A collector needs several bottles of different sizes for different types of insects.

Several chemicals are available for use as killing agents in the bottles; ethyl acetate and cyanide are the most satisfactory. Chloroform and carbon tetrachloride may be used as substitute killing agents when the other compounds are not available. Regardless of the killing agent used, the bottle should be clearly labeled POISON. It is advisable to tape glass bottles to reduce breakage hazards.

Ethyl acetate is readily available and bottles prepared with it are comparatively safe for use. The compound does not kill so quickly as cyanide, but insects do not recover from its effects as they may do when cyanide is used. Also, specimens can be kept longer in ethyl acetate bottles than in cyanide bottles without becoming brittle and discolored.

An ethyl acetate killing bottle is easily made. About ½ inch of a mixture of plaster of Paris and water is poured in the bottom of the bottle. The plaster of Paris is allowed to set and dry completely. Drying may be hastened by setting the bottle in an oven. When the plaster of Paris is thoroughly dry it is saturated with ethyl acetate. The bottle is then ready for use and will remain effective for months if kept tightly closed. When the bottle loses its effectiveness it may be dried and recharged.

Cyanide has been the most widely used compound in making killing bottles (Fig. 321). Any one of three forms; calcium cyanide, sodium cyanide, or potassium cyanide may be used. Calcium cyanide is the most satisfactory. The granular form of calcium cyanide is

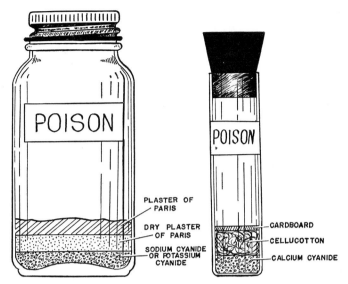

PLASTER OF PARIS

DRY PLASTER OF PARIS

SODIUM CYANIDE OR POTASSIUM CYANIDE

CARDBOARD

CELLUCOTTON

CALCIUM CYANIDE

FIG. 321. Killing bottles.

placed in the bottom of the bottle or vial and covered with a plug of cellucotton which is tamped firmly in place. A piece of card-board, perforated with a few pinholes, is cut to fit tightly in the bottle or vial on top of the cellucotton. The bottle is then ready for immediate use. If sodium cyanide or potassium cyanide is used, the bottom of a perfectly dry bottle is covered with the powdered or granular cyanide. On top of the cyanide is added about $\frac{1}{2}$ inch of dry plaster of Paris or a fine grade of sawdust, which is then covered with a wet layer of plaster of Paris, $\frac{1}{4}$ to $\frac{1}{2}$ inch thick. The plaster of Paris must set and dry before the bottle is closed.

Cyanide is a deadly poison and must be handled with extreme care. Bottles containing cyanide must be conspicuously labeled and kept away from those who are not aware of its deadliness. When a bottle is broken or is no longer to be used, it should be carefully disposed of, preferably by burying.

Best results are obtained from a killing bottle through proper use. The bottle should be kept closed and not opened except to put in and take out specimens. Moisture often condenses on the in-side of the bottle. This should be wiped out periodically and a few pieces of absorbent paper, such as cleansing tissue, should be kept in the bottle and frequently replaced. A separate bottle should be kept for moths and butterflies, as scales from their wings stick to other specimens and spoil their appearance. Insects that die slowly, e.g., beetles, also should be kept in a special bottle and never placed with fragile specimens. Killing bottles should never be overloaded with specimens. Insects in cyanide bottles should be removed as soon as they are dead. If they remain in a cyanide bottle too long they tend to discolor, and when removed they soon become brittle.

Other Collecting Items

An aspirator is useful in collecting small insects. Probably the simplest form is the vial type (Fig. 322). Insects are drawn through

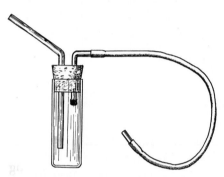

a tube into the vial by sucking on the mouthpiece. A cloth covers the inner end of the mouthpiece tube to prevent insects from being drawn into the mouth of the collector.

Small insects in trash are most easily collected by use of sifters of various types. The material should be sifted on a cloth background where movements of the tiny insects will reveal their presence. The

FIG. 322.   Aspirator for collecting small insects.

insects may be picked up with an aspirator or a wet camel's hair brush.

Large numbers of small insects may be collected by means of a separator which is commonly known as a Berlese funnel. Basically, the separator consists of a sieve, for holding the litter or trash, which fits into the top of a funnel. The insects move downward through the sieve as the litter dries, and drop through the funnel into a killing bottle or a jar containing a preserving fluid. The drying of the litter may be hastened by placing a light bulb or some other source of low heat above the sieve.

Light traps of several types have been made, and used in surveys to determine the distribution and abundance of certain insects. A large number of different insects may be collected in these traps. A convenient way of collecting at a light is to hang a white cloth, such as a sheet, so that the light shines against it. The insects are captured as they collect on the white background or at its base.

Baits of different kinds are useful in collecting insects. "Sugaring" for moths is commonly practiced. A sugary solution is mopped or painted on logs, tree trunks, and stumps to attract the insects. Several mixtures are used for "sugaring," but a fermenting mixture is probably the most satisfactory. The bait is applied before dark and should be visited at intervals during the night.

Other collector's items include a dip net for aquatic insects, forceps, camel's hair brushes, a strong knife, hatchet, vials of preserving fluid, boxes for temporary storage of specimens, and some type of knapsack for carrying the equipment.

MOUNTING AND PRESERVING INSECTS

After specimens are collected they must be preserved for future study. Larvae and other soft-bodied forms may be preserved in 80 percent alcohol or 4 percent formaldehyde. Most hard-bodied insects are mounted on pins. With proper care they will keep indefinitely. Those too small to pin may be mounted on "minuten" pins, card points, or microscope slides.

Relaxing Jars

It is advisable to mount insects soon after they are collected, but this is not always possible. When specimens dry they become brittle and may be damaged in pinning. They must be relaxed before they can be pinned. Any wide-mouth jar with a tightly fitting cover can be made into a relaxing jar. The bottom of the jar is covered with wet sand or sawdust. A few drops of carbolic acid is added to prevent molds. A piece of cardboard is cut to fit into the jar on top of the sand or sawdust. Insects in open boxes are placed in the jar which is then tightly covered. Usually specimens are sufficiently relaxed to be mounted after one or two days.

Pinning Insects

Insect pins may be obtained from any entomological supply house. Common pins cannot be used as they are too short and thick, and soon rust. Insect pins are made in several sizes. For most purposes sizes 2 and 3 are satisfactory.

Insects are pinned vertically through the body. The place where the pin is inserted depends upon the type of insect (Fig. 323). The following rules are followed in pinning the different groups of insects.

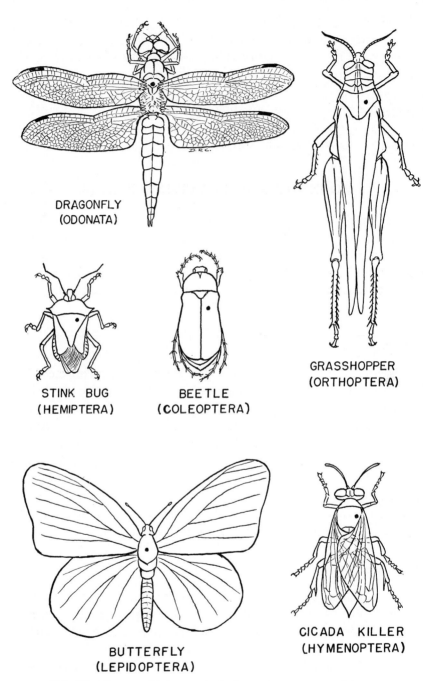

DRAGONFLY
(ODONATA)

GRASSHOPPER
(ORTHOPTERA)

STINK BUG
(HEMIPTERA)

BEETLE
(COLEOPTERA)

BUTTERFLY
(LEPIDOPTERA)

CICADA KILLER
(HYMENOPTERA)

FIG. 323. Correct pinning methods for common groups of insects.

1. *Orthoptera* (Grasshoppers, Crickets, etc.). Pin through the back of the pronotum, slightly to the right of the middle line.
2. *Hemiptera* (Stink Bugs, etc.). Pin through the scutellum, slightly to the right of the middle line.
3. *Coleoptera* (Beetles). Pin through the right elytron (wing cover) about midway of the body.
4. *Lepidoptera* (Butterflies and Moths). Insert the pin between the base of the front wings.
5. *Diptera* (Flies) and *Hymenoptera* (Bees, Wasps, etc.). Pin through the thorax, slightly to the right of the midline.
6. *Odonata* (Dragonflies and Damselflies). Pin through the middle of the thorax. To conserve space in the collection they may be pinned horizontally through the thorax.

A collection should appear neat, with the specimens uniformly mounted. The insect should be mounted about an inch above the point of the pin. Labels on the pin should be uniformly arranged also. Uniformity is most easily obtained by use of a pinning block (Fig. 324). A pinning block in common use is a block of wood with three steps. In each step a small hole is drilled. Beginning with the first (lowest) step, the holes are ⅜, ⅝, and one inch deep, respectively.

Spreading Boards

Some insects, such as moths and butterflies, are usually mounted with their wings spread. Spreading boards are used for this purpose and are important collector's items. Different sizes and types may be purchased or made at home. Figure 325 shows the general type of construction and average dimensions. Soft wood top pieces should be used to facilitate the insertion of pins.

Certain rules are followed in spreading the wings of insects. The front wings of moths and butterflies should be spread with the rear margin at a right angle with the body. The front margin of the hind wings should be under the rear margin of the front wings. Strips of paper are pinned across the wings to hold them in position until the specimens are dried. In spreading the wings of dragonflies, damselflies, grasshoppers, and most other insects the front margin of the hind wings should be at a right angle with the body and the front wings pulled forward sufficiently so the wings do not touch.

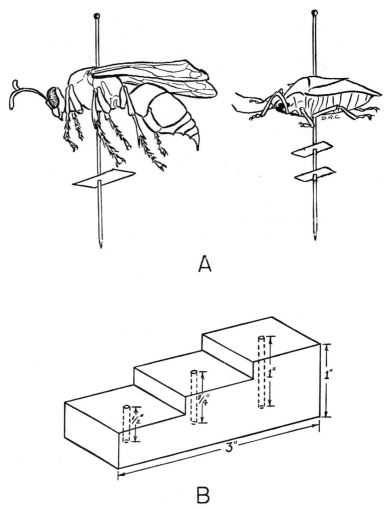

A

B

FIG. 324. **A,** Illustrations showing correct positions of insects and labels on pins. **B,** A pinning block used to adjust both specimens and labels to correct position on pin.

Labeling Specimens

Unless a specimen in a collection is accompanied by a label bearing certain essential information it is of little scientific value. A label should always give the date and locality of the insect's capture. Additional information giving the name or initials of the collector and the hosts or habitat of the insect is desirable. One or two labels may be used. If only one label is used it should bear the locality, date, and name or initials of the collector. When two labels are used

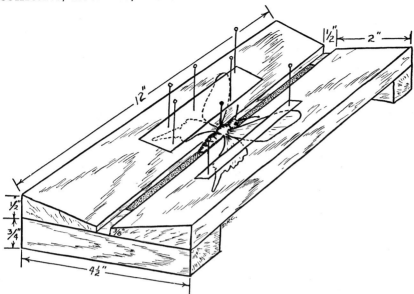

FIG. 325. A spreading board with average dimensions.

the first should give information on locality and date, and the second the name of the collector and hosts or habitat.

Labels should be of uniform size, about ¾ inch long and ¼ inch wide and made from stiff paper. Lettering may be done by hand, printed, or obtained partly printed from entomological supply houses. A very satisfactory plan for obtaining supplies of labels is to type a number on plain white paper. This paper is photographed and prints made. The labels may be cut from the prints as they are used. Identification labels are usually plain white or bordered, about ½ by 1¼ inches in size, and pinned against the bottom of the box. Samples of labels are shown in Figure 326.

Insect Boxes

Boxes for housing pinned specimens should have the bottom lined with a soft material such as cork or balsa wood, and they need to be as pest proof as possible. The best known type is the Schmitt box which is readily obtained from supply houses. Cigar boxes are most frequently used by the beginner. Also, heavy cardboard boxes are satisfactory for temporary use. The collection needs to be checked frequently for museum pests.

Large collections in institutions are frequently housed in cabinets which contain glass-top drawers. The drawers are fitted with

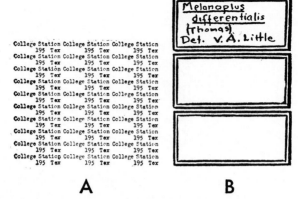

College Station College Station College Station
195 Tex   195 Tex   195 Tex
College Station College Station College Station
195 Tex   195 Tex   195 Tex
College Station College Station College Station
195 Tex   195 Tex   195 Tex
College Station College Station College Station
195 Tex   195 Tex   195 Tex
College Station College Station College Station
195 Tex   195 Tex   195 Tex
College Station College Station College Station
195 Tex   195 Tex   195 Tex
College Station College Station College Station
195 Tex   195 Tex   195 Tex
College Station College Station College Station
195 Tex   195 Tex   195 Tex
College Station College Station College Station
195 Tex   195 Tex   195 Tex
College Station College Station College Station
195 Tex   195 Tex   195 Tex

A   **B**

FIG. 326. Samples of printed labels. **A,** Strips of printed labels giving locality and space for date. **B,** Identification labels providing space for scientific name, the name of the describer of the species and name of person identifying the insect.

trays of different sizes which facilitate rearrangement without having to shift individual specimens.

Riker Mounts

Riker mounts are convenient for display and teaching purposes. A Riker mount is a shallow cardboard box about one inch deep, filled with cotton and with a glass top. The insects are placed on the cotton background and are held in position by the glass cover. Various sizes of Riker mounts may be purchased or made. The size most commonly used is eight inches wide and 12 inches long.

Riker mounts are easily made. All the items needed are a supply of cardboard boxes (such as hose boxes), window-pane glass, glass cutter, cotton, and tape. The top of the lid of the box is cut out, leaving a margin about $\frac{1}{4}$ inch wide. A piece of glass is cut to fit in the top and secured with tape along its edges. Covering the sides of the Riker mount increases its durability and improves the appearance. Black tape makes a better appearing mount. The mount may be filled with cotton of any type which is covered with a layer of medicated cotton to improve the appearance and provide a smooth surface. The cover is secured by pins pushed into the mount through the sides and ends.

Protecting Collections from Pests

Insect collections are attacked by dermestid larvae, ants, and other pests. If precautions are not taken the collections may soon be reduced to fragments and powder. Naphthalene (flakes or balls) is most commonly used in the protection of collections. This compound is a satisfactory repellent, but it will not kill the pests when once the collection has become infested. If an infestation has developed it is necessary to use a fumigant, such as paradichlorobenzene (PDB), carbon tetrachloride, carbon disulphide, or ethylene dichloride. Painting the inside of the boxes with DDT will also prevent infestations.

GLOSSARY

Abdomen the third or posterior division of an insect's body.

Accessory cell a wing cell usually not present; a closed cell in wings of many Lepidoptera between branches of the radius.

Accessory vein a secondary longitudinal vein in an insect wing.

Acuminate tapering to a point.

Adfrontal areas two narrow oblique plates on head of lepidopterous larvae.

Aestivation dormancy in summer, or during a hot, dry season.

Agamic reproducing without mating.

Ametabolous insect development without metamorphosis.

Annulate ring-like; with ringed divisions or segments.

Antecoxal piece a metasternal sclerite in front of the hind coxae.

Antenna (*pl.* **antennae**) a paired segmented appendage located on the head; commonly known as a feeler.

Antenodal preceding or before the nodus.

Aorta the nonchambered dorsal blood vessel opening into the head region.

Apposition eye an eye of day-flying insects which absorbs oblique rays of light in the pigmented walls of the ommatidia.

Apposition image in diurnal insects an image built up in eyes by apposed points of light falling side by side and not overlapping.

Aptera insects which are wingless.

Apterygota a subclass of primitively wingless insects.

Arista a large bristle on antenna of certain Diptera, usually dorsally located.

Asexual independent of sexual processes.

Basement membrane thin, noncellular membrane forming the inner lining of the hypodermis of the body wall.

Beak a jointed, protruding mouthpart structure of a sucking insect.

Binomial pertaining to two names; the zoological system of nomenclature consisting of a generic and a specific name.

Book lung a respiratory sac containing leaf-like plates (found in spiders).

Bucca the mouth in adult Diptera.

Caecum (*pl.* **caeca**) a blind sac, one of a group of appendages opening into the anterior region of the ventriculus.

Calypters a pair of scales at the base of the wings above the halteres.

Campodeiform pertaining to larvae resembling certain members of the Thysanura; i.e., the body elongate and flattened with the legs, antennae, and cerci well developed.

Capitate with a head, a type of antenna terminating in a knob-like process.

Capitulum a false head anteriorly borne (in ticks).

Caraboid resembling a carabid larva.

Cardiac valve a valve at the junction of the proventriculus and ventriculus.

Cardo basal segment of the maxilla.

Carina a ridge or keel.

Caterpillar the larva of a butterfly or moth.

Caudal pertaining to the anal end of the body.

Cephalad pertaining to the anterior end of the body.

Cephalothorax the combined head and thorax of Crustacea and Arachnida.

Chaetotaxy arrangement and nomenclature of setae on the exoskeleton of an insect, particularly in Diptera.

Chelicerae (*sing.* **Chelicera**) anterior paired appendages in Arachnida, representing modified second antennae of the Crustacea.

Chitin a nitrogenous compound occurring in the cuticula of Arthropoda.

Chordotonal pertaining to organs for the perception of sound.

Chorion shell of an insect egg.

Chrysalis (*pl.* **Chrysalids** or **Chrysalides**) the pupa of a butterfly.

Clavate clubbed, thickened gradually toward the tip, e.g., a clavate antenna.

Clavus triangular or oblong anal area of the front wing in Hemiptera and Homoptera.

Closed cell a cell bounded on all sides by veins.

Clypeus the sclerite between the frons and the labrum.

Coarctate larva a larva resembling the puparium of *Diptera;* the hibernating stage of a blister beetle larva.

Cocoon a silken covering constructed for protection of the pupa.

Coelom body cavity.

Collophore a ventral tube on the first abdominal segment of Collembola.

Colon that part of the alimentary canal between the ileum and rectum.

Commissure the nerve cord connecting two ganglia.

Compound eye an aggregation of visual elements (ommatidia), each represented externally by a facet.

Corbicula (*pl.* **corbiculae**) the pollen basket on the hind tibia of bees.

Corium the elongate basal part of the front wing of Hemiptera.

Cornea outer covering of a compound eye, of a visual element (ommatidium) in particular.

Cornicles a pair of dorsal tubes on the posterior region of the abdomen of aphids which secrete a waxy substance.

Costa a longitudinal vein extending along the anterior margin of the wing.

Coxa basal division of leg which joins it to the body.

Cremaster hook-like process on end of abdomen of pupae of Lepidoptera.

Crochets spines on tip of prolegs of caterpillars.

Crop dilated part of the alimentary canal behind the esophagus for the reception of food.

Ctenidia (*sing.* **ctenidium**) rows of stiff spines on head and thorax of fleas.

Cubitus a longitudinal vein of an insect wing behind the media, usually two-branched.

Cuneus a triangular piece at apex of corium of the hemelytron, and separated from it by a suture (Hemiptera).

Cuticula outer covering of the body wall of an insect composed of a noncellular layer of chitin.

Discal cell a cell located in the basal or central part of a wing of an insect.

Discoidal area the middle of an area or a field such as in the wing of an insect.

Ectoparasite a parasite living upon the body of the host.

Ejaculatory duct tube through which the spermatozoa pass from the vasa differentia.

Elytron (*pl.* **elytra**) a horny, veinless front wing of Coleoptera, Dermaptera, and some Homoptera.

Embolium a narrow part of the corium, separated by a suture, along the costal margin in front wing of Hemiptera.

Empodium (*pl.* **empodia**) a single, pad-like or bristle-like structure often present between the tarsal claws of insects, either between paired pulvilli or alone.

Endocuticula the inner layer of the cuticula.

Endoparasite a parasite living within the body of the host.

Epicuticula the thin nonchitinous outside covering of the exocuticula.

Epimeron the posterior sclerite of a thoracic pleuron.

Epipharynx a mouthpart attached to the inner surface of the labrum.

Episternum the anterior sclerite of a thoracic pleuron.

Eruciform resembling a caterpillar, with cylindrical body and with both thoracic legs and prolegs.

Exarate pupa a pupa with the appendages free and not glued to the body.

Exocuticula the outer layer of the cuticula.

Exoskeleton a skeleton on the outside of the body.

Exuviae (no *sing.*) cast skin of immature stages of arthropods.

Facet the lens which forms the base of the visual element, the ommatidium, visible on the surface of the compound eye.

Femur (*pl.* **femora**) the middle or third leg division between the trochanter and the tibia.

Filiform thread-like or hair-like; that type of antenna with the segments quite uniform in size.

Flagellum   the apical part of the antenna, attached to the pedicel.

Frenulum   a bristle or a group of bristles arising from the humeral angle of the hind wing in many Lepidoptera and extending underneath the front wing.

Frons or **front**   that region of the head lying between the eyes and the clypeus.

Furcula   a springing organ on the ventral surface of the abdomen of Collembola.

Galea   the outer lobe of the maxilla, attached to the stipes.

Ganglion   a bundle of nerve cells, supplying nerves to that part of the body where located.

Gaster   that part of the abdomen of ants behind the petiole.

Gena   that part of the head below the compound eye and to the side of the frons; the cheek.

Genus   a group of closely related species, the first name of a scientific name.

Glabrous   smooth, devoid of hairs.

Glossa (*pl.* **glossae**)   one of the paired lobes of the labium between the paraglossae.

Grub   a thick-set, usually sluggish larva with well developed head and thoracic legs.

Gula   a sclerite on the ventral surface of the head.

Gynandromorph   an abnormal individual with morphological characteristics of both sexes.

Haemocoele   general body cavity in which the blood flows.

Haltere or **halter** (*pl.* **halteres**)   small, knobbed organ, one on each side of the metathorax, representing the hind wing of the Diptera.

Hamuli   minute hooks on the anterior margin of the hind wings of Hymenoptera, with which the front and hind wings are held together.

Hemelytron (*pl.* **hemelytra**)   front wing of true bugs (Hemiptera).

Hemimetabolous   pertaining to incomplete metamorphosis as in the Ephemeroptera, Odonata, and Plecoptera.

Holometabolous   pertaining to complete metamorphosis with egg, larva, pupa, and adult stages.

Honeydew   a sweet liquid excreted from the anus of a number of Homoptera.

Hypermetamorphosis   a form of complete metamorphosis in which the larval stages vary morphologically.

Hypodermis   the cellular layer of the body wall which secretes the cuticula.

Hypostome   a structure with recurved teeth located in a median position and arising from the basis capituli (in ticks).

Ileum   anterior part of the hindgut between the ventriculus and the colon.

Imago   an adult insect.

Instar the stage of an insect between successive molts.

Intercalary vein a supplementary longitudinal wing vein lying between two preëxisting veins.

Jugum a finger-like process extending from the base of the front wing underneath the hind wing (Lepidoptera).

Labellum (*pl.* **labella**) the modified tip of the labium of a number of Diptera.

Labium the lower lip of an insect's mouthparts.

Labrum the upper lip of an insect's mouthparts.

Lacinia inner lobe of the maxilla arising from the stipes.

Lamella (*pl.* **lamellae**) a plate-like structure.

Lamellate pertaining to leaf-like or plate-like structures or segments.

Larva the immature stages between the egg and the pupa of an insect with complete metamorphosis; the six-legged stage or first instar of a tick or mite.

Ligula the distal lobes of the labium, the glossae and the paraglossae.

Maggot a legless dipterous larvae without a well defined head capsule.

Malpighian tubes long blind tubes of excretory function arising from the anterior end of the hindgut.

Mandibles the paired primary jaws of an insect's mouthparts.

Maxillae the paired secondary jaws of an insect's mouthparts.

Mentum the distal part of the labium bearing the ligula and palpi.

Mesenteron the midgut or ventriculus of the digestive tract.

Mesosternum ventral sclerite of the mesothorax.

Mesothorax the second or middle segment of the thorax.

Metamorphosis changes in form in development.

Metasternum ventral sclerite of the metathorax.

Metathorax the third and last segment of the thorax.

Micropyle opening in an egg through which the sperm enters to effect fertilization.

Molt the shedding of the skin.

Moniliform segments rounded, bead-like (e.g., moniliform antennae).

Myiasis disorder produced by invasion of dipterous larvae.

Naiad an aquatic nymph of insects with hemimetabolous development.

Nodus the stout cross vein near the middle of the front margin of the wing of a member of the Odonata.

Notum the dorsal part of a body segment.

Nymph the young of insects which do not have a pupal stage; immature stage of ticks and mites which have eight legs.

Obtect pupa pupa which has the legs and wings glued to the body, as in Lepidoptera.

Occiput that part of the head that lies behind the vertex, eyes and genae.

Ocellus simple eye of an arthropod with a single lens for the entire eye.

Ommatidium (*pl.* **ommatidia**) the visual unit of a compound eye.

Ootheca (*pl.* **oothecae**) the covering or case of an egg mass of certain Orthoptera.

Operculum a cover or lid.

Order a group composed of related families.

Osmeterium (*pl.* **osmeteria**) eversible sac-like structures provided with scent glands, usually borne on anterior region of the body of caterpillars of certain butterflies.

Ostia (*sing.* **ostium**) openings on the sides of the heart through which the blood enters.

Ovariole one of the egg tubes which collectively form the ovary.

Ovary a mass of tubes lying one on each side of the body cavity of the female insect in which the eggs are developed.

Oviduct tube leading from the ovary through which the eggs pass to the vagina.

Oviparous reproducing from eggs laid by the female.

Ovipositor egg-laying organ of the female insect.

Ovoviviparous the production of living young by the hatching of the eggs before they are laid.

Paedogenesis reproduction in the sexually immature or larval stage.

Palpi (*sing.* **palpus**) segmented appendages borne on the maxillae and also on the labium.

Palpifer small lobe or sclerite articulated to the stipes which bears the maxillary palpus.

Palpiger small sclerite on the labium which bears the palpus.

Paraglossa (*pl.* **paraglossae**) one of the paired lobes borne on the distal end of the labium, to the side of the glossae.

Parasite an animal smaller than its host upon or within which it lives continuously for at least a part of its life cycle, and the host is not immediately killed by its attacks.

Parthenogenesis reproduction from eggs without fertilization.

Paurometabolous development in which the young resemble the adult, live in the same environment, and have the same food habits.

Pectinate comb-like in appearance (e.g., pectinate antennae).

Pedicel the second segment of the antennae.

Pedipalpi the second paired appendages of an arachnid.

Penellipse in caterpillars, the figure formed by the crochets in a uniserial circle with a part of them absent.

Pharynx that part of the foregut between the mouth and the esophagus.

Phylum one of the major divisions of the animal kingdom.

Pleuron the lateral side of a thoracic segment.

Plumose feathery (e.g., plumose antennae).

Polyembryony the production of two or more embryos from a single egg.

Postgena that part of the head which extends downward and back of the gena.

Postlabium the basal or proximal part of the labium.

Predator an animal usually larger than the prey, which may be devoured in one meal.

Prelabium the distal part of the labium comprised of the prementum, the ligula, and the palpi.

Prepupa a quiescent stage between the larva and the pupa.

Proctodeum the hindgut extending from the ventriculus to the anus.

Proleg a fleshy abdominal leg of some insect larvae.

Pronotum dorsal surface of the prothorax.

Propodeum the first abdominal segment in the Hymenoptera which is joined to the thorax.

Prothorax the first of the three thoracic segments.

Proventriculus the gizzard, the posterior part of the foregut which joins the ventriculus.

Pseudotrachea (*pl.* **pseudotracheae**) a structure having the appearance of a trachea; a false trachea.

Pteropleural bristles bristles located on the pteropleuron of Diptera.

Pulvillus (*pl.* **pulvilli**) pad-like structures between the claws of the tarsi.

Pupa (*pl.* **pupae**) the quiescent stage between the larva and the adult in holometabolous development.

Puparium (*pl.* **puparia**) the larval skin which serves as a covering for the pupa in the higher Diptera.

Pupiparous giving birth to mature larvae which are ready to pupate.

Pygidium the dorsal surface of the last abdominal segment.

Retinula the sensory part of the ommatidium, composed of seven or eight elongate cells which surround the rhabdom.

Rhabdom the optic rod lying in the axis of the retinula.

Rostrum snout or beak.

Scape the first segment of the antenna.

Scarabaeiform larva a grub-like larva, cylindrical, curved and with short thoracic legs but no prolegs.

Sclerite a plate of the body wall of an insect, bordered by sutures or membranes.

Sclerotized of the cuticula, hardened in definite areas.

Scutellum a posterior sclerite of the thoracic notum.

Scutum the middle sclerite of a thoracic notum, anterior to the scutellum.

Seminal vesicles pouch-like structures in which seminal fluid of the male is stored.

Serrate saw-like (e.g., serrate antennae).

Seta (*pl.* **setae**) a hair-like appendage.

Spermatheca receptacle in the female which receives and stores the sperm of the male.

Spinneret a structure from which silk is spun.

Spiracle an outside opening to the tracheal system.

Sternum the ventral part of a body segment.

Stipes the second segment or part of the maxilla.

Stomodeum the forgut of an arthropod.

Stylus (*pl.* **styli**) a short, slender process on the ventral surface of the abdomen of Thysanura.

Subesophageal ganglion the ganglion located below the esophagus.

Submentum the postlabium, the basal sclerite of the labium.

Superposition image image produced by superposition or overlapping of points of light from a number of facets.

Suture a groove or seam in the cuticula between sclerites.

Taenidium (*pl.* **taenidia**) a spiral chitinized thickening in the wall of a trachea.

Tarsus (*pl.* **tarsi**) the distal division of an insect's leg attached to the tibia and consisting of one or more segments.

Tegmen (*pl.* **tegmina**) the thickened or parchment-like front wing of Orthoptera.

Tenaculum a structure on the ventral side of the abdomen of Collembola which holds the furcula or springing appendage.

Tergum the dorsal region of a body segment.

Testis (*pl.* **testes**) sex organ of the male which produces the sperm.

Tibia (*pl.* **tibiae**) the fourth division of an insect's leg between the femur and the tarsus.

Trachea (*pl.* **tracheae**) an air tube lined with taenidia.

Tracheole a terminal branch of the trachea, not chitin lined.

Triungulin larva the first larval instar of Strepsiptera and certain beetles.

Trochanter the second division of an insect's leg between the coxa and the femur.

Tympanum a membrane covering the auditory organs.

Vagina structure formed by the union of the oviducts of the female reproductive organs and opening to the outside.

Vas deferens (*pl.* **vasa deferentia**) sperm duct of the male.

Ventriculus the midgut or stomach of an insect.

Vermiform larva a worm-like, legless and headless larva.

Vertex the top of the head, between the eyes and anterior to the occiput.

Viviparous producing living young, and not laying eggs.

A SELECTED BIBLIOGRAPHY

The list of references given below is not by any means a complete bibliography of the subject material in the text. It is offered as a further source of information for both the teacher and student. A number of the texts listed contain excellent bibliographies. Other bibliographical sources are: *Biological Abstracts,* Philadelphia, Pa.; *Index to the Literature of American Economic Entomology,* American Association of Economic Entomologists Special Publication, 1917—; and *The Agricultural Index,* New York, H. W. Wilson Co., 1916—.

Most of the detailed information on insect pests is found in bulletins and other publications of the United States Department of Agriculture and State Agricultural Experiment Stations. Many of these publications may be obtained free or at little cost.

GENERAL AND ECONOMIC ENTOMOLOGY

Baerg, W. J., *Introduction to Applied Entomology,* 3rd ed., rev., Minneapolis, Minn., Burgess Publishing Co., 1948, 191 pages.

Bishopp, F. C., *et al., Insects,* U.S.D.A. Yearbook, Washington, D.C., Government Printing Office, 1952, 780 pages.

Borror, Donald J., and DeLong, Dwight M., *An Introduction to the Study of Insects,* New York, Rinehart & Company, Inc., 1954, 1030 pages.

Brues, C. T., Melander, A. L., and Carpenter, F. M., *Classification of Insects,* Harvard College Museum of Comparative Zoology Bulletin, vol. 108, Cambridge, Mass., 1954, 917 pages.

Chamberlin, W. J., *Entomological Nomenclature and Literature,* 2nd ed., Ann Arbor, Mich., Edwards Bros., Inc., 1946, 135 pages.

Chapman, R. N., *Animal Ecology,* New York, McGraw-Hill Book Company, Inc., 1931, 464 pages.

Chu, H. F., *How to Know the Immature Insects,* Dubuque, Iowa, William C. Brown Co., 1949, 234 pages.

Clausen, C. P., *Entomophagous Insects,* New York, McGraw-Hill Book Company, Inc., 1940, 688 pages.

Comstock, J. H., *An Introduction to Entomology,* Ithaca, N.Y., Comstock Publishing Associates, 1940, 1064 pages.

Cotton, R. T., *Insect Pests of Stored Grain and Grain Products,* rev. ed., Minneapolis, Minn., Burgess Publishing Co., 1950, 244 pages.

Craighead, F. C., *Insect Enemies of Eastern Forests,* U.S.D.A. Miscellaneous Publication 657, Washington, D.C., Government Printing Office, 1950, 679 pages.

Doane, R. W., Vandyke, E. C., Chamberlin, W. J., and Burke, H. E., *Forest Insects,* New York, McGraw-Hill Book Company, Inc., 1936, 463 pages.

Essig, E. O., *College Entomology,* New York, The Macmillan Company, 1942, 900 pages.

Essig, E. O., *Insects of Western North America,* New York, The Macmillan Company, 1938, 1035 pages.

Ewing, H. E., *A Manual of External Parasites,* Springfield, Ill., Charles C. Thomas, 1929, 225 pages.

Felt, E. P., *Plant Galls and Gall Makers,* Ithaca, N.Y., Comstock Publishing Associates, 1940, 364 pages.

Fenton, F. A., *Field Crop Insects,* New York, The Macmillan Company, 1952, 405 pages.

Fernald, H. T., and Shepard, H. H., *Applied Entomology,* 5th ed., New York, McGraw-Hill Book Company, Inc., 1955, 385 pages.

Folsom, J. W., and Wardle, R. A., *Entomology with Special Reference to Its Ecological Aspects,* 4th ed., Philadelphia, Pa., Blakiston's Son & Company, Inc., 1934, 605 pages.

Frost, S. W., *General Entomology,* New York, McGraw-Hill Book Company, Inc., 1942, 524 pages.

Graham, S. A., *Principles of Forest Entomology,* 2nd ed., New York, McGraw-Hill Book Company, Inc., 1936, 410 pages.

Herms, W. B., *Medical Entomology with Special Reference to the Health and Well-being of Man and Animals,* 4th ed., New York, The Macmillan Company, 1950, 643 pages.

Howard, L. O., *The Insect Book,* New York, Doubleday, Page & Company, 1910, 429 pages.

Imms, A. D., *A General Textbook of Entomology,* 7th ed., New York, E. P. Dutton & Co., Inc., 1948, 727 pages.

Imms, A. D., *Insect Natural History,* London, William Collins Sons & Co., 1947, 317 pages.

Jaques, H. E., *How to Know the Insects,* 2nd ed., Dubuque, Iowa, William C. Brown Co., 1947, 205 pages.

Keen, F. P., *Insect Enemies of Western Forests,* U.S.D.A. Miscellaneous Publication 273, rev., Washington, D.C., Government Printing Office, 1939, 210 pages.

Kellogg, V. L., *American Insects,* 3rd ed., rev., New York, Henry Holt and Company, Inc., 1914, 694 pages.

Leach, J. G., *Insect Transmission of Plant Diseases,* New York, McGraw-Hill Book Company, Inc., 1940, 615 pages.

Lutz, F. E., *Field Book of Insects,* New York, G. P. Putnam's Sons, 1935, 510 pages.

Mallis, Arnold, *Handbook of Pest Control,* 2nd ed., New York, MacNair-Dorland Co., Inc., 1954, 1068 pages.

Matheson, Robert, *Entomology for Introductory Courses,* 2nd ed., Ithaca, N.Y., Comstock Publishing Associates, 1951, 629 pages.

Matheson, Robert, *Medical Entomology*, 2nd ed., Ithaca, N.Y., Comstock Publishing Associates, 1950, 612 pages.

Metcalf, C. L., and Flint, W. P., *Fundamentals of Insect Life*, New York, McGraw-Hill Book Company, Inc., 1932, 581 pages.

Metcalf, C. L., Flint, W. P., and Metcalf, R. L., *Destructive and Useful Insects*, 3rd ed., New York, McGraw-Hill Book Company, Inc., 1951, 1071 pages.

Morgan, Ann H., *Field Book of Ponds and Streams*, New York, G. P. Putnam's Sons, 1930, 448 pages.

Needham, J. G., and Needham, P. R., *A Guide to the Study of Fresh Water Biology*, 3rd ed., Ithaca, N.Y., Comstock Publishing Associates, 1935, 88 pages.

Painter, R. H., *Insect Resistance in Crop Plants*, New York, The Macmillan Company, 1951, 520 pages.

Patton, W. S., and Evans, A. M., *Insects, Ticks, Mites and Venomous Animals of Medical and Veterinary Importance*, pt. 1, Medical, England, H. R. Grubb, Ltd., 1929, 785 pages.

Patton, W. S., *Insects, Ticks, Mites and Venomous Animals of Medical and Veterinary Importance*, pt. 2, Public Health, England, H. R. Grubb, Ltd., 1930, 740 pages.

Peairs, L. M., and Davidson, R. H., *Insect Pests of Farm, Garden and Orchard*, 5th ed., New York, John Wiley & Sons, Inc., 1956, 661 pages.

Pennak, Robert W., *Fresh-Water Invertebrates of the United States*, New York, The Ronald Press Company, 1953, 769 pages.

Pfadt, Robert E., *et al.*, *Fundamentals of Applied Entomology*, New York, The Macmillan Company, 1962, 668 pages.

Pierce, W. D., *Sanitary Entomology*, Boston, Richard G. Badger, The Gorham Press, 1921, 518 pages.

Quayle, H. J., *Insects of Citrus and Other Subtropical Fruits*, Ithaca, N.Y., Comstock Publishing Associates, 1938, 583 pages.

Richards, A. Glenn, *The Integument of Arthropods*, Minneapolis, University of Minnesota Press, 1951, 411 pages.

Richards, O. W., *The Social Insects*, New York, Philosophical Library, 1953, 219 pages.

Roeder, Kenneth D., *et al.*, *Insect Physiology*, New York, John Wiley & Sons, Inc., 1953, 1100 pages.

Ross, H. H., *A Textbook of Entomology*, New York, John Wiley & Sons, Inc., 1948, 532 pages.

Smart, John, *Insects of Medical Importance*, England, British Museum (Natural History), 1943, 272 pages.

Snodgrass, R. E., *A Textbook of Arthropod Anatomy*, Ithaca, N.Y., Comstock Publishing Associates, 1952, 363 pages.

Swain, R. B., *The Insect Guide, Orders and Major Families of North American Insects*, Garden City, N.Y., Doubleday & Company, Inc., 1948, 261 pages.

Sweetman, H. L., *The Biological Control of Insects*, Ithaca, N.Y., Comstock Publishing Associates, 1936, 461 pages.

Torre-Bueno, J. R. de la, *A Glossary of Entomology*, Lancaster, Pa., Science Press Printing Co., 1937, 336 pages.

Ward, Henry B., and Whipple, George C., *Fresh-water Biology*, New York, John Wiley & Sons, Inc., 1918, 1111 pages.

Wardle, Robert A., *The Problems of Applied Entomology*, New York, McGraw-Hill Book Company, Inc., 1929, 587 pages.

INSECTICIDES

Brown, A. W. A., *Insect Control by Chemicals*, New York, John Wiley & Sons, Inc., 1951, 817 pages.

De Ong, E. R., *Chemistry and Uses of Insecticides*, New York, Reinhold Publishing Corporation, 1948, 345 pages.

Dethier, V. G., *Chemical Insect Attractants and Repellents*, Philadelphia, Pa., Blakiston's Son & Company, 1947, 289 pages.

Frear, D. E. H., *Chemistry of Insecticides, Fungicides and Herbicides*, 2nd ed., New York, D. Van Nostrand Company, Inc., 1948, 417 pages.

Metcalf, R. L., *Organic Insecticides, Their Chemistry and Mode of Action*, New York, Interscience Publishers, Inc., 1955, 392 pages.

Shepard, H. H., *The Chemistry and Action of Insecticides*, New York, McGraw-Hill Book Company, Inc., 1951, 504 pages.

NEAR RELATIVES OF INSECTS (SPIDERS, MITES AND TICKS)

Baker, E. W., and Wharton, G. W., *An Introduction to Acarology*, New York, The Macmillan Company, 1952, 465 pages.

Banks, Nathan, *A Revision of the Ixodoidea or Ticks of the United States*, U.S. Bureau of Entomology Bulletin, Technical Series No. 15, Washington, D.C., Government Printing Office, 1908, 60 pages.

Comstock, J. H., and Gertsch, W. J., *The Spider Book*, Ithaca, N.Y., Comstock Publishing Associates, 1948, 740 pages.

Gertsch, W. J., *American Spiders*, New York, D. Van Nostrand Company, 1949, 285 pages.

Hooker, W. A., Bishopp, F. C., and Wood, H. P., *The Life History and Bionomics of Some North American Ticks*, U.S. Bureau of Entomology Bulletin 106, Washington, D.C., Government Printing Office, 1918, 239 pages.

Nuttall, G. H. F., *et al.*, *Ticks, a Monograph of the Ixodoidea*, pt. 1, 1908; pt. 2, 1911; pt. 3, 1915; pt. 4, 1926, England, Cambridge University Press, pts. 1–3, 550 pages; pt. 4, 302 pages.

Prichard, A. E., and Baker, E. W., *A Revision of the Spider Mite Family Tetranychidae*, San Francisco, Pacific Coast Entomological Society, 1955, 472 pages.

EPHEMEROPTERA (MAYFLIES), ODONATA (DRAGONFLIES),
AND PLECOPTERA (STONEFLIES)

Burks, B. D., *The Mayflies or Ephemeroptera of Illinois*, Illinois Natural History Survey Bulletin 26, Urbana, Ill., 1953, 216 pages.

Frison, T. H., *Studies of North American Plecoptera,* Illinois Natural History Survey Bulletin 22, Urbana, Ill., 1942, pp. 235–355.

Morgan, A. H., *A Contribution to the Biology of Mayflies,* Annals of Entomological Society of America 6, 1913, pp. 371–426.

Needham, J. G., and Claasen, P. W., *A Monograph of the Plecoptera or Stoneflies of America North of Mexico,* Lafayette, Ind., Thomas Say Foundation, 1925, 397 pages.

Needham, J. G., Traver, J. R., and Hsu, Y., *The Biology of Mayflies,* Ithaca, N. Y., Comstock Publishing Associates, 1935, 759 pages.

Needham, J. G., and Westfall, M. J., Jr., *A Manual of the Dragonflies of North America (Anisoptera),* Berkeley, Calif., University of California Press, 1955, 615 pages.

Tillyard, R. J., *The Biology of Dragonflies,* Cambridge, Mass., The University Press, 1917, 396 pages.

ORTHOPTERA (COCKROACHES, GRASSHOPPERS, ETC.) AND ISOPTERA (TERMITES)

Blatchley, W. S., *The Orthoptera of Northeastern America,* Indianapolis, Ind., Nature Publishing Co., 1920, 784 pages.

Hebard, Morgan, *The Blattidae of North America, North of the Mexican Boundary,* Entomological Society of America Memoirs, No. 2, Philadelphia, 1917, 284 pages.

Hebard, Morgan, *The Dermaptera and Orthoptera of Illinois,* Illinois Natural History Survey Bulletin 20, Urbana, Ill., 1934, pages 125–279.

Kofoid, C. A., *Termites and Termite Control,* 2nd ed., Berkeley, Calif., University of California Press, 1934, 795 pages.

Morse, A. P., *Manual of the Orthoptera of New England,* Boston Society of Natural History Proceedings, vol. 35, no. 6, 1920, pages 203–556.

Snyder, T. E., *Catalogue of Termites (Isoptera) of the World,* Smithsonian Institution Miscellaneous Collections, vol. 112, Washington, D.C., 1949, 490 pages.

Snyder, T. E., *Our Enemy the Termites,* rev. ed., Ithaca, N.Y., Comstock Publishing Associates, 1948, 257 pages.

Uvarov, B. P., *Locusts and Grasshoppers,* London, Imperial Bureau of Entomology, 1928, 352 pages.

MALLOPHAGA (CHEWING LICE), ANOPLURA (SUCKING LICE), HEMIPTERA (TRUE BUGS) AND HOMOPTERA (APHIDS, SCALES, ETC.)

Blatchley, W. S., *Heteroptera or True Bugs of Eastern North America, with Special Reference to the Faunas of Indiana and Florida,* Indianapolis, Ind., Nature Publishing Co., 1926, 1116 pages.

Britton, W. E., *et al., The Hemiptera or Sucking Insects of Connecticut,* Connecticut State Geology and Natural History Survey, pt. 4, Hartford, Conn., 1923, 807 pages.

Ewing, H. E., *Taxonomy, Biology, and Distribution of the Gyropidae,* U.S. National Museum Proceedings, No. 63, 1924, pp. 1–42.

Ferris, G. F., *Atlas of the Scale Insects of North America,* series 1–7, Stanford University, Standford University Press, 1937–1950.

Ferris, G. F., "The Mallophagan Family Monoponidae," *Parasitology,* no. 16, 1924, pp. 55–66.

Ferris, G. F., *The Sucking Lice,* San Francisco, Calif., Pacific Coast Entomological Society, 1951, 320 pages.

Kellogg, V. L., *A List of Mallophaga taken form Birds and Mammals of North America,* U.S. National Museum Proceedings, No. 22, 1899, pp. 39–100.

MacGillivray, A. D., *The Coccidae,* Urbana, Ill., Scarab Co., 1921, 502 pages.

Patch, E. M., *Food-plant Catalogue of the Aphids of the World, Including Phylloxeridae,* Maine Agricultural Experiment Station Bulletin 393, Orono, 1938, 431 pages.

Van Duzee, E. P., *Catalogue of the Hemiptera of America, North of Mexico, Excepting the Aphididae, Coccidae and Aleurodidae,* University of California Publication, Entomology, Technical Bulletin, vol. 2, 1917, 902 pages.

COLEOPTERA (BEETLES) AND STREPSIPTERA (STYLOPIDS)

Blatchley, W. S., *An Illustrated and Descriptive Catalogue of the Coleoptera or Beetles of Indiana (Exclusive of Rhynchophora),* 2 vols., Indianapolis, Ind., Nature Publishing Co., 1910, 1385 pages.

Blatchley, W. S., and Leng, C. W., *Rhynchophora or Weevils of Northeastern North America,* Indianapolis, Ind., Nature Publishing Co., 1916, 682 pages.

Boving, A. G., and Craighead, F. C., *An Illustrated Synopsis of the Principal Larval Forms of the Order Coleoptera,* New York, Brooklyn Entomological Society, 1931, 351 pages.

Leconte, J. L., and Horn, G. H., *Synopsis of North American Coleoptera,* Smithsonian Institution Miscellaneous Collection, 26(507), 1883, 567 pages.

Leng, C. W., *Catalogue of the Coleoptera of America, North of Mexico,* Mount Vernon, N.Y., John D. Sherman, Jr., 1920; five supplements 1927–1947; 470 pages.

Pierce, W. D., *A Monographic Revision of the Twisted-winged Insects Comprising the Order Strepsiptera,* U.S. National Museum Proceedings 54, 1918, pages 391–501.

LEPIDOPTERA (MOTHS AND BUTTERFLIES) AND TRICHOPTERA (CADDIS-FLIES)

Comstock, J. H., and Comstock, A. B., *How to Know the Butterflies,* Ithaca, N.Y., Comstock Publishing Associates, 1936, 311 pages.

Dyar, H. G., *A List of North American Lepidoptera and a Key to the Literature to this Order of Insects,* U.S. National Museum Bulletin No. 52, 1902, 723 pages.

Forbes, W. T. M., *The Lepidoptera of New York and Neighboring States, Primitive Forms, Microlepidoptera, Pyraloids and Bombyces,* Cornell University Agricultural Experiment Station Memoir 68, Ithaca, N.Y., 1923, 729 pages.

Forbes, W. T. M., *Lepidoptera of New York and Neighboring States, Geometridae, Sphingidae, Notodontidae and Lymantriidae,* pt. 2, Cornell University Agricultural Experiment Station Memoir 274, Ithaca, N.Y., 1948, 263 pages.

Forbes, W. T. M., *Lepidoptera of New York and Neighboring States, Noctuidae,* pt. 3, Cornell University Agricultural Experiment Station Memoir 329, Ithaca, N.Y., 1954, 433 pages.

Holland, W. J., *The Moth Book,* New York, Doubleday, Page & Company, 1913, 479 pages.

Holland, W. J., *The Butterfly Book,* New York, Doubleday, Doran & Company, Inc., 1931, 424 pages.

Klots, A. B., *A Field Guide to the Butterflies,* Boston, Houghton Mifflin Company, 1951, 349 pages.

McDunnough, J. H., *Check List of the Lepidoptera of Canada and the United States of America,* Southern California Academy of Science Memoirs, Los Angeles, Calif., pt. 1, 1938, (Macrolepidoptera), 274 pages; pt. 2, 1939 (Microlepidoptera), 171 pages.

Peterson, A., *Larvae of Insects,* pt. 1, *Lepidoptera and Plant Infesting Hymenoptera,* Ann Arbor, Mich., Edwards Bros., 1948, 315 pages.

Ross, H. H., *The Caddis Flies or Trichoptera of Illinois,* Illinois Natural History Survey Bulletin 23, Urbana, Ill., 1944, 326 pages.

Seitz, A., *Macro-Lepidoptera of the World,* vol. 5, *The American Rhopalocera,* Stuttgart, F. Lehmann, 1924, 1139 pages.

DIPTERA (FLIES) AND SIPHONAPTERA (FLEAS)

Aldrich, J. M., *A Catalogue of North American Diptera,* Smithsonian Institution Miscellaneous Collections, vol. 46, Washington, D.C., 1905, 680 pages.

Baker, C. F., *A Revision of American Siphonaptera or Fleas,* U.S. National Museum Proceedings 29, Washington, D.C., 1904, pp. 365–469.

Betten, Cornelius, *et al., The Caddis Flies or Trichoptera of New York State,* New York State Museum Bulletin 292, Albany, University of the State of New York, 1934, 576 pages.

Carpenter, S. J., and La Casse, W. J., *Mosquitoes of North America,* Berkeley, Calif., University of California Press, 1955, 360 pages.

Curran, C. H., *The Families and Genera of North American Diptera,* New York, Published by the Author, 1934, 512 pages.

Fox, Irving, and Ewing, H. E., *The Fleas of North America,* U.S.D.A., Miscellaneous Publication, No. 500, Washington, D.C., 1943, 128 pages.

Hall, D. G., *The Blowflies of North America,* Entomological Society of America, Thomas Say Foundation Publication, vol. 4, Baltimore, 1948, 477 pages.

Hubbard, C. A., *Fleas of Western North America,* Ames, Iowa, Iowa State College Press, 1947, 533 pages.

Lane, J., *Neotropical Culicidae,* vols. 1 and 2, Sao Paulo, Brazil, University of Sao Paulo, 1953, 1112 pages.

Matheson, Robert, *Handbook of the Mosquitoes of North America,* 2nd ed., Ithaca, New York, Comstock Publishing Associates, 1944, 314 pages.

Russell, P. F., Rozeboom, L. E., and Stone, Alan, *Keys to the Anopheline Mosquitoes of the World,* Philadelphia, Pa., American Entomological Society, The Academy of Natural Sciences, 1943, 152 pages.

West, L. S., *The House Fly,* Ithaca, N.Y., Comstock Publishing Associates, 1951, 584 pages.

Williston, S. W., *Manual of the Families and Genera of North American Diptera,* 3rd ed., New Haven, Conn., James T. Hathaway, 1908, 405 pages.

HYMENOPTERA (WASPS, BEES, ETC.)

Creighton, W. S., *The Ants of North America,* Harvard University Museum of Comparative Zoology Bulletin, vol. 104, Cambridge, Mass., 1950, 585 pages.

Grout, R. A., Ed., *The Hive and the Honey Bee,* rev. ed., Hamilton, Ill., Dadant & Sons, 1949, 652 pages.

Muesebeck, C. W. F., Krombein, K. V., Townes, H. K., *et al., Hymenoptera of America North of Mexico—A Synoptic Catalogue,* U.S.D.A. Agricultural Monographs, No. 2, Washington, D.C., Government Printing Office, 1951, 1420 pages.

Rau, Philip, and Rau, Nellie, *Wasp Studies Afield,* Princeton, N.J., Princeton University Press, 1918, 372 pages.

Root, A. I., *The ABC and XYZ of Bee Culture, An Encyclopedia Pertaining to Scientific and Practical Culture of Bees,* revised by E. R. Root, H. H. Root, and M. J. Deyell, Medina, Ohio, A. I. Root Co., 1950, 703 pages.

Viereck, H. L., *et al., The Hymenoptera, or Wasp-like Insects of Connecticut,* Connecticut State Geology and Natural History Survey Bulletin 22, Hartford, Conn., 1916, 824 pages.

Wheeler, W. M., *Ants; Their Structure, Development and Behavior,* New York, Columbia University Press, 1926, 663 pages.

MINOR GROUPS

Banks, N., "A Classification of the Psocidae," *Psyche, 36,* 1929, p. 321–324.

Chapman, P. J., "Corrodentia of the United States of America, I, Suborder Isotecnomera," *New York Entomological Society Journal, 38,* 1930, pp. 219–290.

Gourney, Ashley B., "A Synopsis of the Order Zoraptera, with Notes on the Biology of Zorotypus hubbardi," Washington Entomological Society Proceedings 40, 1938, pp. 57–87.

Mills, H. B., *A Monograph of the Collembola of Iowa,* Ames, Iowa Collegiate Press, 1934, 143 pages.

Moulton, D., *Synopsis, Catalogue, and Bibliography of North American Thysanoptera,* U.S.D.A. Bureau of Entomology Technical Series No. 21, Washington, D.C., Government Printing Office, 1911, 56 pages.

Ross, Edward S., *A Revision of the Embioptera, or Web-spinners of the New World,* U.S. National Museum Proceedings 94, 1944, pp. 401–504.

Watson, J. R., *Synopsis and Catalogue of the Thysanoptera of North America,* University of Florida Experiment Station Bulletin 168, Gainesville, Fla., 1923, 100 pages.

INDEX

(The more important page references are indicated by boldface type.)